The Amazing Life of Cecilia Chattergee

Bernie Morgan

Cover photography courtesy of Shutterstock

Cover Design by Danji's Designs

About the author

Bernie Morgan is Cecilia Chattergee's great-granddaughter. From early childhood, she was intrigued by the snippets she could glean of Cecilia's story, but it was only when she researched it recently that she discovered it was much more eventful than she had imagined. She decided to write Cecilia's history as a way of honouring her achievements and her memory. Piecing together her great-grandmother's remarkable past and bringing it to a wider audience inspired Bernie to found Amazing Women, Invisible Lives website and podcast www.amazingwomeninvisiblelives.co.uk, as a way of recognising remarkable females who go unnoticed all too often.

Bernie was a stay-at-home mum for 14 years. Then she went to university for the first time and gained a Master's Degree. After just seven years in full-time work, where one of her roles was writing the design brief for the Diana, Princess of Wales Memorial Playground, she became the first CEO of Responsible Finance leading the development of that industry in the UK. She took the industry's worth to more than half a billion pounds in eight years, raising over £85m investment in the process. She was an advisor to HM Treasury and worked closely with a variety of government departments. She has appeared before two Select Committees. She also had an international role, guiding governments in financial policies that support vulnerable people and communities.

Bernie has also been a cleaner, a stand-up comedian and was, for five years, the owner of a chocolate café in Margate.

She lives with her partner in Kent and enjoys spending time with her children and grandchildren.

Acknowledgements

There are many people who helped in the preparation of this book. My cousin, Susie Longstaff, who is a genealogist, helped with lots of facts and family lore.

Nikki Mortimer of Travel Counsellors, organised the research trip to India and was flexible with finding places to stay in non-tourist areas.

My aunts, Myrna and Christine, supplied anecdotes and background information.

My children Grace and Steve with their spouses, Tim and Katy, sent me on a writing course with the Arvon Foundation, which was pivotal to giving me the confidence to complete the project.

Sessions at Margate Bookie inspired me to get on with writing on a daily basis.

Taryn Johnston and her team at Chronos Publishing were hugely supportive – my thanks to them.

Thanks also to Grace, my daughter, and Diane Harris did a sterling job with early reading and providing other support during the writing process.

Huge thanks and love to Mark, who was a rock and constant sounding board.

Dedication

This book is dedicated to all Cecilia's descendants.
May we learn from her intelligence and resilience.
And may we never forget her.

Chapter One

Cecilia finished putting kohl around her eyes and looked in the mirror. She smiled, suppressing the sadness that threatened to engulf her. She took the blue and silver sari off her bed and expertly wrapped it around her thin frame, securing it with the seven folds and waist tuck that her ayah had taught her. There was a knock on her door. 'Come in, Papa,' she called, smiling with a little more conviction than before.

As he walked into her room, he gasped, 'Oh Cecilia, you were my little girl. Now you are a beautiful young woman. You look so lovely.'

'It is my nineteenth birthday, Papa. I want to look nice for my party.' She kissed him on the cheek. 'I still don't know who you've invited. Are you going to tell me now? It's nearly time for it to start.'

Her Papa looked down, 'I tried to do it the way your Mama would have wanted. I invited all the family, some friends and their families. Some of your college friends too. I asked musicians to come because I know how much you love to dance.' He hugged her hard. 'But I think your Mama would have organised it better. In fact, I know.'

'Oh Papa, Papa,' Cecilia laid her head on his shoulder. 'I am sad too.' She sighed. 'I know Mama would feel proud. She is watching us from heaven. She would not like us crying on my birthday. Cheer up, Papa. I am sure you have organised a fine party. We will dance together!'

Her Papa laughed, 'Bette. I never could dance. Your Mama used to tease me about it. I never had her rhythm or her timing. I will be treading on your toes all night.'

'You will be as light as a feather, I know. Now come, come.' She took his arm.

In the early evening glow, they walked to the party hall. Even though sadness weighed on their shoulders, they walked lightly in unison. Little puffs of red dust rose with each of their steps. The evening warmth heightened the scent of the hardy hibiscus growing haphazardly along the way. Cecilia's sari sparkled as it swirled around her tiny body, silvery-gold in the low sun.

'Cecilia, I have invited the Sorabjis. Francina was a good friend of Mama. But they are a very busy family; I know not all of her daughters can come. Cornelia is still studying but I think Susie and Alice will be there. They are so committed to the education of girls. You are like them. Also, I invited Bhikaiji Rustom, another friend of Mama's. She works hard to make life better for poor people. What women we Parsees produce! You are all so intelligent and passionate, wanting to improve life for others.'

'I want to make sure that Mama would be proud of me.' She smiled, her face lighting up.

'Your Mama was proud of you – whatever you did.'

The guests were already assembled in the packed room when Cecilia and her Papa entered. She saw an array of bright colours, pinks, yellows, greens and blues, sparkling with sequins and gold threads. Among the luminescent Indian saris were duller hues of British clothes, smatterings of brown, florals, and greys.

As soon as they saw her the crowd, cheered and clapped and sang:

Happy birthday to you
Happy birthday to you
Happy birthday dear Cecilia
Happy birthday to you.

She had heard that song before, just recently at her cousin Pritti's birthday party. It was a new song that people of all ages liked. The guests sang with an enthusiasm that outperformed their ability. She heard a semi-melodic cacophony of Hindi, Urdu and English. She smiled and nodded in appreciation of their efforts. Her younger brothers, Joseph and Stanislaus, smiled back. Next to them was her stepmother, heavily pregnant. Her little sister, Susie, was hiding behind their stepmother's glittering sari. Her family, how she loved them all.

She noticed they had decorated the hall with banners and bunting, made of fabrics from the local market. Like the saris, they added a riot of happy colour to the room. A delicious smell of spices and curry wafted from the kitchen, where a small group of women were busy chopping and chatting.

Cecilia looked around. There was Alia, Poonam and Naren. Priya and Sameen next to Mary, Margaret, and Sophia. All friends from different parts of her life. They were all smiling, eager to talk to her and wish her well.

Standing in the corner, she glimpsed a tall, good-looking young man in a soldier's uniform. He was smiling at her. Her heart quickened. Who was he? Who invited him?

She saw her mother's sisters come striding towards her. Neither Jaishree nor Bhakti had the petite, lithe grace of their younger sister, her Mama. They were short and solid. They wore brightly coloured, patterned, sparkling saris. Somehow, these glamorous clothes only served to make them look older and frumpier. They formed the nucleus of the 'auntijis', who seemed to be in everyone's family. Sturdy, plain and opinionated. She braced herself for the onslaught of strong sentiment that would be coming her way.

Then she remembered them both at her mother's graveside, wailing and weighted by grief. They would be hurting too today. They had lost their beloved sister. She must remember to be kind to them.

'Auntiji,' she hugged Jaishree, whose eyes were welling over.

'Oh, Cecilia – you are so beautiful. All grown up. You are so like your mother. You have her lovely dark brown eyes and her beautiful skin.' She wiped her tears away. She turned to her sister, 'Oh Bhak- look at her. So like Sally.'

Bhakti rolled her eyes and folded her plump arms. 'Don't say Sally. I don't like it. It's not her real name. Deepali was a perfectly good name. Why did she change it?'

'Shh,' said Jaishree, 'don't say anything. It's Cecilia's party. We don't want to upset her.'

'I don't care,' retorted Bhakti, 'it's ridiculous. And Padmesh. Changing his name to John. I don't understand it. I am never calling him John. He will always be Padmesh to me.'

Bhakti glared at her sister, 'Keep quiet,' she hissed. 'Do you ever give up?'

Cecilia felt her throat tightening. She gulped to stop herself from crying. The auntijis bickering about her Mama and Papa was not what she wanted. She turned away, knowing they would barely notice her rudeness.

She was right. They just carried on voicing their opinions to no one in particular. Cecilia noticed the soldier was still there, talking to another soldier. He looked in her direction. They locked eyes. For a moment, the party faded into silence and she saw only him. He nodded and moved his eyes towards the opposite corner of the room, signalling that he would meet her there. Her heart fluttered as she started to make her way there, trying not to rush.

'Cecilia!' boomed a loud voice. Uncle Saarik appeared in front of her. He was short, large with a bristling grey moustache. 'Happy birthday! You look beautiful.' As her father's best friend, Saarik was a constant presence, along with his wife and daughters, all of whom hovered behind him. Like the auntijis, they wore glittering saris, only theirs were all made of the same material, light blue with silver threads. They were so close together it was hard to tell where one began and another ended.

Uncle Saarik was lurching forward.

'Uncle Saarik, Auntiji Radihka, Fulki, Edha, Chandrika,' she kissed and hugged them all in turn, taking the compliments and birthday wishes with as much grace as she could muster. She cast a furtive glance over to the corner. The soldier was there, still looking at her. Still smiling.

'I am so pleased you could come. But I need to meet more guests, otherwise they will think I am ignoring them. I don't wish to be rude.'

'Of course, of course,' they chorused and obligingly moved aside. Cecilia stepped again towards the soldier, trying not to appear too eager.

'Happy birthday!' called out her friends, Channa and Veena. She turned towards them, inwardly irritated and outwardly delighted. 'Hello,' she said, through a forced smile.

Channa hugged her tightly, 'I love your sari.'

Cecilia swirled the delicate blue fabric, 'Thank you. My ayah helped choose it.'

'It sparkles beautifully,' said Veena.

Cecilia lowered her head and gathered them to her with a whisper. 'Don't look, but there is a soldier over there I want to talk to.'

Both girls turned in unison to look at the soldier. He was still smiling. They waved at him. He waved back.

'Stop it!' cried Cecilia, her cheeks burning up, 'Stop it!' she pleaded. 'Let me get to him. Everyone is in my way.'

Channa and Veena immediately put themselves to work. They laughed as they intercepted guests beelining for Cecilia, charming everyone as they diverted them to the food or introduced them to other people, locking arms and steering them away. Trying not to rush, Cecilia made her way towards the soldier. He was still looking at her, still smiling. At last, she reached him, then could not think what to say.

He was taller than she had thought. He had bright green eyes. His thick red hair was swept back, giving him a carefree air. Cecilia could feel her heart beating faster. His uniform, red and black, tightly fitted his muscular body.

He said softly, 'You have lovely eyes and a beautiful smile.'

'Who are you?' she said briskly, immediately regretting her brusque tone.

'My name is Maurice Roche.' He gestured to his uniform, 'Royal Dublin Fusiliers.'

'Hello Maurice Roche, Royal Dublin Fusiliers. I'm Cecilia Chattergee. Law student.'

'I know who you are.'

'But I don't know you – so what are you doing at my party?' Cecilia knew she was being a bit too direct.

'I was invited by Tashka Gupta, over there.' He pointed towards a small family group. 'He is stationed with me. His mother knew your mother.' His eyes dropped, 'I was sorry to hear your mother passed away. I heard she was very kind and beautiful and that you look like her. I can see now that that was true.'

His eyes seemed to pierce through her. Cecilia felt a current of electricity run between them. She was sure he felt it too.

He broke the spell by saying, 'Cecilia Chattergee, law student, would you do me the honour of dancing with me at your birthday party?'

She threw back her head and laughed, 'Yes, Maurice Roche. I will let you dance with me at my party. I have come here to dance, for sure.'

Her father had booked an Indian band called Savera. Their music was lyrical and swaying, their melodies melting; notes which encouraged dancing without being too loud or too fast. Cecilia and Maurice moved in unison to the mellifluous rhythms without touching each other, careful not to cause a scandal among the auntijis.

No one else mattered to them. When the dance was over, guests clapped and cheered. They had seen the invisible spark between them. Maurice kissed her hand and went away.

Channa and Veena rushed up to her demanding, 'Well?'

'What's his name?'

'What was he like?'

'Do you like him?'

'That was champion dancing.'

'He is handsome.'

'Are you going to see him again?'

'Please,' she shouted to stop the noise they were making, 'I will tell you about him if you sit down here with me.'

As she was giving them all the news, she caught her Papa's eye. He smiled, raising his eyebrows. She nodded. She looked over to the corner where Maurice was still smiling at her.

'Papa seems pleased,' she said to Channa and Veena, 'I wonder if he will invite Maurice to our house, to meet everyone properly.'

Channa and Veena squealed in excitement. 'But you only had one dance together. You must dance some more.'

'It's your party, you are allowed to ask him.'

She knew she was being bold as she walked over to him and asked. He said yes. And that was the beginning of her love for him. She knew without doubt that he was the man she wanted to marry. Even though she had never thought of marriage before. As the evening drew to a close, he kissed her forehead and asked to take her to a dance the next week.

'Yes, please,' she said, but then thought a little more, 'you will need to ask my Papa though.'

She had no idea why he should ask Papa, but she knew it was expected. She didn't like the way that men agreed with men about what women should do. But it was certainly the way of things.

She saw Maurice speaking to Papa. It looked a friendly conversation. They shook hands. Maurice came over to Cecilia with a broad smile on his handsome face. He told her she was allowed to go to the dance with him. He would be calling next Friday at 6pm. If she wanted to bring her friends, she would be welcome, he said. But Cecilia said no, she was happy to be with him alone.

She took Papa's arm as they walked home. Suffused with excitement, she talked breathlessly about Maurice. 'He is in the Army, Papa. It is a good job.'

'A soldier though, Bette? I had thought you might prefer a doctor or a lawyer.'

'I have never thought about men before, Papa. I had no thoughts like that at all. Maurice is the man I want to be with.

Anyway, he is a ferry engineer in the army, so he is not just a soldier.'

He gave a little laugh, 'My Bette, always so strong minded, so determined. I love you.'

'I love you too, Papa. Thank you for letting him take me to the dance next week.' Even though it angered her that she had to thank him for agreeing to something on her behalf.

'Spend more time with him, Bette. Then you can decide what you feel about him.' Papa patted her arm and smiled.

All week, leading up to seeing Maurice again, Cecilia could barely conceal her excitement. She attended lectures, but she couldn't concentrate. Her thoughts were about Maurice and what would happen when they saw each other again.

The interminable wait was over inevitably and eventually, Friday arrived. Cecilia spent the whole day trying on saris – asking for opinions from her siblings, who soon grew bored and ignored her. She chose her orange sari, edged in green and yellow, which suited her coffee-coloured complexion. Her slipper-style shoes were yellow with gold sequins. Veena had lent them to her and she thought they would bring good luck. She added the ten gold bangles that Channa had lent her. She felt happy and desired.

Maurice knocked at the door and Papa answered, bringing him into the kitchen to wait. She heard them talking pleasantly but not what they were saying. She was so nervous that she nearly decided not see him. A steely resolve tightened inside her. She used it to help her walk into the kitchen.

Maurice stood up as soon as he saw her. 'You are even more beautiful than I remember,' he told her.

Papa said nothing, letting Maurice pay court. Maurice held out his arm and Cecilia took it. He turned to Papa. 'I will have her home before 10 pm, as you have requested Sir.'

'Enjoy yourselves,' said Papa.

As they strolled to the dance hall, Maurice told Cecilia he had thought only about her all week.

'It was the same for me,' she replied, 'I hardly heard my lectures.'

'Lectures?'

'Yes, for my law studies.'

'Of course. It is impressive that you are studying.'

'Thank you. Not many people think that way.'

'My mother was a teacher. I am very proud of her. It's honourable that women work and can be independent.'

'Oh, let's not talk about that now. I want to dance tonight like we did last week.'

'Only perhaps closer? There will be no auntijis watching us this time.'

He gave her a brief kiss on the lips. She felt her body tingle.

It was a traditional Indian dance evening. They laughed as they learnt the moves, isolating their heads sideways from their necks, lifting their knees high and moving them back in turn. Moving their arms with fluidity and their legs with jumps. It was fast and challenging. Cecilia did not know any of the moves but she loved trying them. So did Maurice, as he caught her a number of times to prevent her falling over, which she enjoyed. Towards the end of the evening, he whispered, 'I want to kiss you. But people here are looking. Shall we go outside?'

'Of course,' she replied, 'but let's wait until people are eating.' She was aware people may see her leave with him. Even though they were not her auntijis, she knew they would gossip about her. Her only, not Maurice, as a woman, she would be the subject of people's talk and censure.

Food was served. Huge dekshis of vegetable masala, pots of pilau rice and vats of tarka dhal were placed on the table.

The spicy smells and steaming warmth did not make her hungry, as they would normally. She was thinking of Maurice and of being alone with him. While people were interested in the food, Cecilia and Maurice slipped out of the hall and into the night. Maurice held her hand and followed the dusty path at the side of the building. They heard music playing, shouts from houses, the brays, barks, and growls of animals. He put her back to the wall and stooped down to kiss her lips. It was a languorous kiss. He was taking his time, enjoying himself, ensuring she was happy too.

He slipped off the top of her sari and fondled her breasts over her choli. Her body shivered as an electric charge darted from her nipples to between her legs. He asked if he could undress her. 'Only if I can undress you too,' she countered, 'I want to be equal.'

So, in the hot, noisy, summer evening, in a semi-public place, they made love. Both for the first time. Afterwards they lay together, his arm around her shoulders, not noticing the rough ground beneath them as they dozed.

They were woken by the town bell striking ten. They jumped. 'Agh,' said Maurice, 'I promised your Papa that you would be home by ten. We have to go. Now.' They dressed and dusted each other down. They held hands as they ran in happiness back to her house. At the door, he kissed her again and said, 'I love you Cecilia Chattergee and would like to see you again.'

She beamed, 'I love you too, Maurice Roche. I want you to love me again. And again.'

'Shh,' Maurice smiled, 'your Papa mustn't hear.'

Cecilia opened the front door, 'Papa I am home. Sorry to be a little late.' She blew a kiss to Maurice as he left.

Papa greeted her holding a gas light, 'Oh Cecilia, your lovely sari is dirty. What happened?' She looked down and saw that it was stained with mud. 'I am not sure, Papa,' she was unable to think of anything convincing. 'I think it was a dirty road – it was hard to see all the mud in the dark.'

Papa shrugged. She could not tell whether he believed her. 'Did you have a nice time, bette?'

'Oh, yes Papa. Maurice is lovely and such a good dancer too. He is kind and makes me laugh. I think I might be in love with him.'

'Bette, you hardly know him. See how things unfold, eh?'

'Yes Papa.' She kissed him on the cheek and went to bed. All night she hugged the secret of Maurice's lovemaking to herself, recalling little memories in flashbacks and remembering the feelings of love and passion they shared. Her body reacted to the memories by repeating the charges of pleasure that had coursed through her. Maurice Roche was the man for her, of that she was sure.

Chapter Two

She had been hidden at the convent for five months now. It was a lonely place except for the other girls who were staying there, also in hiding because they were pregnant. The convent was stark and lacked warmth of any kind. Decorated only by forbidding holy pictures looking down on her – the adult Jesus with his heart exposed and bleeding from a crown of thorns, Jesus dying on the cross, Saint Sebastian bleeding to death from arrows all over his body. There were no comforting images, such as those of the Madonna and Child or Mary, Joseph, and Jesus. Where the walls were empty, they were brown and stained by the passage of time. The rank smell of damp permeated everywhere. It caught in her throat, threatening to choke her.

The dormitories were stiflingly hot all day with barely any air to breathe. They stayed like that well into the evening. There were a few open spaces in the walls to let in air, but they were small and didn't work very well. It was impossible to sleep until the heat of the day had fully dissipated, usually around midnight. The beds had metal frames with hard, uncomfortable mattresses. They were topped by thin sheets and covers made from an itchy cotton, which scratched her skin making her to bleed. The uncomfortable state of pregnancy, along with the uncomfortable state of the dormitory, meant none of the girls were really rested.

The nuns woke their charges around 5am for Mass in the convent chapel. It was said every day by the visiting priest, Father Pereira. This was the only time when the nuns were lively and alert, Cecilia observed. His visit was the highlight of their day. He was a young man and nervous about the attention he received from them. Tall with greasy dark hair and pockmarked skin, he had an easy blush and a ready stammer. Cecilia did not think that he was at all attractive. It was clear that the nuns, including the aloof convent head, Mother Teresa, found his company utterly charming. They fawned around him with girlish giggles and fluttering eyelashes. It was as if a button were switched on with his arrival and would be switched off when he left. The nuns took care to ensure he had nothing to do with the girls – they may lead him astray. After all, they were fallen women. But it was not difficult to keep them apart, he could barely bring himself to look at the girls in their varying stages of pregnancy. He could just about speak to the holy sisters through his blushes and stammers. He would say Mass, chat briefly to the simpering nuns, ignore the girls and leave as quickly as he was able.

The nuns were tough women with the smugness of those who led perfect lives, unblemished by sex or any other sin. They demonstrated their purity through their dark habits and severe wimples. Just as the girls demonstrated their 'sins' through their swollen bellies. Cecilia noticed how cruelly the nuns spoke to the other girls. They were not quite so cruel to her. Her Papa had paid a lot of money for her to stay here. He was reluctant to do so, but wanted to protect her from the shame she would bring to the family with her unmarried pregnancy. Of course, the nuns did not want her to complain to Papa, otherwise they may lose a source of income.

Even though she was treated slightly better, she was still subjected to the punishing regime of the convent. All twelve girls were young and unmarried. Almost all had been in love and become pregnant by accident, often with no idea how it had happened. Cecilia counted herself as one of those; she had only found out afterwards, from her auntijis, that unprotected lovemaking could lead to a baby. She had felt so sad, because she was sure that if her mother had been alive, she would have explained it to her before it happened. Yet she was excited to be having this baby, her love for Maurice, and his for her, was stronger than ever. Three girls at the convent told her stories of how they had been raped by male relatives. Stories which shocked her to the core. She had no idea that such things could happen. She felt the unfairness of their situation deeply.

All of the girls' parents wanted them to have their babies adopted as they would bring shame on the family if they did not. They had been sent to the convent where they would give birth, and then give their babies away. After, they were to return home and resume their lives as if nothing had happened. Of course, nothing would ever be normal again, for any of them. They would always carry the unbearable weight of emptiness in their hearts. Cecilia wanted to keep her baby, she did not want to give him or her to anyone else. She planned to marry Maurice and become a family. She was unwavering. She was the only girl at the convent planning to keep her baby and the other girls were staggered by her confidence. They were convinced that it was not possible. But Cecilia could feel that same steely core tighten inside her as she spoke of her plans. She was going to keep this baby, whatever anyone else said or thought.

The nuns made life difficult for the girls by discouraging them from talking. They insisted on silence at mealtimes, hard work during the day, and lights out at 8pm. Once the girls were too heavily pregnant to clean floors and make beds, they were allowed to cook and read the Bible. But they were still not allowed to talk. They passed each other little notes, whispered secrets in dormitories and took clandestine walks together whenever possible. They were united in their joint experience of rejection, as well as their desire to break the nuns' sterile regime. Their youthful spirit could not be squashed entirely, whatever the nuns thought.

But the nuns still ruled. They never concealed their contempt for their charges and did little to look after their health and welfare. The food was plain: dhal and rice with a few vegetables from the convent garden. As well as the daily Mass, prayers were said at midday, mid-afternoon and early evening. All the girls were expected to join in, whatever the stage of their confinement. There were no visits from doctors, the nuns just waited for the girls to show signs of giving birth, however early or late that may happen in relation to their due date, before they did anything to help.

Whilst in labour, a girl was taken to the medical room. No one said what happened to her afterwards; they never came back. No news ever arrived about the birth, the health of the mother or baby or the sex of the child. It was as if this 'fallen woman' had plunged into a chasm and disappeared forever.

Cecilia was sleeping when her waters broke. She had been warned by the other girls that this might happen, so she was expecting it now she was past her due date. She manoeuvred out of the wet bed and went to find a nun. As she passed the other girls, she whispered her goodbyes and touched their hands. They woke in turn and watched her leave, blowing kisses and quietly wishing her luck.

Cecilia found Mother Teresa in her study, reading her Bible by the gaslight which stood on the table.

'My time has come, Mother,' she said, clutching the door handle to steady her swollen body.

Mother Teresa placed her book on her desk without responding. She picked up the gaslight and made her way down the corridor to the medical room. Cecilia followed her in the darkness. She moved slowly, pausing every few steps to gather her breath. Her contractions were quickening in their intensity.

There were no kind words or warm gestures from Mother Teresa as she lit lights in the medical room. She nodded at the bed and Cecilia realised that she was supposed to get in it. She remembered the other girls saying it was better not to get into the bed so early as the contractions were less painful if you walked around when you had them.

'If you do not mind, Mother Teresa,' she ventured, 'I would like to walk around until very near the end.'

In the half light, she could not see the nun but she did hear her snort of disapproval, followed by a long silence. Another contraction ripped through her body, Cecilia held onto the bed while she tried not to cry out in pain, biting her lip and breathing deeply.

'Get into the bed,' hissed Mother Teresa, 'now.'

The next few hours were unbelievably painful as the contractions came like waves, crashing through her body with increasing, unrelenting intensity. Cecilia barely had time to register the shock of the pain or take a breath before another contraction built up and took over her body.

Occasionally, the nun moistened her lips with a cloth but otherwise she said and did nothing. Mother Teresa had been joined by three other nuns who busied themselves in the room doing nothing useful that Cecilia could understand.

Cecilia wondered when the labour would stop. The darkness of the night gradually turned into a glimmering dawn, throwing rays of light into the gloomy room. The young nuns switched off the gas lights. No one spoke or soothed her sweating brow. It seemed that this was the pinnacle of the way they wanted to punish her: to ignore her in her time of agony and when she was so desperate for kindness. They were teaching her a lesson – this was what she should expect for laying with a man. The pain served her right for sinning, was the clear message in the nuns' eyes. Eventually, with one last unbearable effort and piercing scream, Cecilia pushed her baby out, feeling it slide onto the bed between her legs.

'It's a boy,' announced Mother Teresa, without any enthusiasm.

'Is he healthy?'

'He's a *chi-chi*,' announced the nun in horror.

'I know that.' Cecilia's tone was defiant, 'But is he healthy?'

Mother Teresa nodded. She was a tall, large-framed nun with a stern demeanour. Her hair was scraped back under her wimple revealing her large forehead and bushy eyebrows over cold blue eyes. It was clear she was not taking any joy from helping this baby into the world.

Cecilia watched as the other nuns wrapped the baby in some shawls, 'Can I hold him now?'

Mother Teresa shook her head. 'Don't be silly, girl. You still need to push the placenta out. Perhaps after that you may hold him.' Cecilia did not know what the nun was talking about – what was the placenta, why did she have to push it out? She was about to ask when she was gripped by another contraction and then another, then another, each as painful as the last, just was they were before the baby had been born. A big lump of red flesh left her body. Mother Teresa was examining it carefully – Cecilia watched with curiosity.

Mother Teresa sighed, 'It is the part the baby feeds from inside you. It has to come out whole or it could be dangerous for you.' It was the first time since Cecilia had arrived at the convent that Mother Teresa had shown any interest in her.

The baby started to cry, 'May I hold him now, please, and feed him?'

The other nuns, young and cowed, looked to the senior nun for permission to hand the baby over. She nodded curtly.

Cecilia rocked her baby and said to Mother Teresa, 'I will need to tell my fiancé, the baby's father.'

'We will only talk to your own father. You and your fiancé,' she spat the word out with disdain, 'have sinned to make this baby. We cannot treat you as if you are married. We will send a telegram to your father only. What will you call the baby?'

'Richard. His name is Richard and his surname is Roche.' Her voice was adamant.

'You can register his birth yourself – we are not able to register bastards.' She turned away.

Cecilia winced. She looked at her little baby, his pink face smooth in serenity. She remembered the time her father had found out she was pregnant. She had fallen in love so quickly with Maurice, their physical love seemed so natural. She didn't know until it was too late that it could lead to a baby. Her Papa guessed as soon as her waist had swelled. He had cried and cried. She remembered him asking Maurice to meet him in their house and the tense words between them about her and her future. A conversation that had excluded her, even though she was in the room. She heard Maurice tell her Papa that he would marry her because he loved her. He would provide for her and their baby, they would be a happy family. That Papa need not worry, Cecilia would be safe with him. But the army would not let him marry until he was stationed in Thatti in the New Year. So, he could marry Cecilia in January, only eight months away. Papa had been relieved. If they married, Cecilia could keep her baby, which is what they both wanted. But she would need to have and keep the baby elsewhere until the wedding. He knew of a convent for fallen women. Cecilia could stay there with the baby until the wedding. They could then move to the barracks in Hyderabad after their wedding. No one need know that the baby was born out of wedlock.

It was Papa and Maurice who decided what would happen to her and her baby. Part of her was pleased Papa was so kind and Maurice really loved her. She had heard of other girls being beaten by their parents for being pregnant and being forced to give their babies up. She had even heard of a girl who had been killed by her parents. But deep inside, she felt angry that they had not asked her what she wanted. Neither of them asked her about her studies and how she might continue them. She decided not to say anything as she did not want to appear ungrateful for their love and protection.

After Maurice had left that day, she said to her Papa, 'I still want to study, Papa, when the baby is born.'

He frowned, 'But you will be a mother, bette, why do you need anything else? People will call your baby a *chi-chi* and it will need you at home to protect it.'

'I know they will, Papa. But I have thought of that. I will ask an Anglo-Indian girl to be my ayah. She will protect the baby as I expect others will have called her a *chi-chi* too, so she will know the insult and won't let it happen. I love my baby already, Papa, but I still want to be a lawyer.'

'I understand, bette. I really do. You have always known what you wanted. There are so many women wanting to be lawyers – but it is not easy as it is not allowed. I believe that the more women who fight this battle, the quicker it will be won. I will help you, bette. We are Parsees and we should be able to change things.'

The baby cried again, and she jumped out of her reverie into the present moment. 'You need to put him on the other breast now,' advised Mother Teresa with disinterest. 'I have sent a wire to your father. He will come tomorrow and see you and the baby. I am sure he will inform your *fiancé*.' The word fiancé was leaden with irony.

Trying not to soak up the nun's approbation, Cecilia turned her attention to the baby, looking at his little face, his downy cheeks and his tiny, clenched fists. An overwhelming wave of love swept through her body. A mother's love. She was determined to keep this baby and love him fully and forever. To build a life with Maurice and make a happy family.

The nuns left the room in stony silence. Cecilia was alone at last with the baby Richard. Exhausted, sore but thrilled, she spent the day marvelling at him, feeding him, kissing him, stroking him, and talking gently to him.

In the morning, after a sleepless night full of excitement and the baby's tears, her father and Maurice came to collect her, bringing Veena and Channa with them. Only her friends were allowed to come into the room, the men had to wait in the convent grounds.

She was so pleased to see them, to hear their happy voices, bathe in their joyful smiles and congratulations. She held Richard out and they held him in turn, clucking and cooing over him. It was such a relief to have people admire her baby and show her care, that she could barely see through her thick hot tears. Veena stroked her cheek. 'Was it awful, living here, Cissy. Did you miss us?'

Unable to speak, Cecilia wept. She wept for all the months of loneliness she had endured here in the convent. She wept as she remembered the pain and drama of her labour and childbirth, the cold silence of the nuns and the lack of joy at the arrival of her son. Her friends stroked her arms as despairing wails escaped her throat. After what seemed like hours, Cecilia's tears dried up. She wiped her eyes and nose. She realised how much she longed to go back home and feel surrounded by love once more. The baby started crying and she fed him while Veena and Channa gathered her meagre belongings into a small bag. Cecilia looked at them, puzzled.

'Mother Teresa told your Papa that you are the first girl here ever to keep your baby, so they don't have room for you here.' Veena told her. 'You must take Richard and go to another convent and wait there until your wedding day. Your Papa and Maurice are waiting in the garden to take you there.'

'But I don't know when my wedding day will be. Where am I going, how long will it all take?' She wiped her eyes again, her voice rising in panic.

'You will move to Thatti to live in married quarters. They will be ready in January so as early as possible that month, we think,' explained Channa.

When they all emerged into the garden, Mother Teresa was waiting with Maurice and her Papa. Mother was smiling widely and congratulating Papa on the birth of his first grandson. She was more animated than Cecilia had ever seen her. Obviously, she was trying to impress him into thinking that the convent was a warm and loving environment. Cecilia noted the nun ignored Maurice. As soon as Mother Teresa had left, Maurice hugged and kissed her and held his precious son with all the bursting pride of a new father.

'Bette,' said Papa, 'we will take you to a new convent where you can stay with the baby until your wedding day.'

'My beautiful Cecilia,' added Maurice. 'We'll be married in Hyderabad on 7th January. It will not be long before we are together. Of course, you must be baptised first, into the Catholic Church. We can do that the evening before.' He glanced at Papa, who nodded his head in agreement.

Channa and Veena chorused, 'We will find you a lovely wedding dress and make sure everything is organised for you – don't worry Cissy.'

She smiled at them all, knowing they were doing their best to help her out of a difficult situation. Their solution meant she could make a family with Maurice and Richard and still keep the good name of her family. But again, dissatisfaction niggled away inside her. Other people, however much they loved her, were deciding her life for her. She couldn't even choose her own wedding dress. And a new religion had been chosen for her. Once again, she stayed silent, knowing this lack of choice was typical for women, especially those who had transgressed the normal way of behaving as she had.

Chapter Three

Cecilia looked up, beaming at Maurice so handsome in his uniform, his gold and silver Regimental badge glinting in the sunlight that filtered through the church windows. His green eyes twinkled with love as he looked back at her. Her heart fluttered. He was her husband now – she felt so lucky and happy. He was hers forever. From today, they would be a family.

She wore a simple sari in a soft buttery colour with a gold-coloured choli loose enough to cover her breasts, which were large through feeding Richard. It had been chosen by Channa and Veena and was silky with a luxurious sheen. She loved wearing it though she was sad that she had not chosen it herself. She reasoned the dress didn't matter; it was trivial compared to the occasion.

The nuptial Mass was a solemn affair; she was learning all Masses were. She was slowly understanding the Latin words and rituals. She found herself increasingly interested in the religion that underpinned them. It seemed kind and caring and based on good values.

Her thoughts strayed to the evening before, when she had been baptised into the Roman Catholic Church. It was a short ceremony requiring her to promise to be a good Catholic and believe all the tenets of the faith. She had to do this, or she would not have been able to marry Maurice. She did not yet believe it all, but felt one day she would and therefore it was acceptable to agree.

Now, taking her new husband's arm and walking down the aisle, she nodded at their guests. She had not invited them. Channa and Veena had. It was a further irritation that she pressed down inside her. She didn't recognise a lot of the congregation, but Maurice had told her that anyone could attend the wedding. It was an opportunity to go to Mass and many members of the congregation would be there for that purpose only. Just the Catholic way, he said. She saw Channa and Veena in the pews, her Papa with her stepmother Susan, and new little brother Harold, her brothers, Joseph and Stani and her younger sister, Susie. All smiling. Even the auntijis were smiling genuine smiles. Cecilia knew that they were not aware of Richard. She feared the beams would not be so quick or so broad if they had known.

As they left the church through its red brick, arched doorway, her father greeted them. Shaking Maurice's hand, he said, 'Look after her, she is precious.'

'I will,' he replied. 'I love her.'

John turned to his daughter and kissed her. 'You're beautiful, like your mother.'

A shard of sadness pierced Cecilia's heart. She wasn't missing her mother just today. She had missed her every day of her pregnancy, throughout her painful childbirth and every single day in the new convent with baby Richard. There she had the advice of a kindly nun, Sister Anna Fernandez, but she still missed her mother.

Papa whispered, 'It is your time to be a happy family now. You have waited a long time. I'll collect the baby tomorrow and bring him to you in the married quarters at the barracks.'

The day was heating up. The hard, red dust swirled around their feet, staining the hem of her sari. She barely noticed; she was so excited. The small group of guests followed them to the church hall, murmuring amongst themselves, the women dusting the bottoms of their saris as they walked. Her younger brothers ran around the straggly line of people, hiding among them and chasing each other around. Cecilia and Maurice laughed and joined in. Soon, all the guests were running around, playing hide and seek, laughing and shouting.

Cecilia decided to rest awhile, and she sought out her step-mother. Susan was dressed in a plain orange sari with a coffee-coloured choli and gold jewellery which clattered gently in time with her steps. She said, 'You must miss your mother today. I know your Papa does.'

Cecilia nodded, 'Yes. You have made Papa happy again. And you have Harold now. Papa is young again.'

Susan smiled and squeezed her hand, 'You know Cecilia, everyone loves you. They love your kindness and joy and sense of fun. And how you always want to help people. You deserve happiness yourself and I am sure Maurice will bring you it.'

They strolled together in a loving silence.

The small wedding breakfast was carefree. It was catered by the auntijis with Channa and Veena helping. She watched the women chattering and busying themselves with laying out the food, including some bickering about who wanted what plate to go where. The special occasion meant they had cooked rogan josh delicious and tender. The smell of turmeric and chilli mingled with the fresh baked scent of naan bread and the wafts of vegetable samosas. It made her realise how hungry she was.

Maurice appeared beside her. He kissed her cheek. 'I love my beautiful wife. We are going to have such a good life. We'll have more babies and our family will be the happiest in the world.'

Forgetting her hunger, she whispered, 'When can we leave here? I want to be alone with you.'

He raised his eyebrows and laughed. 'So do I. If we spend a little more time here, just a little, then we can leave without anyone thinking we are rude.'

'But it is my wedding day – surely I can do what I like. After all, you only have one wedding day in your life.'

Maurice knew what she was thinking and laughed out loud, 'Oh my love. That is why I love you so much. You are so forthright and funny. You don't behave like other ladies, you have so much energy and love for life; I am lucky you are my wife. We have to behave but not for much longer, I hope.'

They sought out Papa and told him of their plan to leave early. He spoke quietly, 'Of course, you must go, bette. You two have not seen each other properly for months. You need time to be together. You go now, I'll tell the guests – when they notice.'

Cecilia kissed him on the cheek, 'Oh Papa. I love you so much.'

Chapter Four

Cecilia was happy. Her life with Maurice was full of fun and laughter. He was kind and loving. Baby Richard was thriving. His ayah, an Anglo-Indian girl called Maria, was attentive and loved him dearly. She was proud of her little family, of the way they had managed the less than perfect start. It seemed that no one, even the auntijis, realised Richard was born before they were married. Now, any sense of scandal surrounding his birth, if there were any, seemed to have faded with the joy he brought to everyone. He was sweet natured, beaming at everyone. Cecilia loved holding him, stroking his little chubby arms telling him about everything she was doing. He seemed to listen to her and absorb everything she said. She was convinced he was the most beautiful and most intelligent baby that had ever been born.

On the occasions when he cried inconsolably, she was glad of Maria's help. The ayah would take Richard for walks and settle him while Cecilia took a rest. The family had settled into a calm routine. She still studied hard at the local college, attending law lectures and working at home, reading and writing essays. She hoped that the newly launched movement to allow women to be lawyers in India – led by her mother's friends the Sorabji family – would be successful and she could soon practise alongside other women. She kept up-to-date by reading newspapers and pamphlets. She was excited by the prospect that women may one day choose how they lived their lives – not have men deciding for them. In the meantime, she was going to study hard, and be a good wife to Maurice and mother to Richard.

Every Friday, Maria stayed overnight so that Cecilia and Maurice could go out dancing. They would meet up with Veena and Channa and sometimes other friends, going to local events around the town. They would dance and dance. She would lose herself in the music and just move the way the rhythms seemed to tell her. Maurice loved to dance with her or sometimes just watch the fluid way she moved at one with the music. He was so proud to be the husband of the best dancer in the room, he would tell her over and over again. After the evening finished, they would walk home linking arms then make tender, passionate love in their little bedroom as Richard slept peacefully in the next room.

When Cecilia started to feel ill in the mornings and her body started to swell, she knew she was pregnant again. She was excited at the prospect of another baby, one that would be born without the shame she was made to feel the first time. This baby would be coming into the world in the 'right' way. When she told Maurice, he twirled her around the kitchen and kissed her with excitement.

'Another baby, my lovely Cecilia. It's really exciting. I cannot wait. Richard will have a brother or a sister.'

She had already told Maurice how sad and lonely she had felt in both of the convents. She knew he was remembering that conversation.

'This time, my beautiful wife, I'll look after you and love you and make up for all the sadness of before. I will not let that happen again to you.'

The local nurse examined her and suggested the baby would be born in the late summer. She also pronounced Cecilia healthy and said that she would have a good pregnancy. The nurse proved right and on 3rd August, 1899 she gave birth to another boy. She was attended by some of the other military wives, who rejoiced at the arrival of this healthy boy. This was such a different experience from last time, she savoured every moment. The baby seemed to sense her joy, opening his tiny blue eyes to stare at her intently.

One of the women ran to tell Maurice at the ferry port. While they waited for him to return home, the other women cleaned the bedroom and washed her so that she was ready to show Maurice his new son. Maria brought Richard in to see them both and he climbed into the bed and gazed in wonder at his little brother.

Maurice burst into the room. 'A boy, a healthy boy! Richard you are a big brother now and my Cecilia is the loveliest wife and mother in the world.' His smile so wide it nearly split his face in two.

He kissed Cecilia on the forehead as she handed the baby for him to hold. Cradling his new son for the first time he said, 'What shall we call him?'

'Richard,' piped up Richard. Cecilia and Maurice laughed. 'Oh bette. We can't have two babies called Richard. We would be confused all the time.'

Two-year-old Richard looked crushed by his mistake, not understanding why he was making his Mama and Papa laugh so much.

Maurice ruffled his son's curly hair, 'Easy mistake, bette. We should give him my name, I say. Then we won't get mixed up.' He looked at Cecilia. She was irritated that he hadn't asked her. She swallowed her disquiet to enjoy this most precious of moments. Her family all together. All happy.

Maria collected Richard and baby Maurice so Cecilia could rest. Maurice lay on the bed next to her. He stroked her arm. 'What a wonderful woman you are, Cecilia. Another beautiful baby son for us.'

She moved close to him, as much as her torn and bruised body would allow. 'I am so happy too. We have two lovely boys. Not sure about calling him Maurice though.'

'What's wrong with Maurice? Perfectly good name. Why don't you like it?'

She smiled, 'Named after you? Poor baby, how awful.' But she couldn't keep a straight face as she saw Maurice's hurt expression and she burst out laughing. 'It's a lovely name really. I was only joking.'

Maurice's face cleared and he began to laugh too, 'You always make me smile. Why don't you choose his second name? I know you chose Richard's name without me. But you were at the convent then and had no other way.'

'Then I shall name him John, after my Papa.' She looked at Maurice and nudged his arm with her elbow, 'That will cancel out him being called after you!' They laughed again and settled down to a happy sleep, cut short when the baby woke up for a feed.

Cecilia and Papa were in the yard with Richard and baby Maurice. They were sitting under the shade of the banyan tree. Marigolds were blooming in the little boxes that leant against the bungalow, providing vibrant clusters of bright orange against the dull walls, cracked by heat. Tiny lizards darted around, disappearing into the dried cracks. The temperature was stifling but the banyan provided welcome shade. They enjoyed watching the boys play with a small bowl of water, splashing each other accompanied by squeals of laughter.

Her Papa smiled at their antics, 'They are such delightful boys, bette, thank you for giving me such lovely grandchildren.'

'I know, Papa, I am so proud of them. Soon Richard will be going to school. I want to make sure he gets the best education. It is so important – as you taught me.'

'Yes, it is important. Your mother and I were sure of that.'

'I keep going to college, Papa. I still want to be a lawyer.'

'Of course, bette, it is even more important now that you are a mother. I understand that now.'

She knew he was referring to the challenge both her children would be facing as they grew older. Being called *chi-chis* by both the British and the Indians was insulting, but the fact they may face more discrimination broke her heart. She knew that a good education would help them break through the constraints of their birth. It seemed Anglo-Indians were fated to work on the railways, but she hoped these two little sons of hers would have a better future and more choices. She hoped they would be doctors, lawyers, teachers, or politicians. There were so many opportunities a good education would give them.

Unexpectedly, Maurice walked into the courtyard, pale and shocked, moving with a flatness of feet she had never seen before.

She looked at him, worried. 'Maurice. Why are you home so early? Is something wrong?'

He sat, his back leaning against the tree trunk, all the life drained from him. Against the sounds of his laughing sons, he whispered, 'I am going to war.'

'War? Where? Why?'

'We are fighting in South Africa. Some of my Regiment are there already. The rest of us go in two days.'

'Two days? Two days?' Cecilia yelped. 'It can't be. You have not long finished your last assignment for them.'

'We need more men to fight. I have no choice. The Regiment is sending all of us, regardless of past attestations.'

Cecilia called out to Maria to collect the boys and take them indoors for their meal. When they had left, she looked at her husband, 'No. No. This cannot be right. You can't go.'

Her Papa stood up, 'You have a lot to talk about. I will go.' He hugged Cecilia, wiping away her tears. He placed a comforting hand on Maurice's shoulder and squeezed it gently, 'Come back safely. We need you here.'

Maurice nodded. They watched him leave in silence and then fell into each other's arms.

'Surely they need you here, on the ferries? I don't understand why you have to go,' wept Cecilia.

'I have no choice, my love. They will find Indians to run the ferries. I have to leave you tomorrow and travel to Karachi. We sail at dawn the next day.'

She could barely speak her next question but knew she had to ask it. 'What happens if you don't come back?'

Maurice did not answer for a long time. Then he said with conviction, 'I will come back, my Cecilia. I will come back to you and our sons. I love you too much to die. The other soldiers tell me that this is the last push, the war is nearly over. I will not be away long.'

That evening the sky was heavy with unshed rain, the heat was still stifling. The weather was as heavy as their hearts. They ate in silence in the yard, a meal prepared by Aktbar, their cook. Cecilia lit some candles. They watched the flames flicker, lost in their own thoughts. Later, they made love in the knowledge that they would not be together again for a long time. After, neither could sleep. They lay in each other's arms savouring every moment.

Maurice started to cry, 'I am scared. I do not want to go to war. I do not want to die or kill anyone.' She held him harder.

He talked more, 'I have seen injured soldiers come back from wars. They are never the same again. Some of them are damaged in their minds too. They are changed men. I don't want to be one of them either.'

Cecilia did not know what to say. She knew that this decision was made by others, people who didn't know them at all. It was a decision that they had to obey. If Maurice did not go to war, he would be hunted down by his fellow soldiers and shot as a traitor. She kissed his shoulder and let her tears fall onto his wide chest as it rose and fell to the sounds of his deep sighs. The night turned to dawn sooner than either of them wanted.

The early morning was quiet, the children asleep. Light was glimmering through the dark clouds and the birds wakened, their chirping contrasted with the sadness that she and Maurice felt. They packed his belongings into his leather issue rucksack. He slung it over his shoulder and took her hand. They walked into the children's bedroom. Both boys were still sound asleep. Richard was sucking his thumb, his damp hair stuck to his head. Baby Maurice was snuffling, his little noises louder in the silence of the room. Maurice stroked their cheeks and bent to kiss them without waking them. He whispered, 'Goodbye my little ones. I will be back soon. I promise. Look after Mama for me.'

In the gateway, they held each other as if they would never let go. When the clock struck six, he gently pushed her away. 'I have to go now, my love.'

She nodded, 'I love you Maurice Roche. Come back to us.'

'I love you too, Cecilia Roche. Look after yourself and the boys. I will come back to you. Soon, I promise.'

He didn't look back as he walked away. His steps were flattened by his sadness. She felt a jolt of cold despite the heat of the morning. It bloomed quickly inside her, turning to panic. She managed to stifle a wail, a pained cry to him to come back and not leave them. She felt nauseous as she watched until he disappeared into the distance.

When her trepidation subsided a little, she walked back into the house. She could hear Richard and baby Maurice waking up, their little cries turning into calls for their Mama. She hugged them to her as hard as they would allow before they wriggled away to start their day. She decided not to tell them about their father. She would answer their questions as honestly as she could when they asked about him.

Later, her Papa returned, bringing Bhakti and Jaishree with him. The auntijis brought the samosas and halva they had made that morning. They laid them on the table and set about making spicy sweet chai. They encouraged everyone to eat and drink, as they always did.

'Have some, have some,' they chorused, looking anxious and determined.

Cecilia understood they were being kind, but she wondered why they always thought food would solve everything. She told them she wasn't hungry.

'But you must eat, bette. You will need your strength.'

'I just don't want to Auntiji. I am not hungry.'

'Bette. You are lucky to have food,' announced Bhakti.

'We grew up in the famine – you should never refuse food,' joined Jaishree.

'We saw many, many people die for many years.'

'We were lucky to have the money to survive, weren't we, John?'

'You must never refuse food. It is too precious.'

'Have some, have some.'

And they went on and on, the way they always did. They annoyed Cecilia more than usual. She pulled her father aside and said, 'Please take them away, Papa. I know they are being kind. But I cannot be with them at the moment.'

'I understand, bette. They were so sorry for you, they have been cooking all morning and wanted to see you. To make you feel better.' He smiled at the irony.

Then she laughed out loud. 'It is funny, Papa. They have come here to make me feel better. But they have made me feel worse. That's very funny. So I am feeling better because I am laughing about feeling worse.'

He looked relieved, 'I love you Cecilia. You always could find the funny side of things.'

The auntijis looked at them laughing and, satisfied they had done their job of cheering her up, took their leave, kissing her, Richard, and little Maurice in turn before they left.

Cecilia looked at her Papa and laughed again. 'Oh Papa, I think I would prefer it if you bring Channa and Veena next time. They will not upset me like that.' She paused, 'Mind you, they won't make me laugh like the auntijis either.'

Changing the tone, Cecilia asked, 'Papa, can you be like a father to my boys while Maurice is away?'

'Of course, bette. They bring such joy to my life and they love playing with little Harold too. It is good that he is a similar age to them.' He tipped his hand forward and back to show he was happy with the idea.

'Yes, Papa. Thank you so much. The Regiment will pay me Maurice's wages and I will go to the barracks every week to collect them. Perhaps we could all go together?'

'That is a lovely idea – it is quite a walk, but the boys have such energy, it'll be fine for them. Less fine for me!' And they laughed again.

A few weeks later Cecilia woke feeling sick for the fourth morning running. She knew what this meant – she was pregnant again. She must have conceived this baby the last night she and Maurice made love – the night before he left for the war. In some ways this was a comfort. She felt this new life was a sign that everything would be alright. But going through another pregnancy without her husband by her side was daunting. She told Channa and Veena. They were at once excited and concerned. They promised to look after her until Maurice came back and they cooed at the thought of Richard and Maurice having a new brother or sister.

On their weekly trip to the barracks to collect Maurice's wages, Cecilia told her Papa. They both watched Richard and Maurice as they chased baby monkeys around the street, shrieking and laughing with delight. The monkeys were too quick to be caught, which excited the boys further.

'Oh, bette, I hope you keep well. Will you continue your studies?' Papa's forehead creased in concern.

'Of course, Papa. I will still do them until my confinement,' she reassured him, 'and I have Maria to help afterwards.'

They arrived at the barracks, the stench of the soldiers' boots – old leather and sweat – overpowered everything, even the smell of elephant dung that accompanied their every walk. Cecilia and her Papa took a sharp intake of breath, as they always did when the soldiers' smells assaulted their nostrils.

As usual, Mr Hugh Weightman was in his office dealing with the line of wives collecting their husband's wages. He was a serious looking young man – about eighteen, she thought. Pale, British and good looking with the accent of an educated gentleman. His voice was clipped yet soft, polite and formal. Unlike many of his type, he was caring. It was his first post in the Indian Civil Service, he had told her many weeks ago. She had watched him as she queued each week and she saw that he took his work seriously. He managed to look interested when the wives updated him with their news. When they handed him their letters, he took them with great care and placed them in a neat pile on his desk. When he had to give them a letter from their husbands, he did so with a kind smile knowing how precious they were to the receiver.

As she reached the head of the queue, a little boy appeared at Mr Weightman's side. He was possibly about eighteen months old and tottered with the unsteady gait of a toddler learning to walk. He pulled at Mr Weightman's trousers to attract his attention. 'Play, play?' he demanded.

Mr Weightman sighed and bent down to speak to him, 'Oh Tommy, you should be a home with Mama. How have you escaped?' He looked at Cecilia by way of apology and said, 'My little brother, Thomas, he is a very lively one, for sure. Quite precocious. Please excuse me a moment while I deal with him.'

'Of course,' nodded Cecilia. Mr Weightman stood up, holding Thomas by his hand, guiding him to the door. An attractive English woman in her late thirties appeared in the doorway. She was tall, slender with red hair and striking green eyes. She wore a pink tea dress with a white lace collar. Cecilia guessed this woman was the mother of Mr Weightman and his little brother. The woman looked worried but her face cleared as she saw the little boy. 'Oh Tommy, there you are! I have been looking everywhere. You must not interrupt your brother while he is working. You naughty boy,' she scolded him.

Little Tommy didn't look at all contrite, he smiled at his mother and looked around at the women in the queue favouring them with a meltingly cheeky grin. Cecilia and all of them were laughing at his spirit. He certainly livened up the tense line of women.

Once his mother had taken little Thomas away, Mr Weightman sat back down at his desk and apologised again to Cecilia. 'I am so sorry – he is a handful, my brother.'

'It is not a problem, Mr Weightman. I have two little boys, they are over there with their grandpapa,' she patted her belly, 'and another baby on the way.'

'Well congratulations, Mrs Roche. Let's hope your husband is back in time to see this one. And let's hope it is not as lively as my brother!'

She handed him her letter to Maurice. 'Thank you, Mr Weightman. I haven't had a letter from my husband for some weeks now. Do you know why that is? Do you know when they are coming home?'

He frowned, 'I am afraid I don't, Mrs Roche. I know it is hard for men to write when they are in the frontline, so that may be the problem. The Regiment tells me that they are unsure of future plans but will let me know as soon as they have some information.'

'Ah, well, you say that every time, Mr Weightman. But I ask every time too!' They smiled at each other in mutual understanding. She turned to leave, 'Come Richard, come Maurice. Papa.' She nodded farewell to Mr Weightman. He called out as she reached the door, 'I promise I will get a message to you, if I hear anything, Mrs Roche. You have my word.'

As they walked back, Richard and Maurice flicked stones in the red dust with sticks they had found. The monkeys had gone so they laughed and chased each other instead, oblivious to the crowds of people around them. Cecilia called to them, but they took no notice, so she watched them carefully to make sure they didn't get lost.

'Mr Weightman is a helpful gentleman, I think,' Papa remarked.

'Yes, he takes trouble with everyone. He understands we wives are in an unhappy position.'

'I wonder if his little brother will take after him?' asked Papa, laughing.

Cecilia smiled, 'I don't think so! I think that little one needs to calm down first.'

'Perhaps he could play with Richard and Maurice – they are about the same age. They would be a positive influence on him.'

She shook her head, 'It's a good idea, Papa. But they are *chi-chis* and the British won't let their children play with *chi-chis*.'

'Such a terrible term, *chi-chis*. Why can't children play together? They wouldn't notice skin colour, I am sure.'

'I agree, Papa. But the British are the power here and they make the rules. They seem to not appreciate Indians or Eurasians.'

'It is not a good way to be, bette. I hear more and more people wanting to free India from British rule. The feelings around the Sepoy Uprising have not settled. It killed many thousands of people. I know it was over forty years ago – but people still feel the hurt. I fear unrest may be coming.'

'Oh Papa, I hope not. If British rule ends, let us hope it is peaceful. When Maurice comes back, he will not want to see fighting here too.'

She took his arm as they arrived at the compound. 'I will make some chai, Papa. Maria will look after the boys. Stay with us awhile.'

Cecilia read Maurice's latest letter again. There had been so few since his departure eight months earlier, she treasured it as she would have treasured gold. It had arrived two months ago and the paper was nearly worn out because she had opened it, read it, and folded it so often:

My dear Cecilia

What exciting news you had in your last letter. A new baby. I hope we will have a girl this time, do you? If I am not back in time, and we have a girl, please will you call her Bridget Mary. They are my favourite names.

How I miss you all. How are the boys? Richard must be nearly at school now. Is he ready for it? And little Maurice – how is he? I expect he is talking more and more by now.

I love you, my Cecilia. I miss you so much. When I am lonely, which is often, I think of you – your beautiful brown eyes, your long hair and smooth skin, us lying in bed together. I think about how much we love each other and how happy we will be when we are together again.

I cannot tell you anything about the war. But I hope to be back very soon indeed.

Your loving husband

Maurice

Every time she read it, the letter made her surge with joy. The newspapers were saying that the war would soon be coming to an end and it was clear that Maurice thought so too. Hopefully, he would be back in the next month, in time to see his new baby due in just four weeks. The boys would have their Papa back. Though they missed him, little Maurice had nearly forgotten him already.

Maria entered, Cecilia put the letter away, folding it with care. Cradling Maurice in the hook of her arm, Richard by her side, Maria handed Cecilia an envelope.

'The telegram boy brought this just now,' she said nervously. Cecilia snatched the telegram from her, knowing it

41

would not be good news. She tore it open and read it in a fit of rising panic.

A howl escaped her lips, she fell to the floor. Richard and Maurice started to cry too, seeing their mother so upset.

Maria picked the telegram up but she could not read it. She looked to Cecilia for answers.

'It says he is missing in action. Missing in action. It says he was brave in serving his King and country.'

Cecilia pulled her heaving body upright using a nearby chair. After she sat on it and got her breath back, she said, 'They haven't said he is dead, have they? Just missing in action. He is alive, I am sure. Maria, please take the boys and find Memsahibs Channa and Veena. Please ask them to come here.'

She went to bed and cried harder than she had ever cried before. She could not imagine life without Maurice. She had been certain he would come back to her. Every day was spent in hope. The telegram was a complete shock, dashing that hope. But she decided she wouldn't believe it until they confirmed that he was actually dead.

She showed Channa and Veena the telegram. They grasped the undercurrent of the message immediately. They hugged her and cried. But she pushed them away.

'He is not dead, I am sure. He can't be. His last letter said he would be home soon.'

'Oh Cissy, Cissy.' Channa's voice was gentle, 'I think this is their way of saying he has been killed.'

'No, no,' she shrieked. 'It can't be. How do you know? I am going to ask that nice Mr Weightman, he will know. He will tell me the truth.' With that, she left the compound, Channa and Veena following in her wake. She moved as fast as her swollen body would allow, weaving between the bullocks and elephants that lived in the streets alongside the homes and shops.

Arriving at the barracks, breathless, she found Mr Weightman in his office, looking through some files. He wasn't surprised to see her, it was clear he had heard the news. She gulped for air, throwing the telegram onto his desk, making Channa and Veena gasp at her lack of manners.

'What does this telegram mean?' she demanded, 'My Maurice cannot be dead, can he?'

Mr Weightman unfolded the screwed-up telegram, flattening it out with careful solemnity. He read it as if he had never seen such a telegram before.

He looked up at Cecilia, 'I am afraid, Mrs Roche, this is an official way of describing someone who has likely been killed.'

'Likely, likely?' she shrieked, 'What is likely? There must be hope, then.'

He shook his head, 'I have worse news for you Mrs Roche, I am afraid.'

'Worse? What can be worse?'

He looked at her with a sad intensity. 'This morning I have had further news about Engineer Roche. Please sit down, Mrs Roche.'

'Why?'

'I think you need to be seated to hear this. Please.'

Her heart was beating fast as she plumped onto the chair opposite him, 'Well?'

'I am afraid he was skinned alive by the enemy, Mrs Roche.' His voice was so quiet, it was barely discernible.

She was instantly sick on the dusty floor, struggling to breathe once more. She could hear Channa and Veena wailing but it didn't seem as if their noise were in the same room as her.

'No, no, no. My poor Maurice.'

'I am so sorry, Mrs Roche. It is such terrible news.'

Channa and Veena were hugging each other in despair.

As Cecilia screamed, a contraction tore through her body. As it subsided, another one followed.

'The baby is coming. It's too early. Help me. I need to go home.'

There was alarm in Mr Weightman's eyes, but his overall demeanour gave no sign of it. 'I will call for some servants to carry you home, Mrs Roche.'

'No that will not be necessary,' she snapped, 'My friends will take me.' Then remembering that he had only been trying to help and that she had been rude, she said 'Thank you for the offer of help, Mr Weightman. And thank you for your honesty.'

The three women made their way through the dirty, noisy streets. Channa and Veena each held a hand, guiding her around the lowing animals, stalls, and detritus on the road. They stopped and propped her up every time she had a contraction. No one took any notice of them.

Channa and Veena made soothing noises as Cecilia kept saying between contractions, 'It's too early, too early,' about the new baby.

All they could do was make the same noises when she gasped for air: 'Skinned alive? No, please no.'

It took them a long time to get home, the street was so dusty that Cecilia's gasps for air seemed to fill her lungs with grime that she kept coughing out. Once they reached the compound, with Channa and Veena's help, she climbed into her bed. Her contractions were coming too quickly for her to speak, or even gather breath. Cecilia bit down with each contraction. Her lower lip was swollen and bleeding but she didn't notice. She did not want to frighten her boys who were playing

44

in the yard with Maria. Channa bathed her forehead with cool water, mummering words of encouragement. Veena ran to collect the nurse.

Ten agonising hours later, she gave birth to a baby girl. The nurse, an old woman in her eighties, wrapped the little bundle in a shawl and said, 'The baby is breathing well, but she is small. She will need great care as she might be sickly – she has been born early.'

Cecilia was relieved the baby was well. 'Her name is Bridget Mary. We must send a telegram to Maurice to let him know he has a daughter.' She paused. 'Oh. He will never know, will he? He will never know now.' She thought of Maurice, of the way he had died. She looked at her daughter, her dark curls and downy skin. This tiny baby would never know her father or how much he loved her. A wave of loneliness swept over her.

She wept.

Chapter Five

'We loved him too Cecilia,' said Channa, placing an understanding hand on Cecilia's arm. 'We miss him.'

Veena nodded. 'He is not coming back.'

'I still don't believe it. I think the Regiment may have made a mistake. He is probably wounded somewhere.'

'He would be back with you by now if they were mistaken. *The Times of India* says that the war in South Africa is nearly over. You have to believe it.'

Cecilia sighed, 'I don't want to, I can't even think about how he died. I loved him so much. The children are growing up without a father. That cannot be right – God would surely not let that happen.'

Channa looked at her friend, 'It happens to many women when there is a war. So many children grow up without their father. Life for a widow is hard. If he had died of illness, they would say you didn't look after him properly. And they would treat you badly. But he was killed in a war and people do not want reminders of war. And they do not want to see that a woman can survive without a husband. They will treat you badly for that too.'

'I don't know what to do. I need to earn money. There is little pension for us from Maurice's service. I cannot keep relying on Papa. I have been going to the law lectures all this time – I think it is time to use what I know and advise people, that will be the best thing. For me and the children.'

Veena gasped, her voice rising in shock 'You cannot do that, it's not allowed. Women cannot practise law.'

'I know. But I need to earn money. I could do it quietly.'

'They will take your children away. They will put you into jail if you get found out. It is too risky.'

There was a long pause. Cecilia picked at a thread on her blue sari. Channa held her head in her hands, Veena paced up and down the room without purpose.

Eventually Cecilia said with a tight smile, 'You have to find me a new husband, then.'

'Perhaps that is the answer. A new husband,' mused Veena.

Channa stood up and went to the cooker where she had a dhansak cooking. Stirring the aromatic pot, she declared, 'We will find you a husband.'

'No, I didn't mean it. I could never love anyone the way I loved Maurice. I don't know that any man would want me and three children who aren't his own flesh and blood.'

'You have to find a husband, you have no choice.' Channa was emphatic.

There was another long pause as Cecilia pondered. The news about Maurice's death had arrived almost a year ago. Yet, she kept expecting him to come back. She knew she had to stop thinking like that. It was time to face the future and stop thinking about the past. She had to do something to change her position. She had the children to consider. She must set about finding a husband as soon as possible.

'Life has been lonely since Maurice went to war, before Bridget was born – she will be a one-year-old in a few weeks' time. I might think about it,' she conceded.

Channa and Veena sighed with relief.

'Good. There is a dance at the barracks on Friday. We are going to it with our husbands. Come with us – it will be good to see you dancing again. Maybe someone will be there that you like. Wear your lovely green sari – it suits you so well.' Veena was firm.

Cecilia laughed. 'Very well, I will come to the dance with you. It will be fun to dance again. And yes, I will wear my green sari, it is my favourite in any case.'

That Friday, she was excited. It had been so long since she had been out. She knew that, whether she met a man or not, she would dance tonight and enjoy herself. She would be as light as air.

Her sari was a deep emerald in colour with a bright trim of gold stripes. She wore a yellow choli and many gold bangles on each wrist. As she pinned her dark hair into a bun, her sari rustled and her bangles jangled. She smiled to herself. It felt good to be happy. She kissed her children goodnight as they went to bed. Richard, who was five, was excited to see his Mama looking so pretty in her make-up and sparkly outfit.

'You look beautiful, Mama. Will you be dancing?' He stroked her arm, playing with her bangles.

'Yes, I hope so, bette. I like dancing. Will you be a good boy for Maria?'

'Yes, Mama. I will look after Maurice and Bridget too.'

She hugged him and gently reminded him, 'We call Maurice by his middle name, now. We call him John as it makes me sad to call him Maurice. It reminds me too much of your Papa.'

He looked at her with earnest eyes. 'When is Papa coming back? When will he stop being a soldier, Mama, I miss him.'

'I don't think Papa will come back now, bette. I do not think we will see him again.'

'Why not, Mama, why won't he come home? I don't understand.'

Cecilia couldn't bring herself to tell Richard that Maurice was dead. It was too hard to explain to this little, earnest son of hers. His big brown eyes stared at her with such childlike hope.

'The war took him, bette, he cannot come back. But I will find you a new Papa, soon, I promise.'

With the acceptance of his age and another kiss from his Mama, Richard settled down into his bed. He turned on his side and his bony frame seemed to relax almost instantly into a deep sleep. Such sweet innocence, she thought with a sad smile as her friends arrived.

Channa was wearing a plain yellow sari and a pale green choli. She had tied her thick hair into a plait. Her long gold earrings stroked her neck as she moved. Veena wore a sky-blue sari with a cream-coloured choli. She wore no jewellery and her thick, wavy hair casually cascaded over her shoulders to her waist.

'You both look lovely,' declared Cecilia as she met them.

'You look beautiful,' they told her. Together they marvelled at Cecilia's tiny waist and her slender figure.

'All the men will want to dance with you tonight,' said Channa.

'They would never guess you have three young children,' Veena told her.

Linking arms, they chatted and laughed all the way to the dance hall. As they drew near, Channa spotted a small hibiscus bush growing randomly near the dusty path. A scrawny black cat was scrapping at it, looking for food. Channa shooed it away. She bent down, plucked a spray, and tucked it behind Cecilia's ear.

'There,' she said, 'you look lovely. The pink goes well with your sari. Hibiscus will bring you luck tonight. You will find a husband now.'

Cecilia touched her friend's shoulder and smiled. They heard the sounds of music and laughter coming from the hall. It was such a relief to her. Life for the last few years had been punctuated by the screams and squabbles of her children. That was all she seemed to have heard, over the sound of her own tears for Maurice.

Cecilia walked into the hall with Channa and Veena, the nascent auntijis, as she always thought of them. 'Right – who can we find for you?' they said with determination.

'There is a handsome soldier with our husbands. Look, look,' said Veena so loudly the whole room could hear.

Everyone turned to look at the soldier. He was white, tall and broad set. He had a thick moustache and a wide smile. He was holding a glass of whisky and laughing with Ravi and Daksha as if he had just heard the funniest joke in the world. His laugh was loud and long. Cecilia thought he looked attractive indeed. She felt a frisson of desire flow through her.

'I think he looks very handsome,' said Veena, 'what do you think, Cecilia?'

She was cautious, 'Possibly. I might like him.'

Channa and Veena took this as all the encouragement they needed. They each took one of Cecilia's arms, marching her towards the group.

'Cecilia, this is Christopher Keating. He is a friend of ours,' said Ravi, picking up the hint from the women.

'And he likes his drink,' said Daksha, raising his own glass.

Christopher's handsome face split into a bigger smile when he set eyes on Cecilia.

'This is Cecilia, our sisterji,' said Channa.

'You are beautiful. I have been waiting for you all my life. Where have you been?' said Christopher, looking at her with appreciation.

'And he is a charmer too,' added Ravi. Somewhat unnecessarily, she thought.

The camaraderie between the men was palpable. It was infectious and the women were drawn into the conversation and laughter. The band struck up – an Irish ceilidh. The lively beat was an invitation to dance. She watched the musicians, tapping her foot.

Christopher noticed her rhythmic movements. 'Shall we dance?' he asked her, as he proffered his arm.

Watching the people on the dance floor, she hesitated, 'I am not familiar with this type of dancing.'

He pointed to a man standing on a box in the corner.

'See that man? He is the caller. He will tell us what to do. Because everyone makes mistakes.' He drained his whisky glass in one gulp, placing the glass onto the table with a flourish.

They danced. They smiled and laughed as they twirled around the room. They listened to the caller, sometimes following his instructions. Other times, they just ignored him and danced their own way, much to the amusement of the onlookers and the annoyance of the other dancers. Christopher's looks and charm lifted Cecilia out of her sadness. She lost herself in the dance she loved so much and had been denied so long. He told her he was a gunner in the Royal Artillery, working as a guard on the North Western Railway. She told him she was a widow with three children and was about to work in law. He didn't seem put off by her widowhood or her children. But he was confused by her wanting to be a lawyer. He asked as they twirled in a do-si-do, 'Why do you want to work? Women should not work. Surely your father will keep you?'

'My father is supportive of women having opportunities.'

'Right hand star,' shouted the caller.

As they formed the star, Christopher raised his eyebrows, 'Such a beauty should never work. What did your husband think? People must have thought he could not keep you, he was not a real man.'

'Promenade, everyone,' yelled the caller, 'Now.'

He squeezed her tight around the waist as they promenaded through the centre of their set. His grip was starting to hurt her.

'He supported me too.' She tried to shake his arm away.

Christopher relaxed a little, loosening his grip on her, 'I can see you are determined and intelligent, so you will succeed, I am sure.' He didn't sound convinced.

Cecilia was not unduly worried about his reaction. It was, after all, to be expected from most men. Her father and Maurice were exceptions. If this Christopher did not want her to work, she would not be with him.

They sat at the table to catch their breath. He smiled at her.

'May I buy you a drink?' he asked as he ordered himself another whisky.

'A gin and tonic, please.' This was such a rare treat. She did not drink alcohol normally. It was unwise when she had three children to look after and studying to manage.

As the evening drew to a close, Christopher slapped his thigh, gulping another whisky, 'I would like to see you again Miss Cecilia. You are beautiful and you have made me laugh. I will walk you home and enjoy your company for a little longer.'

Channa and Veena looked pleased as they left the hall. Ravi and Daksha shook hands as if they had completed a deal. They were happy to let Christopher walk their sisterji home – he was a good man.

Cecilia and Christopher walked arm-in-arm through the crowded streets. The evenings always brought people outside, the cooler weather being a welcome relief from the overbearing heat of the day. They were surrounded by the noise and chatter of the night as they strolled along, wrapped in their own little world. When they got to the edge of her compound, Cecilia stopped.

'You live here.' It was a statement, not a question.

'Yes.'

'You have a very large compound. You must be wealthy.'

'Yes, I said my family are Parsees. We are high caste.'

He kissed her cheek, 'Your wealth doesn't matter to me. You do. You are so beautiful. I would be honoured if you stepped out with me again.' He smiled his charming smile again.

Cecilia smiled back, 'I think that will be possible.'

'Thank you. I will call on you very soon.' He plucked the hibiscus from her hair and put it in his pocket. He turned and left with a jaunty step.

She skipped into the house – her happiness carrying her feet almost faster than she herself could move. She flopped down on her bed. All was quiet in the house – Maria and the children were obviously asleep. Bliss. She thought about the man she had just met. He was captivating with kindly eyes, an easy smile and caring manner. He had a steady job. He loved children. He surely would make a good father to hers?

She fell asleep full of hopeful, peaceful thoughts: Christopher may well be the answer to her problems. She looked forward to seeing him when he called, as he had promised.

A few days later, Maria ran into the with kitchen Bridget in her arms. The baby was crying as if she were in considerable pain. Her wails were ear-piercingly loud. Maria had panic in her eyes.

'She does not seem well, Memsa'ab. She is clammy.'

Cecilia took the baby, 'Go back to Richard and John. I will see to her.'

She felt Bridget's forehead, 'My goodness, she is hot. Feel her, Channa, what do you think?'

'She is too hot. She needs medicine. I will get the doctor for you.'

Waiting for the doctor, Cecilia tried to calm Bridget. She walked her up and down, sang to her, tried to feed her – she was too feverish to feed – changed her nappy, rocked her in her crib. Bridget would not be comforted. She was getting hotter and seemed to be in increasing pain.

Cecilia was worried – her older children had times when they could not be comforted – but this seemed different. A mother's instinct told her Bridget was extremely ill.

With panic rising inside her, she tried to appear calm as she willed the doctor to come quickly.

Bridget started gagging then vomited everywhere. After she finished, she calmed down and stopped crying, as if the purge had solved the problem. Cecilia sighed with relief and after wiping Bridget's face and dabbing her clothes, placed her gently in her crib. The crisis seemed to be over.

Aktbar, who had been sweeping the yard, heard the commotion, came into the kitchen with a mop and wordlessly started to clean the floor. Cecilia dabbed at her sari with a cloth and looked at Bridget as she lay sleeping, seemingly content.

Channa burst into the room with the doctor. He was a young Indian man with a calm manner and guileless expression.

'How is baby? I hear she has a fever,' he said.

'She was sick and now she is sleeping,' Cecilia nodded towards the crib, 'I think that it has helped her.'

The doctor looked at Bridget saying, 'I am not sure.' He picked her up. Her arms, legs and head flopped alarmingly.

'This baby is unconscious, not sleeping,' he said. He felt Bridget's forehead and listened to her heart, 'She is critically ill. I am afraid she might not survive.'

Cecilia sat down in shock, 'That cannot be. No, no.'

'I am afraid time is running out. We need medicine that is not available here.' He turned to Channa, 'Go to the telegraph office and call the hospital in Karachi. Ask them to send some quinine quickly. A boy on a bike could bring it here.'

The doctor turned to Cecilia, 'Where is your husband, Memsa'ab? He works on the ferry doesn't he?'

'He went to war. He has been missing in action for months.' She did not want to tell him the truth about Maurice, the words always choked in her throat.

'Who is nearby for you?'

'Well, Channa, who you have seen. And Veena. And Papa.'

'Send your cook to get them. Now.'

He laid the baby down and listened again to her heart, felt her pulse. He said nothing, raising his eyebrows and shrugging his shoulders.

Trying not to give in to panic which was threatening to engulf her, Cecilia picked Bridget up. She held her close, walking up and down, 'My baby, my baby,' she whispered. 'Don't die, Bridget, please don't die. It will be your birthday soon. We will have a party and your brothers will bring you presents. We will sing songs and dance. Your auntijis and uncles will be all here. You will be the luckiest, happiest baby in the world. Please don't die Bridget, please don't die. Please. I love you so much.'

Her tears fell on Bridget's unknowing head and trickled down her little cheeks as if they were crying together, both fearing the very worst parting of mother and child. They were oblivious to everything around them.

Veena arrived and Channa returned a few minutes later with Papa.

'The hospital is sending the medicine now. I told them it was for a baby, they said they would be quick,' Veena told them in a voice breathless with terror.

The doctor lifted Bridget from Cecilia's arms. 'I am afraid it is too late.' He laid her dead body in the crib.

There was an unending, shattering scream, one that seemed to rent the walls. In the unbearable heat, everyone who heard it shivered to the bone. It was her own scream, Cecilia realised later. Channa and Veena held onto her, to comfort her and themselves. Papa slumped into a chair, holding his head in his hands, groaning as if in physical agony.

Maria hurled herself into the kitchen followed by Richard and John, 'What has happened, Memsa'ab?' The little boys, frightened by the noises of the adults, hid behind Maria's skirt.

Cecilia, Veena and Channa were crying so loudly they didn't hear Maria's question. So, the doctor told her.

The ayah started yelping and shrieking. And following suit, Richard and John began howling too. Still crying, Maria ushered them out of the room, glancing at Bridget's lifeless body as she left.

The doctor gently touched Cecilia's arm, 'I have to go now, Memsa'ab. There is no more I can do here.' He paused, clearly waiting for something. His money, she supposed, but knew he did not want to be indelicate.

She reached for the jar on the shelf, pulling out some money and passed it over. 'I should have called you earlier – but I didn't know how ill she was. I thought it would pass.'

'You weren't to know, Memsa'ab. This plague is a violent fever. I have had other little ones die the same way. Babies get bad quickly. There is no explanation, no reason. It is not your fault that God has taken her. It is his will.'

Cecilia picked up her dead baby and kissed her warm cheeks, her tears still falling. 'What about my boys, Richard and John. Will they catch it?'

'They will be safe, Memsa'ab. They are older and stronger – the plague has taken babies and older people but it is nearly over now. I will check them to be sure.'

Richard and John were acquiescent when the doctor examined them, picking up the sadness in the household.

'Well, Memsa'ab, one can never be sure of these things – but I feel these young men will not be affected by this plague. They are both healthy and strong. Your baby was always a little sickly, am I right?'

'Yes. She was born early, after I had a terrible shock.'

'I am sorry this has happened to you. After your husband is missing in the war too.' He left with a soft tread.

She stroked Bridget's face, talking to her in a soft voice. A voice of full of sadness and longing,

'Oh, bette, bette, bette. You are with your Papa now. He will look after you. Be happy, bette. I love you so much.'

Wiping their own tears away, Channa and Veena decided to take charge.

'Cecilia,' said Channa, 'I will go to St Patrick's and arrange the funeral.'

'I will stay with you and Bridget,' said Veena.

Cecilia and Veena held hands, silent in their shock and grief. They waited for Channa to come back with the news of the funeral.

'Father Gomez will bury her this afternoon. We will have a funeral Mass before,' she told them.

Channa and Veena set about making all the arrangements, Cecilia was too distraught to do anything but rock her precious dead baby in her now useless cradle.

The family gathered to say goodbye. They were all numb. They loved Bridget and her sweet nature, a happy smile. Cecilia's father was broken at the passing of his grandchild. He brought little Harold with him. Cecilia looked at her half-brother, just four-years-old. She felt a tear of envy that he was alive and her own baby was dead.

The pain of the funeral Mass and burial were unbearable. She held her head high, jutting her chin as every sinew of her body strained to keep her tears at bay. She knew that she would have to give way to the burden of grief soon, but was determined to stay calm in front of everyone.

For three days after, Cecilia lay in bed facing the wall. An invisible weight was pushing her body down, crushing her so much she couldn't get up. She wondered if she would ever again. Richard and John were concerned and bewildered about what had befallen their mother and baby sister. They ran into their mother's room often, pulling her arms, trying to drag her out of bed. She would hold them and tell them that she loved them but that she was too ill to play with them. Maria was an excellent ayah – Cecilia felt that she was not needed. For the first time ever, she wasn't interested in attending college either.

Maria knocked on the door and entered the room with a quiet step.

'Memsa'ab, there is a man at the door asking for you.'

'Tell him to go away. I don't know why anyone would be calling on me.'

'He is very keen to speak to you, Memsa'ab. He says his name is Christopher and that you would remember him.'

Cecilia rolled on the bed to face Maria, 'I do not know a man called Christopher – but if it takes only me to send him away, I will do so. Please ask him to wait for a few minutes in the yard.'

She started to feel a little better with something to actually do – send this Christopher away. A surge of determination coursed through her. She had no idea who he was, but was looking forward to telling him not to come back.

She changed quickly from her pyjamas into a dull sari and smoothed her unruly hair, just a little. He stood up as she strode towards him in the yard. There was something familiar about him. The events of the last three days had taken over so that she couldn't remember anything. Her mind felt foggy as she tried to work out where she had met him. He was tall, handsome with bright blue eyes, a bushy moustache and a shock of very dark hair. He was wearing a soldier's uniform. He was smiling at her with a lazy grin. He took her hand and kissed it, she was somewhat taken aback by his personal approach.

'Ravi told me about your baby. I am so sorry. I have come to pay my respects.' He sat back down.

'Thank you,' she said, sitting on the other chair. He obviously knew who she was, she felt that she could not send him away as readily as she had planned. She still did not remember him.

A long pause followed, he seemed to be wanting her to say something.

'You said I could call on you,' he explained, when he realised she didn't remember him, 'we met at the dance at the barracks last week.' He reached into his pocket and pulled out the hibiscus spray, now shrivelled but with the flowers still on the stalk.

The flowers seemed to jog her memory. She recalled, in a piecemeal way, the lovely evening she had spent with this man, just a few days before Bridget died. Little memories of dancing and laughing penetrated her mind.

She nodded, 'Yes, I remember you now. It's just that the shock of Bridget's passing has taken my memory at the moment.'

'Of course, of course,' he replied, 'it was a terrible thing. I know this plague has taken so many lives, lots of tiny babies, so very quickly.'

If she had had any more tears inside her, Cecilia would have cried again. Her eyes were swollen, sore with dryness and sorrow. She took a long breath, saying nothing.

'I want to bring some happiness into your life. Will you allow me to call on you again? You did agree to walk out with me the night we met.'

She saw eagerness in his startling blue eyes, someone who wanted to be with her.

'Yes please, I would like that.'

As he stood up to leave, he was slightly unsteady on his feet, staggering a little before he straightened himself, using the chair to support him. It was a hot day, she thought. She probably she should have offered him some water – but it hadn't occurred to her. He leaned in to kiss her hand again. She thought she could detect the smell of whisky on his breath, although she wasn't sure. He smiled up at her with the charm that had attracted her when they first met. 'I will call tomorrow. I will take you out for a walk. It will be good for you.'

Chapter Six

Some weeks later, Christopher said, 'I have fallen in love with you, Cecilia, you are beautiful and kind,' his beaming smile wide and warm.

'But we have not known each other for long.'

'I am sure, though. As soon as I met you, I knew you were the girl for me.'

Cecilia wasn't sure about her feelings for him. She had an inkling that he wasn't being honest. But she knew she needed a husband. She enjoyed his company and he seemed kind. She pushed her concerns down and tried to think of the good things that could come from this, saying 'We suit each other, I say.'

'We do. Perhaps it is time for me to meet your father.'

'He would like to meet you too – I have told him about you.'

'Then you must arrange it as soon as possible,' he commanded.

Christopher and John met each other a few days later, with Cecilia introducing them in the manner of a young girl, she was so nervous. They all sat in John's lounge, slightly tense and making small talk. Eventually, Christopher looked at Cecilia and said, 'I would like to speak to your father alone, please.'

She waited in the kitchen, listening to the sounds of the street outside. The dogs barking, monkeys screeching, children yelling, hawkers shouting about their wares. Time slowed as she sat alone.

She guessed Christopher was asking Papa for her hand in marriage. She hated the idea that, as a grown woman a widow and mother, she wouldn't be asked directly.

John entered the kitchen with his usual soft step and sat down. 'Bette,' he whispered, 'Christopher has asked my permission, he wants to marry you. What do you think?' His voice was laden with concern.

Surprised, she replied, 'Oh, Papa, thank you for asking. I don't like you men sorting out my life for me.'

'You are my little girl, bette, you always will be. I know you are an independent woman now too. That is why I am asking.'

Cecilia kissed him. 'Yes, Papa, I do want to marry him. He has a good job – he will be a kind father to the children. And I can stay in Karachi, continue my studies and still be near you and my friends.'

Her Papa frowned. 'He seemed nice enough, bette. But I am not sure about him. He seems a little too charming to me. A charming man is an angry man, in my experience. I could smell whisky on his breath. I think he has demons.'

Cecilia was struck by how much Papa was echoing her own concerns. She decided to be honest with him, 'I do understand what you mean, Papa. I have wondered about him too. He might have had a whisky today to calm himself before meeting you, so I think that's alright. I have thought about this carefully and decided he loves me. I need a husband. I can't earn any money yet. And I cannot live as a widow.'

He thought for a little while. Then asked, 'Shall I tell Christopher that he can marry you? I will tell him no if you want me to.'

'Please tell him yes.'

Papa left to tell him the good news. Moments later, Christopher bounded into the kitchen. He picked her up, twirled her around shouting, 'Marry me, my love, will you marry me? Please, please say yes.'

'Yes, I will.'

'I can't wait any longer - we must marry as soon as possible. Let's go to the church and get the banns read now.'

Excited, Cecilia agreed. Hand in hand, they ran to St Patrick's Church to organise the reading of the banns. Then they would have three weeks to plan the wedding. The children would be so thrilled. They would have a Papa again now.

It was the start of the monsoon season. They had timed the wedding for after the day's downpour. Cecilia held Richard and John in each hand as she walked to the church. The air was heavy with moisture. Each step made them all sweat, their clothes sticking to their bodies. The puddles of water in the streets were evaporating, plumes of steam rising from them. No one, not even the children, said anything. The tension was as heavy as the humidity.

Cecilia felt a wash of doubt as the church came into view. She was not sure about this marriage. Everything had happened so quickly. She barely had time to think about it. She needed a husband, she told herself and Christopher had offered. So, she pushed her doubt down, breathed the damp air into her lungs and carried on walking.

Terrible memories of Bridget's funeral in this church so recently nearly overwhelmed her as they reached the door. Her Papa was clearly thinking about the tiny coffin he had carried into the church just a few weeks ago. They looked at each other in a moment of understanding. He hugged her as they both fought the tears that were filling their eyes. She nodded, a nod which told him she was ready to focus on this day.

She was wearing a light cotton dress, made for her by a local British seamstress. It was lilac with a pink trim. It had a delicate lace collar with puffed sleeves, a tight waist and flared skirt. She was pleased with it and even more pleased because this time she had chosen it herself. Leaving Richard and John with Channa and Veena, she took her father's arm and walked up the aisle to be married. Again.

It was a small wedding. On her side, her family were there, along with Channa and Veena and their close relatives. Cecilia had also invited the kindly Sister Anna Fernandez to be a witness because the nun had helped in the second convent when she was learning how to look after baby Richard. Christopher had no family in India. He had asked a handful of his fellow soldiers and railway colleagues. The Latin Nuptial Mass was simple. They said their vows smiling at each other, both moved by the importance of the moment. Cecilia could smell whisky on Christopher's breath, which she decided was to be expected from a groom on his wedding day.

The wedding breakfast was held at her Papa's house. Her auntijis had been working all morning to prepare the tasty food: chicken farcha, rogan dhansak, patri ni machhi for the spicy savouries. Sev ravo, faluda and kulfi for the sweetest desserts. The mellow scents of spices and sugar hung in the air, heavy like the damp. The food was spread out on an overladen table in the kitchen where guests could help themselves and wander into the garden sit under the trees to eat and to chat. It was a subdued affair, there was little of the merriment that had marked her wedding to Richard.

As the evening wore on, the air began to lighten and it was easier for everyone to relax and breathe. Cecilia was making an effort to be happy, doing her best to thank everyone for coming, holding light-hearted conversations. But it didn't lighten the muted feel of the party.

She kept glancing at Christopher. He was drinking more whisky than was necessary and exhorting as many people as possible to join him. Ravi and Daksha were not keen, they were working later that evening. Christopher's friends were drinking along with him with the jollity that they were used to creating in the barrack bar.

Channa and Veena were looking after the children, having given their ayahs a free day. They were playing games with them, keeping them out of the way of the adults. Papa was quietly watching Christopher and his friends drinking as they became louder and more coarse. Papa looked unhappy. His faced was creased with concern.

Cecilia saw the auntijis were immune to Christopher's charm though he tried to win them round. He admired their looks, was enchanted by their saris, and complimented their cooking. They folded their arms, pursed their lips, and raised their eyebrows.

As soon as everyone left, Cecilia kissed Richard and John goodbye. They were staying the night with Channa and Ravi. The newlyweds had planned to sleep in Christopher's quarters. Cecilia was disappointed to see Christopher slurring his words and staggering, unable to stand properly. She turned to his best man, also drunk, 'Please Patrick, can you help me get him back to the barracks?'

Patrick, a short round man with few teeth, laughed. A leering uncomfortable sound, 'Of course. You need him in your bed tonight, don't you?'

She did not reply but glanced over to her Papa. He was still frowning. She shrugged her shoulders, the message in her eyes telling him not to worry.

Patrick and Christopher leaned on each other for support on the way to the barracks, singing and slurring. Cecilia walked beside them, disappointment bearing on her shoulders. As they arrived at the barracks, Patrick seemed to have sobered a little. He shouldered the metal gate open and hauled Christopher to his quarters, throwing him unceremoniously onto the bed. He staggered out of the room without another word.

The drunken groom stirred and started to wake.

Their lovemaking that night was not happy. Christopher was brief and brutal. She was bereft. She lay beside him awake as he snored in post-coital satisfaction. She wondered what she had done, in marrying him.

The next morning Christopher woke with a bad headache. She fetched him a glass of water. He took a glug and smirked, 'Good morning, Mrs Keating. We are moving tomorrow, so you need to pack your bags and the children's things.'

'Sorry? I do not understand.'

'I said we are moving to Mahoba tomorrow.'

'I still don't understand. Why are we moving? Where is Mahoba? I have never heard of it.'

'I have been posted to the Great Indian Peninsular Railway there. They need new guards. They are building a major junction at Jhansi. There will be chances for promotion. It's really exciting. There will be work for your boys there when they are older. And our own children. They will get work as they are *chi-chis*. Mahoba is the right place for us.'

She listened to his little speech in an astonished silence. What on earth was he saying? She was stunned, she couldn't take it in. She sat on the floor with her head in her hands. 'No, no, no,' she ran her hands through her hair, 'We can't move, we can't.'

His voice was cold, 'You have no choice, Mrs Keating. You are my wife and we are moving tomorrow.'

'But where is Mahoba?'

'About a thousand miles away. We will be properly together – just us and the boys.'

'A thousand miles? But I can't move that far. I have my family here. I will miss them too much.'

'Don't be silly. You have got me now. You don't need them.'

'But what about my studies?'

'You are my wife. You do not need to study. Now be quiet with your moaning. It's making my headache worse. I need to lie down. Go and pack your bags and the boys' clothes too. Now'

It took Cecilia a few minutes to understand what he was saying. Leaving her home, her family, her friends and stopping her studies. Moving a thousand miles away. Tomorrow. Why had he not mentioned this before? Why tell her now, after their wedding and after they had consummated their marriage? Why did he not ask her about it?

Once more, her future had been decided by a man. Her life she was beginning to understand was not, and never would be, in her control.

She felt the core of steel tighten inside her. She would have to go to Mahoba with him. She had no choice. But she decided she would carry on with her studies somehow, whether he liked it or not. He had tricked her. She was not sure she would ever forgive him.

She needed to talk to her Papa. Christopher was in a deep sleep, so would not notice her disappearance. The boys would be fine with Channa and Ravi for a little while longer. She ran to her Papa's house. Her feet were fleet with her need to talk to him.

'What is wrong, bette?' he asked with an edge of dread in his voice as he saw the state she was in, dishevelled, wide-eyed and short of breath.

'Oh Papa, Christopher says we are moving to a place called Mahoba tomorrow. He has a new job there. He only told me this morning.'

Papa sighed, heavy with sadness but lacking in surprise, 'Oh bette, what a shock for you. And me too.'

She lay her head on his shoulder and he held her tight as she cried and cried. As her sobs subsided, he moved her away from him and, holding her shoulders, looking at her with sadness.

'With a good job, he may change his more unappealing habits. And there will be chances for the boys to work on the railway when they are older.'

'But I don't want them to work on the railways. They should have more choices.'

'The boys may want to work on the railways, you know. The British seem to think the Anglo-Indians are the best railway workers and give them all the jobs. Mahoba may actually be the best thing for all of you.'

She wasn't convinced but said nothing more about it, 'I will miss you, Papa, so much.'

'I will miss you too, bette, more than you will ever know.'

'We will write letters and send telegrams for urgent things, won't we?'

'Yes, of course, we will.'

'Will you help me pack the house?'

'Of course, I will help. But your husband should be doing this really.'

'He has a headache.'

Together they walked through the streets of Karachi, oblivious to all the sights, sounds and smells that normally would have assaulted their eyes and ears. They walked in their own bubble, acutely aware that this would be one of the last moments they would be together for a long time. On the way, she went to see Aktbar and Maria. They both agreed to come with them to Mahoba. Cecilia knew it was less out of loyalty than the fact they would still have work. They would also provide some stability and continuity for the children, so she was content.

After they had packed, Cecilia and Papa went to collect the boys and tell them the news. At the ages of five and three, Richard and John had no qualms about moving. They were going on a train and it would be a big adventure, so they were eager to get going.

Channa and Ravi were less convinced.

'Why did he not say earlier?' asked Ravi.

'We will all miss you, Cecilia, it is not fair.' Channa began to cry.

'I don't know what to say, Channaji, I really don't. I am as surprised as you. He says he already has the job and there will be more opportunities there as they are building a big railway junction at Jhansi which is nearby.'

'What about your studies?' asked Channa through the tears that were forming rivulets down her cheeks.

'He doesn't want me to carry on with them. But I will find a way. I have studied too much to stop now. I will find a college near there that will take women. I can go to the lectures when he is at work.'

'Ah, bette,' said Papa, 'always finding a way. You always have and you always will.'

Chapter Seven

They arrived at Mahoba station late in the evening. There was still enough light to see the surroundings. It was in the hills, where rocky outcrops studded the countryside as if they had been dropped from the skies by an angry god. They were hot, dusty, and tired. The children were fractious, the novelty of the train having worn off many hours ago.

Cecilia heaved a sigh as they piled out of the carriage and stretched their legs, 'How far will we have to walk now?'

Christopher smiled and pointed over the station fence, 'It is just here. We have the shortest walk. Come on.'

He led the way to a spacious bungalow next to the platform. The sign above the front door said, 'Section Engineer'.

She frowned, 'You are not a Section Engineer. Why is this our home?'

As he turned the key, opening the door with a flourish. 'Because they think so much of me – they are letting me have this house. See, it is large, enough room for all of us. There is a yard where the children can play. A verandah for us to sit out in the evenings. And little huts for the servants to live in at the end of the garden.'

She had to admit it was a nice house with plenty of room for them all. But it hadn't been lived in for a long time and was dilapidated. She coughed as the dust invaded her throat and lungs.

70

'Aktbar will clean it,' Christopher reassured her. 'And look,' he swung her around to look through the shutters in the front room. 'It's the railway workers hospital. Just over the road. So, there will be doctors and nurses nearby if the children are ill. Or,' he squeezed her waist suggestively, 'if we have more children.'

The memory of Bridget's loss pierced her as she deftly moved away from him and peered further through the shutters, 'I can only see railway homes here. Is there a town?'

'It's just short walk away, my love. Not far at all.'

Still peering, she asked, 'And where is your office?'

'Oh, it's not here. Don't you remember? I told you I will be working at Jhansi. It is a train journey away, so I will stay there and come back here every so often.'

She frowned. 'I don't remember you saying anything. Why did they not give us living quarters in Jhansi?'

She saw a shadow flit over his deceitful face. He paused and said, 'I don't quite know. I think the quarters in Jhansi are not big enough.'

She was not convinced – after all there were only four of them. There were many railway families with more children. But, she reasoned, if he were away some of the time, there would be more chances for her to study. Living in Mahoba may be a good thing after all, just as Papa had said.

But it was not as she had hoped.

The railway quarters in Mahoba were near the station, convenient for Christopher and his travel to Jhansi. But not for the family. Mahoba town, with its shops and schools was around two miles away, a long walk for the children. There were no families in the railway quarters for them to have friends nearby. It was mainly single men who worked long hours. There were no other women around and Cecilia began to feel isolated.

Mahoba was a railway town. There was an endless line of old men, porters weighed double by the loads on their backs, picking their way through the streets to the station. They looked like the rows of ants which troubled their kitchen when the children left fruit out, she thought. Other than these porters and a small weekly market, there was nothing in the town. No monuments or temples, nowhere green to play. Mahoba was isolated and, for all of them, dull.

She found a college in Allahabad, Ewing College, where she could attend lectures. It was a long way to travel. She had to leave her children with Maria, sometimes for days. She was able to keep her secret from Christopher because he was away so much. When he was home, his behaviour was difficult and aggressive. Increasingly, every time he came back, he smelt of drink, shouted at them all and spend most of the time nursing a headache.

She knew that she should never have married him. She was lonely and miserable, but not about to give up on their marriage. Every time he came home, she was hopeful that things would improve between them and they would be happy again. She was sure that he was a good man, really, and that he just needed to get used to them all. But he crushed her hopes every time.

Cecilia sighed. She looked at Maria's lowered head. 'Well, if you are not happy and you are missing your Mama and Papa, then you should go home.'

Maria looked relieved. Her face lit up as she asked, 'May I leave now, Memsa'ab?'

'Not quite now. I will need to find a new ayah first. I am due to have this baby in three months – I cannot be without an ayah.'

'Memsa'ab, I have spoken to a friend of mine. Her name is Supriya. She lives this side of the town and wants to be an ayah.' Maria's voice was tentative, as if she should not be making this suggestion.

Cecilia didn't mind – she was keen to find a replacement. Maria had not been happy since they moved to Mahoba, nearly a year ago. Her sadness had pervaded the house and added to Cecilia's loneliness.

'What is this Supriya like?'

'She likes children, Memsa'ab. She is kind and honest and works hard.'

'That sounds fine but I would like to meet her. Please could you fetch her for me.'

Supriya was young – about fourteen, Cecilia guessed. She was pretty with large brown eyes and soft coffee skin. But she had a sulky manner. Her eyes were dull and disinterested. Her pouty mouth was downturned as if she disapproved of the whole household. As though she were superior to them all.

'What experience do you have of looking after children?' Cecilia asked.

'I have three little brothers, Memsa'ab. I have looked after them all.' But there was no enthusiasm in her voice.

'What about helping in the house? We have a cook, but you will be asked to help out on occasions, I am sure. And cleaning too.'

'I am a hard worker Memsa'ab. I can do any task you ask of me.' Her face changed a little, to force the modicum of interest she knew was necessary to get the job. Cecilia had doubts but thought she would try Supriya out. She needed a new ayah as a matter of urgency. She was prepared to over-look this girl's manner in the hope she would improve with time.

'Are you able to start tomorrow?'

With a little curtsey, she replied, 'Yes Memsa'ab. I will be here at 7am.'

'Good,' said Cecilia, by way of dismissal, 'we will be wait-ing for you.'

She helped Maria pack her clothes and took Richard and John with them to the railway station to say goodbye to her. The train pulled in belching plumes of grey smoke. Cecilia hugged Maria, 'Thank you for looking after my boys for all these years. And thank you for looking after little Bridget too. All the children love you.'

'And I loved them too, Memsa'ab. They were a joy to me. And little Bridget was so precious, I miss her.'

Nodding and wanting to change the painful subject, Cecilia said, 'Please send my regards to your parents and tell them how much we love you. I wish you well in your new endeav-ours.'

'I hope this new baby is fine and well too, Memsa'ab.'

Richard and John cried and clung to Maria's skirt, trying to stop her getting onto the train. As the guard blew the whistle, Cecilia prised them off, 'You have Supriya to look after you now.' Maria stepped onto the train and, as its piercing whistle blew, Maria leaned out of the window and waved. They all waved back until they could see her no more.

The boys were downcast. It was market day. Cecilia de-cided that they would walk the distance into the town and stop at a stall to buy some *gulab jamun*.

In the market, saris fluttered in the breeze, hung up outside little shops. Dekshis shone under the glaring sun as if they were the most precious of silver jewels. The sweet stall was a

74

riot of sugary treats, bright colours and inviting scents. The boys cheered up as they ate the sticky, sweet, nutty treat. How easy it was to make them happy, she reflected. If only *gulab jamun* had that power over her own life.

He body was aching from the weight of the baby. She was looking forward to having this child but had moments of complete dread too. The memory of Bridget's death was still raw – she worried that it may happen again.

She wondered if it was just work that kept him away. Perhaps it was another woman. She realised that she didn't much care. His behaviour was so unpredictable. Sometimes he was kind and gentle, others he was temperamental and aggressive. She never knew which Christopher he would be when he returned from work or even an hour later, so quickly could he switch personalities. She was beginning to be scared of him. But she knew he was looking forward to being a father and she hoped things would change for the better once this baby was born.

Christopher held his newborn daughter in his arms, his smile as wide as Cecilia had ever seen it. 'We should call her after you.'

'You mean Cecilia?'

'Yes, why not? You always say women should be equal. And men call their sons after themselves. Why shouldn't women do the same with their daughters?'

Cecilia thought about what he said. 'You are right. If we give her my first name, we should give her my second name too. We shall call her Cecilia Mary.'

'We should shorten her name to Cissy. That way we won't get you two mixed up,' he said, still grinning.

Cecilia laughed, 'Yes, it would be easy to mix us up. Me and the baby.'

Christopher looked at his daughter. 'She is beautiful, my darling. I love her and will be a good father to her.' He paused. Then he looked at her, 'I have not been a good husband to you. I know that. But this is a new day, a new dawn. This baby gives me the reason to be a good husband and father. I will try harder in the future. I will be better. I promise.' He sounded sincere.

Cecilia took the baby from him to feed her, slightly concerned that he was promising to be better because of the baby. It was clear that she alone hadn't elicited a similar change of heart in him. She was too excited to think about it for long. Little Cissy was pink and healthy. She was born on the exact date that she was due, 25 August 1903. Cecilia smiled to herself. She had been so worried. Bridget's death had haunted her, but that was over now. She was pleased that Christopher was going to change – things would be much happier for her little family now.

She could carry on her studies while he was away – she still wouldn't tell him. She sensed that, even in his new way of being, he still wouldn't like her going to the college. She wouldn't tell him.

Aktbar made a celebratory dessert. He called it Cissy's Anglo-Indian treat. It was bread and butter pudding spiced with cardamom and cloves. Cecilia knew he had taken the trouble to invent the dish because he, too, was relieved that the baby had arrived safely. He had been with her when Bridget died. This was his way of showing he cared and was happy for them all. The new dessert was sweetly aromatic and tasty. She thanked Aktbar for being so clever in melding Indian and British cuisines. Christopher was bemused at first but pronounced it delicious after a few mouthfuls. Richard and John, who tended to eat everything that was put in front of them, gobbled it up without comment.

Christopher was holding Cissy as she started to cry. The boys were mesmerised as he gently rocked her and sang to her – his Irish voice lilting in the lullabies. Richard and John had never seen their Papa be so kind. He encouraged them to kiss their little sister and stroke her cheek. As they did, Cecilia watched, suffused with happiness at the happy scene. The boys ran off to play in the yard where Supriya was waiting for them. The baby settled down again. Christopher looked at her with a smug smile, 'I am such a kind Papa, aren't I?'

She bit down the immediate riposte that one day as a father was not the greatest test and his step-parenting abilities were somewhat lacking. But she said instead, 'You are a fine Papa. She is lucky to have you.' She wanted to build on the lovely atmosphere pervading the house.

Christopher left for work later that day; he said a gentle goodbye to his family. He told her he would be back in a week to see them all.

Cecilia lay back on her bed to rest after the rigours of labour. But once the euphoria of producing a healthy baby wore off, her body felt weak and she was not well enough to move far. The doctor told her she must rest in bed until she was stronger. He gave her no reason for her weakness but advised her not to have another baby for a while.

'Therefore, Memsa'ab, no intimate relations with your husband until you are properly better.'

Christopher did not return a week later, as he had said he would. She was a little relieved as she still was not well. She feared he would want to make love to her. Three days later than he promised he burst in, smiling. Cecilia was wary as she could smell whisky when he stooped to kiss her. But he seemed relaxed and amiable.

'I am sorry to be late, Cecilia. My workmates wanted to wet the baby's head, they were so happy for me. For us, I mean.

They wanted to congratulate me. Well, us, really. But it was only me there, of course. And I missed the next train back. Then there wasn't another train for two days.' He shrugged, 'Sorry.'

She noted that this was the fullest explanation he had ever given for any of his many absences. And he had apologised too. Was it guilt, she wondered?

She decided not probe. 'Well,' she asked, 'did you enjoy the celebration?'

'Yes.'

He changed the subject, 'How is little Cissy – how has she been?'

'She is thriving nicely, thank you. She is asleep in her crib at the moment.' Cecilia knew her voice was a little sharp.

'Oh, and the boys? Have they missed me?'

'They always miss you. They always ask for their Papa. I didn't know what to tell them when you were so late. We wait every day for you, never knowing when you are coming back.'

'I am sorry – I really am. I said to you I would be a good husband and Papa. I am trying but I wanted to celebrate with my friends. Is that so wrong?'

'No, it isn't,' she said, 'It is just that you were three days late – that is a long celebration.'

'I know, I know.' He changed the subject again. 'How are you? How are you recovering?'

'I have been very weak. I still am.'

He rushed to her side and knelt beside her chair, 'Oh my love, I am sorry. I didn't know.' He saw her stern look at that comment, 'I couldn't know, could I? I was at work. But I am sorry to hear this. How are you now?'

'I am only a little better. The doctor says it will take weeks to recover and that I am to rest.' She paused, wondering how to tell him. Taking a big breath, she blurted, 'He said we must not have sexual relations until I am better.'

She watched a range of conflicting emotions flicker across his face. She saw anger and frustration battle with empathy and gentleness. She saw the angry Christopher fighting the calm Christopher. With relief, she saw the calm Christopher win.

'Alright, we must wait until you are stronger. If the doctor says so, that is what we will do.'

She relaxed a little. She did not know how long he would be this reasonable. It might be days or hours or just minutes. She decided to make the best of this situation while it lasted, laying on the bed to rest. She stared at the walls of the bedroom with their old, faded pink wallpaper and stains from the previous residents. She closed her weary eyes.

His good mood lasted about an hour while Christopher cuddled little Cissy and played a game of catch with the boys in the yard. Then he rushed into the bedroom and announced he was leaving for work.

'But you have just got here,' Cecilia was surprised.

The look in his eyes told her that he was lying as he said, 'I forgot to mention that we are short of shed men. I have to go back to help out.'

She could see that he was doing his best to contain anger. His body was tense, his voice flat and forced through clenched teeth. She knew it was because she couldn't lay with him yet. He had come home for physical relations only. That was obvious now.

'If they need you, you have to go,' she said, happy to be rid of him.

'Very well. I will come back when I am not needed there.' He threw some money on the table, 'This is from the last shifts.' Without a goodbye he left the house, slamming the door behind him.

Cecilia felt so alone again. She had three children to look after and no husband to help her. Her body was still not strong so she couldn't yet be active. Supriya tended to sulky idleness. Aktbar was a good worker and she was grateful that he cooked the meals every day and cleaned the house and yard regularly. But he was not a companion, he was a servant. She felt the need for the company of another adult. But not Christopher. Though she was lonely and lost, she was relieved he had gone back to work. He was too unpredictable and she was too uncomfortable when he was near her.

She sighed and stood up slowly, her many silver bangles jangling. She promised herself she would make life happy for them again, whatever way she could. She felt her steely core of resolve find its way through her weakened body and strengthen her once more.

Cecilia arrived at Mahoba station after the evening lecture at Ewing College in Allahabad. The train was late and she had waited for hours. She had telephoned the telegram office in Mahoba asking them to send a message to Supriya and Aktbar telling them she would be delayed.

Thank goodness their bungalow was so near the station, her body was still weak and she couldn't walk far. She was feeling guilty for being away from her family for longer than she had planned and she decided to take them all out for a treat tomorrow. Opening the front door, she intended to rush straight into the children's bedroom to see them but she stopped short. Christopher was slouched in the lounge, a bottle of whisky in his hand staring into the space in front of him. She had no idea that he would be back, she hadn't heard from him for three weeks.

'Where have you been?' he demanded.

Taken aback and unable to think of anything to say, she replied, 'I have been out.'

'Where have you been?' he spat and slurred.

Her stomach involuntarily contracted. She decided to stand her ground, 'I was out.'

'But where?' he growled. His eyes flashed in anger but then fogged over with drink. His head lolled to one side and he passed out, dribble winding its way down his stubbly chin.

Tiptoeing passed him, she went into the children's bedroom. Moonlight filtered through the shutters; she could see them sleeping. They were breathing deeply, so innocent in their slumbers. Her heart swelled with love and pride. Her children were the most precious things in her life. Everything she did, she did for them. Her little ones were worth every moment of hard work and energy. Her love for them propelled her every day. She crept into her own bed, leaving Christopher asleep in the chair in the lounge. Hopefully, he would stay there all night.

The next morning, she rose to the smell of chai simmering on the stove. Aktbar was, as usual, in the kitchen cooking for the family in silence.

She was having breakfast with the children when Christopher walked in. His eyes were red and weary, his stubble grown hard on his chin, his clothes awry. He was rubbing his forehead declaring, 'My head is so sore. I was so tired I slept the night on the sofa.'

She watched him warily. Aktbar handed him a glass of water which he drank with the urgency of a man who depended on it to live. Then he looked around the kitchen and seemed to see them all for the first time. His eyes settled on her.

'You were back late last night. Where were you?' he demanded of Cecilia.

Ready for him now, she had decided what she would say. 'I was visiting Reema. I wasn't late. You were asleep on the sofa, I didn't want to disturb you.' She was relying on him not remembering last night.

He looked puzzled, as if he didn't quite believe her. But couldn't quite refute her either because his memory was too cloudy. The pause, while he thought about it, was tense, like a dekshi that was about to boil over. But suddenly the strain evaporated, as he shrugged and sat down with a grunt. The moment was over. She breathed a sigh of relief as the tension seeped out of her.

'Papa,' said Richard, 'I like my school.'

'That is a good, young man,' he replied as he ruffled Richard's hair and took Cissy onto his knee, cuddling her while he spoke. It was as if he had not been angry just a few moments ago. 'Your Mama and I want you to like school. It is important that you learn lots of things now to help you when you grow up.'

'Yes Papa, I know. You have told me before.'

Christopher laughed.

John joined in, 'I want to go to school, Papa. I want to learn lots of things soon.'

Cecilia smiled at him, 'You will be starting school soon, but you can still learn things before you go.'

Christopher's head seem to clear more as he shook it from side to side. He said, 'Let's do something fun today, shall we? It is not a school day, so perhaps we should all go out for a walk and buy some food from a street stall, shall we? It is market day today.'

Christopher carried Cissy while Cecilia took one boy in each hand. They wandered through the loud, colourful, smelly, animal-strewn streets. As ever, the sights and scents assaulted their senses. The railway quarters were not like these streets at all. They were quiet, with spacious boulevards and the only noise came from the trains and passengers in the station. Here, in the centre of Mahoba on market day, everything was malodourous, noisy, and chaotic. People and animals were everywhere. The line of bent over porters still plodded its way to the station, carrying sacks of goods. Monkeys waited by the stalls, ready to pounce on any food that strayed onto the ground or was held in an unwary hand. Cows sat in the middle of the street untroubled, flicking flies from their hind quarters with their tails.

Cecilia felt both boys straining at her arms, trying to join the crowds or stroke the animals. She held them even tighter, fearing for their safety. They were becoming frustrated with her so she turned the walk into a game for them. She chased them from tree to tree, buying them a treat from nearby stalls as she caught them. The boys ran around the dogs, cows, and horses, sitting or lying in the heat. They jumped around the beggars and the street sellers, laughing and squealing as they tried to escape her.

When they had all had enough, Cecilia suggested that they go to the barrage on the other side of the town to cool down. They made their way to the lake where local families gathered to play and paddle. Seeing the sun silver-shimmering on the gentle water, the boys broke free and began splashing each other, laughing and screaming.

Cecilia and Christopher were distracted by a man nearby who was standing on a box and speaking Hindi with impassioned fervour. Out of curiosity, they went to join the crowd gathering around him, although Cecilia kept glancing over to her sons, making sure they were still happy. Other little boys had joined their game. They were all having fun, so she relaxed and listened to the speaker. The man had a notice at his feet saying, 'INC, Bal Gangadhar Tilak, talking here today'. He was in his forties, rotund with sagging flesh. Speaking in Urdu, his voice was firm and loud as he extolled the rationale for freeing India from British rule. Cecilia understood him and listened with rapt attention. But Christopher soon grew bored.

'What is he saying?'

'He is from the Indian National Congress – a new organisation. I read about it in *The Times of India*. They want to stop British rule.'

Christopher snorted. 'He had better stop talking like that or he will be in trouble.'

'That's true. I am sure they will imprison him if they know about this.'

Christopher grabbed her by the elbow, pushing her back to where the boys were playing, 'I don't want to hear him anymore.

I don't want to stand and listen to that sort of nonsense. I am a white man among Indians there.'

'Do you think the British should leave, like he is saying?'

'Of course not! Where would we be then? I am British and work here. If the British withdraw, what will happen to us, to you and me? The children are all *chi-chis*. They will never be welcome anywhere.'

'But I don't think the children – or even us – are welcome anywhere even now. You are a British man and I am an Indian woman. Many people don't like us being together and married.'

'Well, the Anglo-Indians will stay together – we have our own community now. The railway jobs all go to us, the British need us to build them. And to run them. That is work forever. If the British leave now, who will build more railways? There will be no work for us at all. No future for the children either.' His voice was becoming more animated as his anger grew.

She didn't want to stoke his fury but needed to challenge him. She was desperate for him to acknowledge their children should have a better variety of jobs to choose from. 'We must give our children more opportunities, not just the railways,' she said determinedly, 'Parsees are campaigning for women to be lawyers, teachers and doctors. Cissy could be any of those if she has a good education.'

He looked at the baby in his arms. Then her turned to Cecilia, 'She is a girl – she doesn't need an education – she can just marry well. She is my princess, I will make sure she has a rich husband.' His voice, now calming down, held an element of contempt.

Cecilia decided not to argue with him, to keep the peace. She changed tactic, 'Richard and John need more opportunities too. They will get more choices through a better education. That is why I am sending them to such a well-known school.'

A dark cloud fleetingly passed over Christopher's face. He shrugged, 'They are not my sons. They are yours. It is up to you what you do. I don't really care. Cissy is mine.' He cooed at his daughter, 'She is mine, she will not study. She will do as I say.'

Cecilia felt her heart lurch in sadness. Up until that moment, she believed Christopher loved her boys as if they were his own. Now she knew it wasn't true. She watched them shouting and splashing about with new found friends. Her poor little boys, rejected by the man they loved as their father.

They strolled home in uneasy silence, buying samosas and laddoos from the street stalls and eating them as they walked. Richard and John were still lively but a little of their energy had worn off with all their water games. They gulped their food and asked for more.

Cecilia laughed, 'There is a book by a man called Charles Dickens. It's called *Oliver Twist*. He always asked for more food as he was always hungry. You two remind me of him.' She bought them more sweet laddoos.

'Mama,' asked Richard, 'Can you read that book to us, please Mama?'

'When you are older, bette, I will. But now it is time to go home and settle down to bed.'

Cecilia realised much later that baby Michael was conceived that evening. After the children had settled in their beds, Christopher made love to her with less than his usual brevity. She could not smell drink on his breath, so she assumed he was more sober than normal. He was not caring, but this time, he was not as rough as usual. That this nicer lovemaking had resulted in another baby, she took as a good sign, a sign that things would get better.

Christopher's improvement after Cissy's birth had not lasted long at all. A few months maybe. But the birth of Michael seemed to give him another boost – another reason to be a better husband and father. Michael was born on 30th November, 1904, which meant she now had a family of four children, aged seven, five, sixteen months and four weeks. The household was busy, full of noisy cries, squabbles, screams and laughs.

Supriya was not much help. She did as little as possible, now there were four children. Cecilia resolved to find another, more useful, ayah. But she was so busy, there was little time to do it and she did not know who to ask. She was unhappy and lonely. She missed her Papa, Channa and Veena with a pain that pierced her heart and an emptiness that lived in her mind every day. At night, even when Christopher was beside her, she cried herself to sleep, aching for the gentle touch of a kind lover, for the whispered words of a caring husband. Longing for Maurice.

When mornings dawned, she relied on the core of steel inside her to face the rigours of the day.

Christopher was away again, he had left just after Michael's birth. She preferred life without him now, so she didn't mind. She was rocking baby Michael in his crib when there was a knock at the door. She answered it and saw a fat, toothless British man in Royal Artillery uniform. He looked familiar but she couldn't remember where she had seen him before.

'Hello Cecilia!' he grabbed her by the waist and swung her around with an enthusiasm that robbed the breath from her. 'How are you? It has been a long time!' He smelled just like Christopher did when he was drunk. A rancid reek of fustiness that made her wince as it attacked her senses.

She was trying to pull fresh air into her lungs to ask him who he was, when he answered her unspoken question, 'I have come to see Christopher, the last time was on your wedding day. And we carried him home to the barracks. Do you remember?'

Ah, he was Patrick. And she did remember him. She remembered that she didn't like him either. And she was wary of him now too, as he was obviously drunk again. She was polite, as she felt she should be.

'Christopher is at work in Jhansi. I do not know when he will be back.'

Patrick looked bemused, 'Oh, I thought he would be here. Jhansi is quite far away, isn't it?'

'Yes, he returns every so often. The trains are not regular, so he cannot always come back when he wants to.'

There was a pause, which she broke by saying, against her better judgement, 'Would you like some chai? I have some on the stove. You must have come a long way today.'

'Thank you, I will. Yes, it has been a tiring, dusty journey.' He looked around the kitchen, taking in its shabby cupboards and tatty furniture.

He caught sight of baby Michael asleep in his crib. 'A baby. He's tiny. Very new?'

'Yes, he is one month old. Michael. We also have another child. She is just over a year old. Cissy.'

He smiled, a lecherous smile, 'Aha, so you have been busy!'

She was silent, feeling uneasy. She ladled his chai into a glass and set it on the table. There was a menace about him which made her skin prickle.

'When is the next train to Jhansi?' he asked, 'I think I will go there.'

She felt relieved he was not planning to stay long. 'It's in about an hour. If you catch it, you will be in Jhansi late this evening. I will write down his address for you. He is in the railway quarters so he will be easy to find.'

Patrick swallowed the chai in one gulp and, placing the glass on the table with a purposeful move, he stood up and moved towards her. His step heavy with menace.

'You must be lonely without him. A beautiful woman like you.' He stood in front of her.

She stepped back as she began to feel a sense of dread take over her body. 'I am not at all lonely. We write letters all the time and we are very happy.'

'But you must miss him.' He stepped towards her once more, 'especially in your bed. At night when you are all alone. With no one to love.' His voice was filled with threat.

Feeling his menace push her, she stepped back again. She knew that the wall was behind her. There was nowhere for her to go now.

'You need a man in bed with you.'

He lunged forward, grabbing her arms and pinning them to her sides. Roughly, he pulled her towards him and landed his lips on hers, forcing his tongue between her teeth. At first, she was too stunned to realise what was going on, but suddenly she felt her steely determination take over. She bit hard down, stamping on his foot at the same time. He dropped his grip as he cried out, blood tricking down his chin. He staggered across the room, clutching at his face.

Aktbar came running in from the yard. In Hindi he said, 'Memsa'ab, what has happened?' He looked at Patrick who was wiping blood from his tongue. 'Do you need help with him?'

She replied in Hindi, 'I am fine Aktbar. Mr Patrick is just leaving. Perhaps you could watch as I show him out of the door?'

'Yes Memsa'ab, I will.'

Incensed by their use of Hindi, Patrick hissed at her, 'No wonder he doesn't love you – he doesn't even like you. You bitch.'

'What did you say?'

'I said he doesn't love you. He never did. He hates you,' his eyes flaring with hatred.

'He married me.'

Patrick picked up his bag and started towards the door, 'You don't know why he married you? Hasn't he told you? You are a fool as well as a bitch.'

Cecilia could feel a cold pit in her stomach. She knew she was about to hear something awful.

Patrick's tongue was swelling up, more blood was now trickling down his chin onto his uniform. He wiped it before he spoke. His tongue was clearly making it difficult but not enough to stem his venom.

'He only married you to get his job and this house. He needed to be married by 10 June. He married you on 9 June. Why else did you think he would take you and your two brats on? No one else would have you and he needed a bride fast. He could smell the desperation on you.'

He continued, 'This house, this bungalow here in Mahoba. Why do you think you are living here?'

'He said it was because the GIPO thought highly of him. They wanted him to have a large house for his family.'

'Huh! That is a lie. They do not think well of him. They didn't want him living in Jhansi and influencing other workers with his bad ways. Mahoba is small and just used for the mining line. They told him to get married so he could have this house. They thought a wife would calm him down. But it's not working, is it?'

She felt sick with the realisation that there was a terrible inevitability to his words. But she wasn't going to give him the satisfaction of breaking down in front of him.

'You are only saying this because I have spurned you. He loves me. And my boys too. I know he does.' But even she could hear the doubt in her voice.

Gathering her courage, she shouted, 'Get out of my house now. You are never to come here again. I will tell Christopher what you did to me. He will not like it. He will not like you anymore either.'

'You bitch. You ugly bitch. No wonder he stays away. There are more beautiful women in Jhansi. I will join him. We will take our pleasure from the women there, like we always did in Karachi. And like he does now.'

Aktbar, realising the tenor of the conversation was deteriorating, took Patrick firmly by the arm and led him out, with a strength that belied his age. Patrick, his evil spewed and spent, cursed under his breath, still stemming the blood from his tongue.

She sat down, bent double, as if all the air had been punched out of her. She was breathing fast and feeling sick. The realisation that Christopher had used her to get his job, had lied about loving her and tricked her into marrying him, was almost too unbearable to contemplate.

She realised there had been signs in the past but she had always ignored them. She was cross with herself, for not facing reality sooner. For blinding herself to his faults with her endless hopeless optimism. For telling herself he was a good man, he loved her and her boys, that his drinking wasn't a problem, that he really did want to change his ways.

Her marriage was a sham. She was far away from Papa, Channa and Veena. She was lonelier than ever. She did not have friends she could talk to in Mahoba. She did not know where to turn.

She hated Christopher and how he had trapped her into this existence.

Yet there was little time to think about it, life was too busy with her studies and the children. She decided to carry on as though Patrick's visit had never happened and ignore the seething and fear inside herself. She needed to protect her four children. Richard and John, rejected for not being his blood. Cissy and Michael who weren't born from love. She knew she could not leave him, the scandal would be too great. The stigma would follow her everywhere and throughout her life, stopping her from realising her ambition.

She decided to make a life with her children and her studies, Christopher would only be a part of it when she faced other people. She needed her studies to be a lawyer and earn money to give her children a good education. She would merely tolerate Christopher when he turned up.

Baby Michael began to stir in his crib. She picked him up and hugged him tight. She drew strength from his little warm body and felt the love flow between them, more poignant than ever.

Christopher turned up a few weeks later, strolling into the bungalow with a light air and ready smile, smelling of drink.

'Hello, my Cecilia. Hello, my babies,' he greeted each child in turn, treating Richard and John in the same way as Cissy and Michael. She sighed with relief. Perhaps he had forgotten that he had told her that Maurice's sons were nothing to do with him.

She would never forget. She felt a prickle of nervousness about the Patrick incident, wondering if he knew about it. She let him kiss her on the cheek, 'Hello. How long are you back for?'

'I don't know yet. Is there any drink here?'

'I have some chai on the stove and there is some Camp Coffee in the storeroom.'

'Chai? Camp Coffee? I meant a proper drink. Whisky.'

'There is nothing in the house. You will probably find some in the market today.'

'Well, I will go there then.' He strolled out with the same jaunty air as he entered a few minutes ago. The children watched him leave and then turned back to their game, without comment.

He staggered in the next morning, drunk and belligerent. She was alone in the kitchen, washing a cup.

'Patrick said you threw him out,' he slurred, 'You threw my best friend out.'

She took a deep breath, 'He attacked me. He wanted to have physical relations with me.'

'I don't believe you. He is my friend,' Christopher was snarling, his exposed teeth yellowed and rotten.

'And he told me you didn't love me. That you only married me to get the job in Jhansi and this house.'

She was hoping against hope he would say Patrick was lying.

He leaned into her ear, taunting her. 'That's true. I needed a wife quickly. You were desperate. I do not care for you or your children. Patrick said you threw him out when he was trying to help you. He is my friend. He would never attack you.'

Her heart was thumping, her knees felt wobbly. She was terrified. But her insides were tightening with resolution. She was determined to stand up to him, 'Well, he did. He said I needed him in my bed.'

'Why are you lying, woman?'

She was unprepared for his lunge, he moved so fast. His face contorted with anger, his teeth baring like a wild animal. He pushed her hard in the chest. She fell hitting her head on a chair. The glass in her hand shattered all around her. Christopher looked at her prone on the floor, helpless and breathless. He kicked her hard. Twice. Then walked out.

Cecilia lay there, holding her side. She was sure he had fractured her rib. She felt a warm trickle down her forehead. Blood flowed into her eye. She realised she had been cut where her head had hit the chair. She lay still with shock. He had knocked the energy and fight out of her.

Aktbar ambled into the kitchen, he had not heard anything nor had he seen Christopher arrive or leave. He stood still with horror as he saw Cecilia on the floor. His face crumpled as if he were about to cry. She saw him hesitate, knowing it was not acceptable to help her up as that would entail touching her.

She spoke to him in Hindi, 'Please help me Aktbar, it is hard to move.'

With the strength he had shown when ejecting Patrick, this time combined with the gentleness of a child, he lifted her and sat her on a chair. He grabbed a nearby cloth and handed it to her to stem the blood. He poured a glass of water and gave it to her to sip. The tears in his eyes spilled onto his cheeks. 'Oh, Memsa'ab. Oh, Memsa'ab. This is not right. You husband is not a good man.' He wiped his cheeks with the back of his hands. He began to sweep up the glass.

Cecilia held her aching head in her hands. She did not know what to say. He was a servant and she did not want to involve him. But he was the only one who knew about her husband, so it made sense that she should talk to him.

In the end, she decided not to say anything for fear of stories getting out among the townspeople and the reputation of her family being ruined. Or more ruined than it already was, she thought ruefully.

Instead, she asked him, 'Please could you help Supriya look after the children? I need to lie down for a while.'

'Of course, Memsa'ab. I think Supriya is not always nice to them. I am happy to help.'

Oh no, she thought with her groggy head, another problem, Supriya. What did Aktbar mean when he said that? She must deal with Supriya soon – but now she needed to rest. Her head was aching, her ribs painful. She had no idea when Christopher would return, he may be travelling back to Jhansi by now, or he may be getting more drunk at a local bar, ready to come back and beat her again.

Her body was tense with the problems and sore, so sore with the injuries. She lay in bed, taking stock. She had a violent, drunken husband and no choice other than to stay with him. She had four young children who needed her. She had to find a better ayah, who would be able to stay over on the evenings that she went to college, which was Supriya's only advantage. She needed to earn money to be independent of Christopher.

As she lay on the bed bruised and battered, she felt a determination rise from the depths of her being, overtaking her mind and body.

It was time to make a decision.

Arriving in Allahabad, she sought out the offices of Dinshaw Edulji Wacha. She knocked at the door. It was answered by a serious young Indian man who looked at her in surprise because women did not usually arrive alone, if at all.

She wasted no time, 'I need to see Pandit Wacha.'

Recovering his composure, he asked, 'Who may I say is calling and what may I tell him it is about?'

'My name is Cecilia Keating. Pandit was a friend of my mother and father. My name was Cecilia Chattergee then.'

The young man closed the door, leaving her outside in the midday heat. He clearly didn't feel the need to be polite. She watched the activity in the street as she waited. Animals were wandering around, some had owners, others were strays. Monkeys were in the trees looking for any opportunity to nab food. Young men were gathered in groups, smoking and talking. Women in bright coloured saris carried urns full of water on their heads. Children were running around oblivious to everything but each other.

The young man opened the door again, this time with a warmer manner.

'Please,' he said, gesturing indoors, 'follow me.'

He opened the door to a large office with a wooden desk, which was covered in papers. Behind it sat a man who looked to be around fifty. He had a shock of white hair and a bushy greying moustache. A smile broke out across his face when he saw Cecilia. He stood up to greet her.

'Bette. Cecilia. I have not seen you since you were a child.'

'I know Pandit. I hope you are well?'

The young man withdrew quietly.

'Yes, bette. I am well and working hard. I was sorry to hear about your Mama. We were friends many years ago.'

'I know. I remember your visits to our house. My parents were always so happy to see you and your wife.'

'They were happy days. Life is busier now. Sometimes too busy.' He stared at the piles of files on his desk.

'I read that you have been busy with the INC. And other Parsees too.'

'Yes, we Parsees want to make this country free of British rule. And kinder to women.'

'That is what I want to talk to you about, Pandit. I need your help. Did you know I have been studying law?'

He looked impressed. 'I didn't. But I am not surprised. You were highly intelligent even when you were a little girl.'

'I have been studying for years now. Attending Ewing College.'

'Yes, I teach there sometimes.'

'That is how I found your office. The address was in the lecture room.'

'So, how can I help you?'

'My husband is not well and can't work,' she said, coming out with her prepared lie, 'We have four children.'

He raised his eyebrows, 'And...?'

She realised that her voice was becoming more urgent, 'I thought you might need help with your law work. You must be busy with the INC and I could do a lot of your more ordinary cases. I could be your clerk.'

'Akil, who you have met, is my articled clerk. You have not finished your studies and you are a woman. You are not allowed to practise law, even though you are allowed to study it.'

She tried to keep the desperation out of her words. 'Possibly I would not be your articled clerk. I would just be in the background, Pandit. I would do the work and prepare your papers. You would attend court and be the advocate and representative. With Akil. No one need know about me.'

He laughed out loud, 'You are cut from the same cloth as your mother. She always broke the rules.'

'You will have more time for your INC work, which is so important for the future of this country.'

He laughed again. 'I like the idea, bette. I am working for more opportunities for women, so I should give women opportunities in my own work, yes? And Parsees must help Parsees, yes?'

'Yes. Yes.' This time she tried not to sound too eager.

'Let us try this. We will not tell many people. Just those we are working with. I cannot call you bette anymore either. I will call you Mrs Keating from now on. Please come to the office next week and we will start.'

She stood up, shaky with relief, steadying herself against the chair. 'Thank you Pandit. We will work well together and show the way to others. We tell them what we are doing. In years to come, I mean.'

'Yes, bette, I mean Mrs Keating. I have work to do now. We will see you next week.'

Cecilia ran back to the station, hardly feeling the pain in her ribcage from Christopher's kicks. Pain that had crippled her since it had happened a few days ago. But pain that had somehow energised her into planning a new life. Despite travelling back for hours on the crowded, oppressively hot train, she felt as if she were free and breathing fresh air.

Suddenly everything was different. She would be financially independent. She could pay for the children's education and give them the life they deserved. She wouldn't tell anyone about her work, especially Christopher. She wouldn't risk his wrath. Pandit must not know her husband was a no-good drunk either, she had to keep the family's reputation intact. She felt so powerful, was sure she could manage it all.

Cecilia fell into a routine of going to work in Allahabad and studying in the evenings. Sometimes, she brought Pandit's files home and worked there. Pandit seemed pleased with her. She enjoyed putting the law into practise. She told Supriya and Aktbar she was visiting an elderly auntiji in Allahabad. She reminded herself that she must find another ayah. That would be the next thing to do. But while Supriya was willing to stay over, it didn't seem to be so urgent.

Cecilia had written to Christopher with the story about her auntiji. An acceptable cover, she thought one that he wouldn't question. She just had to ensure that, if she had papers at home, they were hidden away when he returned. The unpredictability of his comings and goings made it a little tricky. But he was returning less and less now, so the problem was receding.

She didn't hear him enter the room, 'Boom!' he shouted, his face in hers, 'I am here!'

She jumped, spilling the legal papers onto the floor. Her heart was pounding from the shock and from the fear that he would look at them and guess that she was working. She quickly decided to welcome him to distract him. He had pungent breath from whisky as he breathed over her. She guided him into the yard to see the children. He was gratifyingly compliant.

Richard and John were at school, but Michael and Cissy were playing watched by Supriya, who was sitting under the shade of the tree, suddenly feigning an interest as she saw them arrive.

'Papa, Papa!' the children cried as they saw him. They threw their arms around his legs, hugging him hard. He was nearly caught off his already fragile balance. 'Hello, my babies, I have missed you.' He kissed them both.

She watched the scene, with mixed feelings. She was happy to see the children loved him, that they had no idea of the man he really was. They saw him as a fun papa who played with them whenever they saw him. But she knew he could only put on this front for a short time. Then his patience would run out. He always left her with the day-to-day problems of being a parent. Yet the children showed him a love that they rarely showed her. She felt the injustice of it, but knew she could do nothing about it. She tiptoed away from the happy scene, to tidy up her papers. She hid them in a pan in the kitchen, hurriedly putting on its lid.

Just as she finished, he appeared in the doorway, making her jump again. 'What are you doing?' he demanded, leaning on the door frame for support.

'I was about to make some chai,' she replied in a casual tone that she did not feel. 'Would you like some?' She pulled an empty dekshi from the shelf and put it on the stove. She added the milk, sugar, tea and spices as he watched her. He hoped she could not see her hands trembling.

'Yes, I think I need some. It might rid me of this headache. I have no idea what causes them. I get so many these days.'

He sat down and waited for the sweet drink to be served to him. His presence was brooding, making the atmosphere taut. She joined him at the table, saying nothing but occasionally sipping her own glass of chai.

'I was having a drink with my Mahoba railway colleagues last night.' He said, breaking the silence.

'Did you enjoy yourself?'

'Of course. But they tell me you are always taking the train to Allahabad.'

He heart started to beat fast again. 'Yes, of course, I wrote to you about it. Auntiji is not well and it is too far for Papa to travel to see her.'

'You make a lot of visits, they said.'

'She is quite ill.'

'One of my colleagues followed you at Allahabad.'

She started to feel even more anxious. 'Why would they do that?'

'Because they wanted to let me know what you were really doing.'

She said nothing but frowned and shook her head as if she did not understand. Her throat was dry, her heart pounding, her stomach churning.

'I did not believe that you have an auntiji in Allahabad. I had not heard about her before. So, I asked them to check up on you.'

The tension rose between them, so thick it could almost be seen. Her heart was pounding harder, her breath was becoming shallower. She could feel her jaws tightening.

'And they found nothing, I assume?' she said with forced casualness.

He slammed his fist down on the table, so hard both chai glasses spilt. Neither of them did anything about it, their eyes were locked in each other's defiant gazes.

'They know that you go to a solicitor's office. They think you must be working there.'

Suddenly she decided to tell the truth, whatever the consequences. She was tired of pretending.

'They are right. I work in Pandit Wacha's office.'

'But I told you not to work,' he hissed, leaning over the table.

'I have no choice. You give me so little money. I have to feed and clothe the children and pay for their schooling.'

He thumped the table again. 'Are you saying I am not man enough to keep my own family? Are you?' His voice was loud and threatening.

'I am saying that I need to earn money.' She hoped her voice was cool.

He sprung at her the way he had done before, teeth baring, eyes flaring. He hit her around the face over and over. He punched her in the stomach, winding her. She was dizzy and confused when he dragged her into the bedroom and threw her onto the bed. In so much pain, she was unable to move, she watched in terror as he undressed himself. He ripped off her sari. Then he forced himself into her, hard and hateful. It took only a few shoves for him to finish.

Then he beat her again. For not wanting him, he said. She was his wife, she should be available anytime. She was his property. She had lied to him and disobeyed him. He had to punish her.

And then he forced himself into her again.

Afterwards, he hissed in her ear, 'You will stop working from now. You will stay at home and be a proper wife. I hope you have learned your lesson.'

With another slap across her face, he left. She heard the front door slam. She let herself breathe again. And sob. And sob. She felt her face, her fingers fluttering with the lightest of touches, it was so painful. She was swollen and tender. Cecilia felt between her legs, she was bleeding and bruised. She could barely move. She ached in her body and ached in her soul. He said she was his property to do with as he pleased. Through her work, she knew he was right in the eyes of the law. But she knew that it was not morally right. It was not right that he could beat and force himself on her, rape her. It was not right that her husband could abuse her and be within the law.

She felt used and worthless, a piece of rubbish. She would never trust him again. Never. She was scared of him after he hit her the last time. Now she was terrified of him. She missed Maurice so much, life was happy with him. As she lay, her bloodied body lit by the half light of the bedroom, she wondered at the contrast of life. Her children innocent and harmless playing outside while their violent father violated their mother. At exactly the same time.

She cried for her lost dreams, her lost hope, her lost Maurice.

Christopher had been gone for nine weeks. This wasn't the first time, of course. He had disappeared many times before. She suspected other women were involved, as Patrick had said. She didn't care. She was glad it wasn't her. She had grown stronger in a strange way since the day he raped her last July. She had already seen him at his worst. She had stopped trying to placate him and started to challenge him about his drinking and behaviour. She reasoned that if his punishment of her was going to be the same, she would not be cowed by him. That way, she at least felt an element of pride in herself for not being weak. She had carried on working too. He would never stop her doing that.

Now, her ears echoed with the harsh words they had exchanged before he left all those weeks ago. The argument was the same one they had had so often before. He had refused to leave the army once again. She had begged him and begged him. Crying, she had told him that she was scared of losing another husband to war. She was sure fighting would come soon, as the movement for independence was gathering momentum. She didn't want to be a widow again. She had pretended she loved him to make him understand. She didn't of course. She just needed a husband to protect her and her children.

Allahabad was becoming a centre for the independence movement and the INC. She was learning so much about the campaign and its main people. Nehru and his family lived in the city in a palatial white house with large gardens. They held many meetings in their spacious rooms. The British were arguing against self-rule for the Indians. The discussions were becoming more heated every week and she feared the Army would be called in to deal with any potential unrest. There had already been bloody uprisings over Lord Curzon's plans to separate East and West Bengal.

Christopher had said she was panicking. There was nothing for her to worry about. He knew more than her. After all, he was in the Army and they had been told not to react to rumours. She was talking nonsense as usual, he said with contempt. In desperation, she felt compelled to tell him the secret that she had been withholding – that she was pregnant again. She did not tell him that the baby was a product of his raping her. She shuddered as she remembered his screaming reaction.

'Not another baby,' he shouted, 'you stupid whore! Why do you keep getting pregnant? I don't want any more children. I hate them. I hate you too.' And he had left, slamming the door with such ferocity it shook the bungalow's walls to their very foundations.

Remembering it all, Cecilia started to feel nauseous. Whether from the pregnancy or Christopher's disappearance – she didn't know. The whole scene had been terrible. She knew it was the reason he hadn't come home since. Perhaps he would never come home now; he had been gone so long. The baby she was carrying would not be born out of love but she would love this baby as much as her other children. Even if Christopher didn't want it. She would protect this precious child forever.

She could hear the children playing in the yard. Their happy laughs were a source of joy, as ever.

She jumped as she heard the front door fly open and Christopher yell, 'I'm back!' He burst into the kitchen with a big smile, waving a piece of paper.

'I've done it!' he cried, 'I've done what you asked. I've left the army. Here look at this.' He thrust the paper at her. It was his discharge note from the Royal Artillery.

'I did it for you. And I am still going to stay working on the railway. We were right to come to Mahoba and Jhansi – the best places for railway jobs. I will still be a guard on the railway. We will be fine. See the things I do for you, my love. I love you.' He kissed her quickly on the cheek, not noticing her flinch. 'My Cecilia. And I am so pleased about the new baby. Honestly, I am.'

Cecilia was stunned. Christopher didn't notice her silence – he grabbed her and twirled her around the kitchen. Her body stiffened involuntarily in his arms as she smelled the whisky on his bitter breath, remembering the time he had raped her. But he didn't seem to notice.

She felt that she should say something encouraging to keep him in a good mood, 'I am pleased you are out of the army. Now our family will be safe.'

'I did it all for you. All because you asked me to. I did it out of love for you.' He kissed her again and then strolled out of the bungalow without another word.

A few days later – he still hadn't reappeared – she was at Mahoba railway station waiting for the train to Allahabad, when one of his soldier friends stopped to speak to her. She couldn't remember his name but recognised him from the times she saw him with Christopher. He was small man with greasy hair, crooked teeth with an unctuous manner.

'Hello, Cecilia,' he said as if he knew her well.

She nodded.

'My name is Peter. Christopher asked me to make sure you are safe.'

'I am able to look after myself, thank you.' Her retort was crisp.

'I was the one who told him you work at that lawyer's office in Allahabad.'

'Thank you.' Her voice laden with insincerity.

He didn't hear her sarcasm and carried on, 'You must be glad the Army got rid of him.'

'Oh?'

'Didn't you know?'

She said nothing, not wanting him to see her react.

'They discharged him for excessive drinking,' He said with pure glee.

'I have seen his discharge papers. That is not true.'

'He asked them to keep his job on the railways and not mention the drinking on his papers.'

'Why would they do that?'

'He told them you were ill with another baby on the way and that you both had lost a baby before. He said he was worried about you.'

Cecilia felt a fire of ire stoke inside her. Christopher had used her and her lost baby Bridget, to make his situation better with the Army and railway. He had lied to her about it, telling her he had left the Army out of love for her. He had no shame. She clenched her teeth to control the maelstrom she was feeling.

'I don't believe you. Why would they let him keep his job if he were drinking too much?'

'He doesn't tell you much, does he?' said Peter, his eyes shining with uncontained triumph. 'They gave him a coal man's job. Much lower position and one where the drinking doesn't matter so much. He can only be a guard when there is a shortage of men to do it. So, he will have even less money for you, even after he has spent it at the Rag.' Peter's grin was wide and spiteful.

Now she knew where Christopher had been spending his time. She had come across the Rag at work in many divorce petitions. It was a brothel in Agra. The British wanted their soldiers to be satisfied physically and safely, so they ensured the Rag's prostitutes had access to doctors and were free from disease. She didn't care that Christopher used the Rag, she was relieved.

Peter was watching intently, waiting for her to say something.

She felt the baby kick inside, as if it were protesting about the behaviour of his father. The kicking was hard and took her breath away. Pausing to clutch her belly gave her time to think what to say to this odious little man. He started to look alarmed. She knew he would be running away soon, too scared to stay and make sure she really was alright. What an irony.

Taking a deep breath to allay the pain, 'I am sure he had good reason to change jobs. He wants to spend more time with his family, so it is a good thing.'

Peter's eyes widened in surprise. He had not expected that reaction. She could see he was disappointed. His words hadn't hurt her as much as he hoped they would.

She decided to twist his poison back to him, 'Besides, I earn a lot of money as a lawyer, so I can support our family and Christopher likes that arrangement.'

She turned with a swish of her navy-blue sari, she walked away as quickly as she was able, leaving him open-mouthed in astonishment and frustration.

She boarded the train to Allahabad.

For the third time in as many years, Cecilia carried a new-born baby through the lychgate of the Sacred Heart Church in Jhansi. Little Alfred James, already known in the family as Alfie, wriggled and fussed clearly wanting to be fed. He was not even three-weeks-old and had made his angry presence felt.

The girls were enchanted with him. The boys were annoyed by the way he took their mother's attention. Cecilia thought about the three Keating children. All born healthy due, no doubt, to her regular visits to the railway hospital across the road from their house. But this new little chap, though full-term and thriving, never seemed to be content.

The train journey had been long and dusty. Alfie had cried the whole time and would not be settled. Supriya had come with them to help, with some reluctance, as usual. It was better than being alone, Cecilia reasoned. Nothing and no one, not even his sisters, could settle baby Alfie. Christopher had not yet met his new son. She had wired the news to Jhansi from the railway telegram room at Mahoba the day after Alfie had been born. She had chosen this baby's name herself. Her resentment over Alfie's conception meant Christopher did not deserve to choose his name. Alfie was her precious baby, not his.

Christopher had wired back from Jhansi a few days later:

> Baptism at Sacred Heart on 7 May. I have chosen his sponsor.

She knew that Christopher had done that to spite her for choosing Alfie's name. She didn't care. She would make sure he had as little to do with this child or, indeed, the other children from now on.

She was shocked when she saw him at the door of the church. As the older children ran to him, she stood still with Alfie in her arms. He had lost weight, his clothes falling off him. He looked years older than when she had last seen him just a few months ago. His skin was yellowing, his hair thin and he seemed to be trembling as the children threw themselves at his body. She walked towards him as he was touching and cuddling the children. He looked up with eyes that seemed clouded by a lack of vision.

'Hello.' He moved to kiss her. She edged her head away. He looked at little Alfie, still squirming in her arms. 'He is a lovely baby, thank you.' His voice was weak and scratchy. He made no move to hold his son.

He nodded at the arched door, 'The others are inside. Let's go in.'

At the big stone font, with its quote from the book of Mark, stood Father Almeida, the priest who had baptised Cissy and Michael. Next to him, to her shock, stood Patrick, grinning a toothless grin. He was clearly here to be Alfie's sponsor. Patrick, who had attacked her, was going to be her baby's sponsor.

She gasped in astonishment and turned to Christopher hissing under her breath, 'Patrick? Why did you choose him? I can't believe you have asked him.' She saw a cold glint in his eyes, it pierced the clouded vision and showed malicious victory.

'He was so upset about what you said about him. I needed to make it up to him. He is my friend, after all.'

She knew that whatever ailed Christopher today, he had not changed. He was as angry and nasty as ever. There was no time to protest or argue; everyone was waiting for the christening to begin. As she stepped up to the hexagonal font at the back of the small, plain church, she caught Patrick's eye. He was still grinning at her. But it was really a sneer of loathing.

'Why are the children still so sleepy? It is nearly their teatime, they should be awake,' Cecilia asked.

'It's hot,' Supriya insisted. 'That's why.'

'Nonsense. Something is wrong. How long have they been like this?' Cecilia's voice was rising in concern. Supriya looked at her feet and said nothing.

Frightened, Cecilia shouted out, 'Aktbar, here! Now! Aktbar!'

The cook came shuffling into the children's bedroom – his elderly feet hampering his pace.

'Aktbar. How long have the children been sleepy like this? Is it since I went away to work? Is it?'

'Memsa'ab, I am sorry but I cannot remember when you went away.' He shook his head.

'It was three weeks ago.'

Aktbar tipped his hand side to side declaring, '*Acha*,' a sign that he was now remembering. But he said nothing. Supriya was still staring at her feet. Cecilia was waiting in furious anticipation. Outside the compound, the noises of Mahoba continued relentlessly. Cocks crowed, dogs barked, people shouted, children sang, monkeys shrieked. The sounds seemed to stop outside the room, which held a cold, expectant silence. They watched as Michael groaned and rolled over without waking. Cecilia went to him and stroked his forehead.

'Aktbar, tell me now', she said in a cold voice as she pivoted on her heel back towards them, 'I need to know. How long has this been going on? How long have they been this sleepy?'

Aktbar shrugged. 'I don't know Memsahib. But likely since you went away. Or maybe before.'

They both glanced at Supriya. Her head was still bowed, her body sagged.

Cecilia shook Supriya's shoulder, 'What have you done to them? What is wrong with them? Tell me, tell me.'

'Nothing Memsahib. It's hot. They are sleepy. That is all.'

'I am getting the doctor for them. Aktbar, wait with them while I find him. Supriya, do not touch them.'

Cecilia ran across the road to the hospital. But the doctor wasn't there. She ran the two miles into the town to find the Indian doctor who had a surgery in the market. Lifting her sari to avoid detritus on the road she weaved her way through the thronging masses of people and animals. Panic rising with every step. Arriving breathless, she leant on the door and gasped at his assistant. 'I need the doctor now. My children are ill.'

The young woman, jumped up, startled. 'I will get him, Memsahib.'

The doctor appeared almost instantly. 'The problem, Memsahib?'

'There is no time now, I will tell you on the way. Come.'

As they hurried their way back, Cecilia talked through her rapid breaths. 'I have been away. The children were all a bit tired when I left. I thought they needed to sleep off an illness. Yet, I am back and they are all still sleepy. Something is not right.' The doctor listened but said nothing. An older man, he was having trouble keeping up with Cecilia whose feet were hurried with the panic of a terrified mother.

At the bungalow the doctor, regained his breath with two or three wheezes, then looked at all the children in turn. Richard, John, Michael, Cissy and baby Alfie were examined slowly, pulses taken, breathing checked, hearts listened to while she watched, too nervous to breathe. When he had finished, the doctor asked Supriya, 'What have you given them? You must tell me. Or you will be in big trouble.'

Squirming through tears, Supriya whispered, 'Opium'.

Cecilia screamed, 'Opium – you gave them opium. Opium?'

'They were not well, Memsahib. I did it to make them better,' her sulky eyes downcast.

'No. No. Make them better? That is wrong. They were not ill. They were fine.'

'But you were not here Memsa'ab. You were working.'

The doctor intervened gently, 'They have signs of opium use. You will need to leave them to sleep it off. I don't think you should have any big problems.' He turned to Supriya. 'Where did you get the opium? I need to know. More people are coming to me with this opium problem.'

Supriya whispered, 'It should be a secret. But I will say because of the children.'

Because you need your job, thought Cecilia.

'There is a man at the market. He sells it. To people he knows or their friends.' Supriya was still looking at her feet.

'You must take me to him now. I have to speak with him. Memsahib, you can pay me when you bring the children to me after they have slept it off.' He picked up his bag. 'Follow me, Ayah. Now.' He grabbed her arm and propelled her out of the room.

'Do not come back here. Ever,' Cecilia shouted at Supriya's retreating back.

She should have dealt with Supriya long ago – but she had been too busy. Now the time had come to do something about her.

'But Memsahib, my clothes, my belongings, my work?' cried the ayah as she was being pushed through the door.

'I will send your clothes and belongings on. You are not working for me anymore. You have no work here.'

After Supriya left, Cecilia slumped to the floor of the bedroom, her head in her hands.

Her children, her poor children. Would they be damaged for ever? She had heard about opium and how bad it was for people. The British grew it and sold it throughout the country, it was a very lucrative business. Many adults were addicted to it, it was doing huge amounts of damage to people and their families. But children, she had never heard of children having opium. She started to cry as she thought about the damage it might have done to her precious little ones.

She wiped her teary hands on her sari. She would need to find another ayah quickly. She had more legal work to do tomorrow. She needed the money to pay the doctor. At least the work was in Jhansi this time, so she would not need to be away overnight. But she needed to trust the new ayah would look after the children properly.

112

She sighed. Once again, she would have to sort out these problems herself. She stood up, dusting her sari off, determined to make things better again.

'Aktbar, look after the children. If they wake, give them cool water. I will be back soon.'

The cook nodded vigorously. 'I will look after them properly, Memsahib.'

Cecilia hurried back through the dirty, noisy streets to the house of her only friend in Mahoba, Silpa. Silpa was another student of law, they had met at college. Her large body belied a sharp intelligent mind and kindness of spirit.

Cecilia sat in Silpa's kitchen and cried. She explained what had happened, finishing with, 'I don't know what to do. How to sort it out.'

Silpa stirred a dekshi of a vegetable dhansak as she listened. She placed a comforting plate of it in front of Cecilia. 'We can help. Bring the children to me tomorrow and my ayah will look after them.' Cecilia gobbled up the dhansak realising she had not eaten properly for days, she had been too busy.

'I don't know if they will be well enough to come to you.'

'Then, I will ask my ayah to take my children to your home and she could look after them all there. That will cover your needs for tomorrow.'

Cecilia sighed with relief. 'Thank you. Thank you. But where can I find a new ayah? I have to keep working. I cannot rely on Christopher for money.'

After a pause Silpa said, 'I know that Rumi's daughter wants to be an ayah. She is 14 now. Perhaps you would consider her? They live just past the marketplace.'

'I have met her and Rumi at your house before. I will go and see them now. Thank you.'

She wiped her mouth with a napkin, kissed Silpa and left. She rushed to Rumi's ramshackle house in the smelly narrow streets of the poorer part of town.

Rumi, a slight attractive women of about 30, looked surprised when she arrived. 'I don't see you very much, Cecilia. You are always working.'

Cecilia shrugged, not wanting to spend time justifying herself. 'My ayah has gone and I need a new ayah as soon as possible. Would your daughter be my ayah?'

Rumi looked pleased. Some work for her daughter would be welcome. She called her daughter in from the filthy street, 'Bala, come here.'

A young girl entered the room and stood by the door, shyly. She was small, pretty with long dark hair and a burgeoning womanly body. She wore a sapphire-coloured sari. Cecilia could she had the makings of being a stunningly beautiful woman. She knew Christopher would be attracted to her and it would not be wise to have her in their house. But she needed an ayah. She had known Rumi for some time through Silpa and knew she would have brought up a good daughter. Anyway, she did not know when Christopher would be back. She swallowed her doubts.

Cecilia smiled at Bala. 'I need a new ayah. Can you help?'

Bala smiled and nodded. Rumi was smiling too.

Cecilia added, 'Can you come with me to my house now to meet the children? I am working tomorrow, so now would be best.'

As they arrived back home after another rushed journey, Cecilia noticed that all the children were playing in the yard. They were unusually quiet, but at least they were awake. Alfie was in a basket, eyes open and looking around, but not his usual squalling self.

'Children,' she said, 'this is Bala, she will be your new ayah.'

The children, still suffering the effects of the opium, said nothing. Only Richard showed any interest, looking at Bala with a touch of curiosity. He then went back to listlessly playing.

'Come, come,' said Cecilia, 'I will show you the kitchen. Aktbar is the cook and he will make the children's food. But you must serve it to them and make their drinks.'

She stopped in shock as she rushed into the kitchen. Christopher was sitting at the table, eyes glazed, hair awry, tie askew. He still looked as unwell as he had at Alfie's christening, possibly even worse, but she did not have time to think about it.

'What are you doing here?' she demanded.

'I live here, in case you've forgotten,' he slurred. His eyes fell on Bala. He smiled. A slow lascivious smile. 'Well, well. Who have we here?'

Through clenched teeth, Cecilia said to Bala, 'Go back to the children and look after them with Aktbar. Now.'

Bala, glancing between them with fear in her eyes, retreated quickly. Cecilia pounded her fist on the table. 'Where have you been?'

'Why do you want to know?'

'I am your wife.'

He laughed – the hollow laugh of someone who was not amused. She noticed there were blisters on his neck and hands. They were raw and red and looked painful. She said nothing.

'How long is it since you have been my wife? How long since you have lain with me?'

She shuddered as she remembered the rape that had led to Alfie's birth. 'Alfie is only four months old. I am working so much because I have no money from you. I don't see you for weeks on end.'

He paused and grinned again. 'Perhaps that young girl can help me if you don't want to. What was her name?'

'I hate it when you are drunk.' She slammed the door as she stormed out of the room, his empty laugh following her and ringing in her ears. She found Bala in the yard.

'Bala. You cannot be my ayah. I am sorry – let me take you home to your mother.'

Bala looked confused. 'I don't understand.'

'I am sorry. Come with me, now.'

They hurried back in silence through the noisy crowds back through the maze of alleyways.

'Mama,' said Bala when they arrived at Rumi's hut. 'I cannot be the ayah and I don't know why.'

Rumi stared at Cecilia, full of unspoken questions.

'Christopher is back,' Cecilia told her, 'is there anyone else you know who could be my ayah?'

Rumi suddenly understood – her eyes showed that she knew. 'Reema's daughter is very plain. She will be fine. Her name is Rupali.' Rumi gave her Reema's address.

Cecilia turned and ran to Reema's house, a tin shack in an even poorer part of Mahoba. Cecilia knew this family would be keen for their daughter to find work. The poverty meant they needed her to have an income and live elsewhere.

'Can Rupali be my ayah?' she asked Reema breathlessly.

Without replying, Reema called Rupali in from where she was talking to friends outside. With some relief Cecilia saw that the young girl was sturdily built and unenviably plain, with a large nose and crossed eyes. She was dressed in a brown sari with a grubby white choli. She would not attract Christopher at all.

'She is not clever but she is kind,' said Reema as if reading Cecilia's mind. Rupali didn't react to her mother's comment.

'I need her soon. When can she start?'

'Tomorrow, if you would like.'

'Yes, yes. Silpa's ayah is helping tomorrow – she can show Rupali what to do.' She looked at Rupali. 'We will welcome you to the house tomorrow, thank you.'

Breathing out a long sigh, Cecilia rushed back to the bungalow. Next, she needed to take the children to the doctor's house for an examination. She couldn't wait until the morning as she needed to be at work then. She knew it would be expensive. She had a locked box of secret money under her bed – there should be enough rupees in there.

The children were still playing quietly in the yard under Aktbar's watchful eye.

Christopher was passed out drunk on the bed. Even though she was sure he wouldn't wake, she tiptoed to the bedside and bent down to reach the box underneath. Feeling it on the edge of her fingertips, she inched it towards her, as silently as she possibly could. Every time it moved, it scratched the floor. He snored loudly with each of the sounds but didn't wake.

She barely stifled a gasp of shock when she finally pulled it out and saw it was empty, the lock broken. The rupees were gone. Her secret source of money, gone. She sat, defeated, beside the bed. How would she pay the doctor now? The children had to see him. Especially tiny Alfie. She had to know if serious damage had been done to them. She held her head in her hands, tears falling from her eyes onto her sari. Had Christopher taken the money? Had Supriya? How could she confront either of them? Supriya was gone – and Christopher would lie. There was no time to think about it now. She had to get the children to the doctor quickly.

Christopher rolled over. The bed creaked. She started, unnerved. She pushed the box under the bed and stood up, smoothing her sari into place without disturbing him.

She took the children to the doctor's surgery. It was a slow journey as she carried Alfie and, in turn, the others when they complained. The children were sluggish and unhelpful. They groaned and moaned with every step, protesting that they were too tired to move. She had not the time or inclination to indulge them, so she shouted at them to keep up. She was exhausted when they reached the doctor's house.

'They have woken up, then?' The doctor asked.

'Only just. I need you to check them, especially the baby. I am really worried about them all, but especially the baby as he is so young. I cannot pay you, Doctor. Not today. I am working tomorrow and can pay you then.'

The doctor had an arrogant air that she hadn't noticed earlier because she was too terrified about the children. He looked at her with cold eyes and said, 'Your husband works, Memsa'ab. Do you not have his money?'

She bit down her irritation and forced a smile, 'Of course. My husband is a guard on the Great Indian Pacific Railway and he works hard indeed. But we have a lot of children to feed.'

The doctor raised his eyebrows clearly not believing her, 'We must look at these children now. You may pay me tomorrow.'

He examined each child, paying particular attention to baby Alfie, as he had been asked.

'They all seem to be fine. Even the baby. But I see problems with adults and opium everyday now. I know nothing about opium and children. I don't think other doctors know anything either. We will just have to wait.'

Cecilia listened, frustrated. She wanted to know more, she wanted to know how her children might be affected. What she, as their mother, should do. But no one knew. She closed her eyes and prayed for a brief moment. Prayed that her children would be safe and well. Prayed that there would be no lasting damage to their bodies. She gathered them to her, nodded her thanks to the doctor and left.

Aktbar was cooking when they returned after another long and difficult walk. Cecilia left the children with him so they could eat their meal. She told him to put them to bed after. Christopher was sitting in the lounge, seemingly sober. He stared at her with barely disguised contempt. 'Where have you been?'

'I had to take the children to the doctor, to see if they were alright. Supriya was giving them opium.'

He laughed out loud. 'I use that. Makes me feel good.'

'Why are you laughing? It is not funny. You are a horrible man. These are your children, they could be damaged. She even gave it to baby Alfie.'

He jumped up, leapt over to her and gripped her arms hard, pulling her towards him so viciously that her head whipped back, 'No wonder I take opium and drink so much, with you as a wife. You are always moaning or nagging about something.' He bit her cheek, drawing blood. She let out a sharp cry of pain, scared that this situation would lead to another beating. Or worse. He let go of her so fast he wrenched neck again. She stifled another scream.

'I am going out. To find someone to be my wife for the night. And other nights.' As he reached the door, he turned back. 'And I took the rupees from under the bed. You are stupid if you think you can hide anything from me.' With a revolting, foul-breathed, leer he added. 'And I bought myself some real pleasure with them. I never asked her name. She was a chilli cracker though. I am going there now. I will be back when I am ready.'

Cecilia lay on the bed, crying sobs that wracked her whole body. Her loneliness swept over her as she touched the bite on her cheek, tracing the blood as it dripped down her face. She rubbed her neck where he had nearly wrenched it from her body. She thought of Maurice. Of how loving he was and how much she missed him.

She decided whenever Christopher bothered to come home again, she would encourage him to drink whisky, pouring him a large glass on arrival and topping it up frequently. Then he would be drunk enough to sleep deeply and leave her alone. In the mornings, she would get up early to be with the children. That way she could avoid his attentions completely.

The telegram was from the railway company, its wording was brief but its message conveyed so much more:

> Coal Man, Christopher Keating seriously ill. Come to Agra as soon as possible.

Reading it, she sighed. She was not surprised that he was ill, she could see that when she looked at him, ever since Alfie's christening. She didn't care. But she cared about her family, her five little innocent children who relied on their parents for everything. She knew the telegram meant he was seriously ill or else it would not have been sent. So, there was a possibility he could die. And she would be a widow again. And with so many children, she would be unlikely to find another husband. Life would become unbearable for them all. She needed him to be get better for the sake of the children.

She asked Rupali, who was proving a much better ayah than Supriya, to stay for a few days in the bungalow so that she could go to Agra and visit Christopher. But the real problem was baby Alfie. At five months he was too young to stay at home but too young to take to come on such a journey, although he needed to be with her. She thought about the options for a long time, torn about what to do. Suddenly she made up her mind. Alfie would have to stay at home. The risk of taking him was too great. She did not want to lose another child.

The train to Agra was hot, crowded and uncomfortable. Her emotions were fluctuating with every bump and lurch of the carriage. She felt guilty every time relief washed over her at the thought of Christopher's death. She knew it would mean a difficult life for her, but she would no longer be living in fear of him. Her relief was laced with the knowledge that it was a terrible thing to be happy because someone had died. Christopher had brought her a little happiness after Maurice and Bridget's deaths. He had married her, taken on her two children and given her respectability. And dying at such a young age was an awful fate, he was only 36 after all. In addition, her children would be fatherless again. Richard and John had already lost their own father and Christopher's death would be another confusion in their young lives. Cissy, Michael and Alfie would grow up not knowing their father. As *chi-chis* and children of a widow.

At Agra station she alighted to throngs of people hurrying in every direction, all weaving among hundreds of other people who were standing looking around in confusion. There were masses of platforms with many trains leaving and arriving to the accompaniment of steam whistles and the deafening roars of brakes and engines. She did not know which way to go. Her vague plan was to find the offices of Great Indian Peninsula Railway and ask for someone to tell her where Christopher was staying, but she couldn't see a sign to the offices. She stood for a moment, bewildered.

'Memsa'ab,' she heard a familiar voice and turned around. Peter was standing beside her, a sly smile on his face.

'Are you here to see your husband, Memsa'ab?' he asked, barely able to contain his excitement.

'I am.'

'Well, he is dying, Memsa'ab. He is in the Railway Hospital in the Cantonment.' Peter was enjoying imparting the dreadful news. 'Too many women at the whorehouse. Venereal disease, the doctor said. Follow me.' Smiling his unctuous smile, he turned to make his way through the heaving horde of people and animals. She followed him concentrating hard not to lose him, trying not to think about the disease that was killing her husband.

'The Cantonment is a high security area,' Peter told her as they arrived at the barrier. 'It is only for the army and railway workers. But do not worry I will make sure the soldiers let you through.'

She still recoiled at the thought of him helping her but she would not have known what to do otherwise. He spoke to the soldiers and, pointing to her, explained that she was the wife of one of patients in the Rag clinic. The soldiers gave her knowing winks and she shivered with embarrassment.

'What did you mean – the Rag clinic?' she asked him once they were through the barrier.

Peter smiled slowly, 'It is the soldier's name for the syphilis clinic. They get syphilis at the Rag. It is a special ward in a separate bungalow in the hospital grounds.'

She looked at him with silent contempt. He didn't notice. They arrived at the small bungalow. A clinic for railwaymen, according to the sign outside, giving no hint about the nature of their illnesses. They were met by a nun, dressed in white robes straining over her stocky body and ample bosom. She had a ready smile and maternal, comforting air. She introduced herself, 'Hello, I am Sister Margaret. I am the nurse in charge here. I am glad you have come. There is little time left for Mr Keating. Just to warn you, we keep the rooms dark so the light does not hurt their eyes.'

The nun led her through the dim, dank corridor to Christopher's room.

As she entered, she gasped. There was just enough light to see him. There had been a terrible deterioration since she had seen him last. Emaciated, he was covered in the huge sores she had seen before. They had grown larger and seemed to have taken over his body. There was little normal skin to be seen. The sores were varying degrees of suppuration. She could only think of the pain he must be suffering and her heart softened.

Christopher weakly turned his head towards her, as if he had heard her arrive. She realised that Peter and Sister Margaret had entered the room with her. She looked at Peter and said crisply, 'Please leave the room now. I need to speak to the Sister alone.'

Disappointed and angry at his dismissal, Peter skulked out, closing the door behind him. She knew he was listening outside.

Lowering her voice, she asked the nun, 'What ails him?' Hoping perhaps that Peter had been wrong.

Looking at her with kindness, 'It is syphilis I am afraid, Mrs Keating. We see a lot of cases among railwaymen and soldiers. It is a very nasty disease.'

'How long will he live?'

'We do not know. I think just a few hours more. Are you able to stay and be with him at his passing?'

She felt her throat tighten with supressed tears and just nodded. She hadn't wanted to, but she felt sorry for him now.

'Good. It is not a disease that wives find sympathy with. Many would not do this for their husbands. They are so angry with their men. I am so glad that you think differently.'

Cecilia shrugged, still unable to speak.

'Syphilis is a terrible disease, Mrs Keating. It can lie dormant for years and then change a man's personality. It can make them bad tempered and aggressive. It is not their fault, they are ill.' She was speaking as if she knew about their marriage, about Christopher's volatility and violence.

Her first reaction was to say he had caught the disease by having sex with other women while they were married, so it would be hard for her to forgive him. But another thought jumped into her head. She had only known Christopher for four years. He may have been infected before they met if the nun's words were true. And his moods and violence were not necessarily because he was a hateful person or didn't love her. It was because he had a terrible disease.

Her tears flowed. For him and for the suffering he had endured. For her and the terrible marriage that needn't have been. For her children, losing their father to such an ignominious disease.

'I will leave you to be with him now,' said Sister Margaret. 'Do not touch his stores. That is how you become infected. The hearing is the last sense to go – so he will hear everything you say to him.' She squeezed Cecilia's arm. 'Be kind to him, please. He told me how much he loved you and that he treated you badly. He was truly sorry.'

She looked at Cecilia, 'I see a lot of men at the end of their lives, Mrs Keating. Many of them are not being true when they say this. But I believe Mr Keating was telling the truth. He loved you and all your children. He wanted to ask your forgiveness. But he cannot talk anymore, his mouth is full of sores. But you can tell him that you forgive him, he will hear you.' With a sad, sage nod she moved to leave the room. As the nun opened the door, Cecilia heard her jump with surprise as she saw Peter crouching on the other side. She heard the nun cuff him around the head and the sound of scurrying as Peter left in a hurry.

Cecilia opened the shutters slightly, she wanted Christopher to have some light in his last moments, but not enough to upset him. She pulled a chair up to his bedside and for a while, she watched as his chest breathed shallow breaths, which came out in tiny scrapes. She could not touch him, there were too many sores. She was relieved that he had no sores when they had lain together in the past. Or even when he raped her, and she became pregnant with Alfie. She had avoided him after that, so she felt safe from the disease. Cecilia felt a little guilty, sitting at his deathbed thinking of herself, but she needed to be healthy for her children now.

Eventually, she found words, 'Oh Christopher. I know you are sorry for all the awful things that happened.' He moved very slightly and she knew he had heard her. She searched her brain for something convincing to say. There was no point in dwelling on the terrible behaviour of this man. He was dying, she wanted to say something kind to bring him some solace.

'Do you remember when we met, how we danced? How you tried to win over my auntijis? The happy times when Cissy was born? We were so happy then, weren't we? And we went for that walk to the barrage and the boys were so excited and happy?'

He moved again, unable to speak, in acknowledgement.

'It is your time soon. When you pass, your Mama and Papa will be waiting for you. They will look after you and you will be healed and happy. You can look after us from heaven too. The children will need your protection.'

His breathing became even shallower, 'You can go peacefully now. Remember that we have forgiven you and still love you. I won't let the children forget their Papa.'

125

With a surge of strength that she did not know he had, she saw him raise his head and heard him whisper in the quietest of voices, 'I am sorry.'

He lay back and drew his last breath in peace.

She stayed with him for a while watching him. Tears fell down her cheeks, tears of relief and sadness. She left the room to find Sister Margaret, gently closing the door in respect.

A new nun was on duty, sitting at the desk in the small office. She was a tiny, wiry woman with a sliver of grey hair poking out of her wimple. Her face was lined all over and her eyes were cornflower blue, shining with wisdom.

'My husband has passed, Sister.'

'I am sorry, Mrs Keating. A sad day for you and your family.'

Cecilia could think of nothing to say. The silence was broken by the nun, 'Now I need to fill out his death certificate so you can have his funeral. He will be buried at the British cemetery here in the Agra Cantonment. There is a small plot of consecrated land by the border with the school. That is where we Roman Catholics are buried.'

Cecilia had had no thoughts about his funeral. This whole turn of events was still a shock. She knew nothing of Agra, except it was the home of the Taj Mahal. And the Rag.

The nun asked for his name and filled it in. Then she asked, 'Occupation?'

'Guard on the Great Indian Peninsular Railway.' Her tone was firm.

The nun frowned. 'I thought he was a coal man.'

'No,' Cecilia lied, 'He was a guard. Sometimes he was a coal man, only when they were short of men.'

The nun raised her eyebrows and wrote 'Guard, GIPR?' on the document.

In the space marked for Cause of Death she started to fill in 'Syph…'

Grabbing the nun's hand quickly, Cecilia said, 'No, no. Please do not write that.'

The nun shook her hand off, 'That is what he died of, Mrs Keating, I must write it. It is the truth.'

Cecilia felt her voice rising in horror, 'No, no! His children will be shamed. They do not deserve that. He needs to be remembered in a respectful way.'

'But I cannot lie, Mrs Keating,' her pen was hovering over the form.

'Of course not. But could you put something else? His skin was covered in sores, could that be the cause? Please.'

The nun sighed and turned back to filling in the document, although she paused, pen poised, while she thought about what Cecilia had said.

'Well, you are right, Mrs Keating. Your children are Anglo-Indians and they will have hard lives because of it. I should not be adding to their difficulties. They are innocent lambs.'

With that, she wrote, 'Carbuncle.' She blotted the ink and gave Cecilia the death certificate with a small smile. 'There you are Mrs Keating. I hope this is helpful to your family. You can take this certificate to Father Sylvester. He is in the church in the Cantonment. You can organise the funeral with him now.'

Overwhelmed with emotion, Cecilia kissed the little nun's warm cheek, saying, 'Thank you so much. Thank you.'

The next day, Christopher's coffin was borne by his colleagues into St Mary's church. Peter and Patrick had wanted to carry it, but she had said no to both of them. She knew they were angry with her, but she did not care.

She looked up at the church noticing it was an incongruous lemon colour, almost bleached white by the blazing sun. It had a happy peaceful aura. She felt neither happy nor peaceful. As she followed the coffin up the few terracotta steps to the main church door, she felt weak and beaten by life.

There were only a few people at the funeral. Some colleagues and a few members of the normal congregation. She ignored Peter and Patrick. When the Mass was over, the coffin was loaded onto a cart and a small bullock pulled it the short distance to the cemetery, wheels scraping relentlessly against the stony path. The caretaker opened the blue metal gates and led them through the white and terracotta archway. He spoke Hindi to the cart man and she understood he was gesturing to the allocated grave. As he did, Cecilia caught sight of a flowering hibiscus shrub nestled at the base of one pillar. Just like the hibiscus she had in her hair on the day she met Christopher. She bent down and plucked a spray, holding it tightly in her hand. The little walking cortège followed the cart, priest and caretaker through the makeshift paths, past the red sandstone colonial gravestones, turning one corner then another and another until they arrived at their destination. As the coffin was lowered, she could hear the incongruous joy of children playing in the nearby schoolyard. How life goes on, she thought.

The priest blessed the coffin with holy water, murmuring prayers in Latin. Cecilia glanced at the small group of mourners. They were nervously looking to each other for a sign to tell them what to do next. She threw the hibiscus spray on top of the coffin and dusted her hands on her sari. She shivered despite the oppressive early morning heat. She looked again at the mourners and she knew she would have to talk to them. The group waited for her expectantly. She moved towards them with firm strides, shoulders back, head held high and eyes tear-free.

They said the usual things: sorry for your loss, we will miss him. She made the usual replies: it's so kind of you, thank you for coming. Ritual words exchanged, they parted ways. Cecilia watched them leave. They walked with an air of relief and increasing speed, their duty done.

Cecilia's posture slumped as soon as they disappeared from view. She walked back slowly to the entrance as though her shoulders carried the weight of the world. When she reached the gate, she saw the caretaker returning to his wooden shelter beside the entrance. She nodded a 'thank you' to him and gave him a few rupees. He smiled in acknowledgement.

She decided to visit the Taj Mahal before returning to Mahoba. She wanted to spend time there, thinking about her life and what to do next. She had read about the Taj. Its recent restoration by the British made her think it would be a good place to find some solace. She started to stroll down the road.

Suddenly she felt a hand grip the back of her arm. And Patrick's voice whispered in her ear, 'You are mine now, we can be together now.'

'Excuse me, I don't understand.' She turned to look at him. His eyes were glinting in the sun, laden with victory.

'We can be married now he is dead. I know you have always wanted to be with me.' He grinned, toothless and full of menace. His breath was rancid. She stiffened.

'I do not understand. My husband is not yet cold. You are his friend. What are you talking about?'

His hand gripped her arm tighter and he pushed her forward through the gate. 'You are coming with me. We will be married as soon as possible. I will be a father to your children. Besides, I am Alfie's sponsor. And we can have our own children as well. I know that is what you want.'

She prised his fingers from her arm. 'You are being ridiculous. I am not marrying you.' She said through gritted teeth.

She started to walk away, fast. He caught up with her, 'You cannot be a widow. Life will not treat you or your children well. Who else will marry you? You have lost two husbands and have five children. You are a bad omen. You are lucky that I am willing to marry you. You should be grateful.'

She spun around and looked him in the eye, 'I wouldn't marry you if you were the last man in India. I will never let you near my children. I do not care what you say, I will never, ever marry you.'

She saw hatred and violence flame in his eyes but she continued, 'Now leave me alone. I never want to see you again.'

She ran as fast as she could all the way to the barriers of the Cantonment. Built by the British, the roads were smooth and uncluttered, so it was easy to run. Only at the boundary did she turn around and look to see if he were still following her. But there was no sign of him, the road was wide and straight, she could see the whole way down. She breathed a sigh of relief as she nodded to the soldiers at the barriers. She started to walk the two miles down Taj Road to the Taj Mahal.

For once, the noise and smells and dust of the streets didn't disturb her. She was lost in thoughts about the incident with Patrick. She was shocked that he had approached her in the graveyard, he seemed not to have been concerned about respecting Christopher's passing or his memory. What sort of a friend was he? She knew that if she took up with Patrick, she would be in the same position again: with an aggressive, drunken, man who used the Rag for women. She knew he would not be a good father to her children, so she was right to reject him and his offer of marriage, whatever the cost to her.

When she entered the grounds of the mausoleum through the resplendent red sandstone West Gate, the beauty of the Taj Mahal took her breath away. It seemed to be so fragile, so delicate. Made from one of the world's heaviest materials, it looked like a filigree of lace floating in the sky. She sat in the lush garden by the streams of gently bubbling water and gazed in awe at its sparkling brilliance, the whiteness of the onion domes and minarets against the still blue of the sky. The British had added the gardens, giving the stunning tomb the most tranquil and apposite of settings. Cecilia doubted that she would ever again see such a magnificent building. She drank in the view, hungry for the beauty and peace it offered.

The light of the heavy midday sun settled over the Taj, making dramatic reflections in the pools below and bringing her some calm. It was almost as if she could leave her troubles in these lush gardens and return home unburdened by life. Almost. But not quite. As she lay on the lush grass peering up at the magnificent edifice, she stopped thinking about anything and just drank in its majestic beauty.

After a time, she did not know how long, she decided to return home. She needed to break the news to the children and sort out their lives and futures. She ran to the station and managed to catch a train to Mahoba without having to wait too long.

By the time it was a few miles away from its destination, she had decided, as she had many times before, that the children's education was the most important outcome of anything she did. Everything else would follow. She decided she would ask the railway if she could keep the bungalow as it was clear that Mahoba only had a few employees and they would probably be glad it was occupied. Being a widow would be easier there as it was a quiet area. The children could still attend their school. They were happy there and the teaching was good. She would carry on her work in Allahabad and so life would be as near to normal as possible.

As she alighted, she could hear a cacophony of screams and wails coming from the railway quarters. Picking up her sari, she ran over the tracks, ducked under the wire fence that separated their bungalow from the station. Instantly, she saw what was causing the noise. Rupali and the children were in the front garden sitting among her furniture and a host of bags. Holding a screaming Alfie in her arms, Rupali was wailing. Richard, John, Cissy and Michael were crying as loudly as they possibly could. Aktbar was standing nearby, head bowed in silent defeat.

For a second she tried to take in the scene in front of her. She said, to no one in particular, 'What has happened? Why are you all out here?'

There was no answer as they all carried on howling, as though she wasn't even there. She ran to the front door. It was locked. She ran around the veranda to the back door. It was locked too. Back in the front garden, with the noise dying down a little, she asked Rupali, 'What has happened?' Rupali, through her tears, said nothing but pointed to the hospital across the road. Cecilia looked. Standing outside were Patrick and Peter. They were looking at her with amusement. She wondered what on earth they were doing there.

But her attention was distracted by Richard's cries.

'Papa. Papa,' Richard was screaming, 'Papa is dead.'

John joined in, 'Our Papa is dead, dead.'

She grabbed her sons and pulled them to her. 'How do you know? Who has told you this?' Looking up, she saw Patrick and Peter striding towards the bungalow. And she knew.

She shouted, 'You told my children. You told them. How dare you tell them? I am their mother. It was my job to tell them. My job.'

Patrick called, in a voice that cloyed with insincerity, 'Oh, I thought we were being helpful. Saving you the trouble. They needed to know. Sorry if it was wrong. It's too late now, though,' he gloated.

She was so outraged she couldn't reply. Rupali and the children had all stopped their noises and were looking at her, agog. She gestured to the furniture and bags and found her voice enough to ask, 'Why are my furniture and bags outside?'

Patrick walked up to her, with Peter following behind. They both had the light of satisfied revenge in their eyes.

'Because,' Patrick said, 'you are no longer married to a railway worker. You cannot live here. This is no longer your house. You are just a widow. You have no home.'

'You have to leave now,' joined in Peter, his eyes glinting with hate, 'We told the Great Indian Peninsular Railway what happened to Christopher. They said you must move out as soon as possible. So, we packed up and locked up.' He smiled. 'We were just trying to make things easier for you.'

Patrick moved towards her and pulled her to him. He hissed in her ear, 'You should have agreed to marry me, you bitch.'

With that, both men walked away, laughing loudly.

The family watched them go. Patrick and Peter jumped over the fence and onto a train that was waiting at the station. As it pulled out and they leant out of the open door and waved enthusiastically, shouting: 'Goodbye!' 'Have fun!' 'Goodbye!'

When the train had disappeared into the distance, Cecilia sat down on one of the suitcases. Rupali handed her a squirming Alfie. The other children gathered around her expectantly. She kissed them and rocked Alfie back and forth.

'Is it true, Mama, is Papa dead?' sniffled Richard. 'Is he?'

'Yes, it is true, bette, I am afraid. Papa was seriously ill and he could not come here to tell us. He was in hospital, so I went to see him. Before he died, he told me he loved you all very much.'

Richard and John started crying again. Cissy and Michael followed suit. Rupali was weeping and wringing her hands. Cecilia tried to think through the cacophony. She had to decide what to do, especially now they had no home. All her planning on the train had come to nothing.

Looking around, her eyes fell on the hospital across the road. Perhaps they would help her tonight. Just for tonight. With Alfie still in her arms, she walked through the door of the hospital and found the doctor who had delivered Alfie just five months ago. He was in his office writing notes. A gangly, bald Englishman, with small glasses and a kind manner. He looked up and smiled at her as she came in. 'Mrs Keating. It is lovely to see you. And how is little Alfie here?'

Alfie had stopped wriggling and smiled at the doctor as if he were the most peaceful and angelic baby ever born. The doctor was entranced, clearly feeling that Alfie's good nature was wholly the result of his own medical brilliance. Cecilia decided to let him think that, as it would surely only further her cause.

'We need help, doctor, please. My husband has died suddenly. We have had to leave our house straight away. The children and I and our servants need somewhere to live until I can sort out a move.'

She saw the doctor was taken aback, but she pressed her case.

'I think it will only be for this night, doctor. I will contact my Papa in the morning and arrange to have the clothes and furniture sent on to him. Then we will follow.'

There was a pause. She filled it with, 'Just for one night. Please, doctor, please.'

He sighed, 'Well, Mrs Keating, this hospital has delivered all three of your younger children, so we have a duty to ensure they are well. May I suggest that your servants stay in the workers' quarters by Platform One at the station? They are only across the platforms. I am sure your furniture will be fine outside for one night. I will ask our caretaker to look out over them. You and the children may stay in the spare beds in the ward. We have two beds, that is all I am afraid.'

'Two beds will be fine, doctor, thank you. Thank you so much.' She nearly cried with relief.

Cecilia barely slept that night, sharing the bed with both Alfie and Michael didn't help. Richard, John and Cissy were all sound asleep in the next bed, so they were not a problem. The real problem was churning in her mind. What to do next. She had told the doctor that she would be contacting her father. It was her only option. She had the furniture to sort out and her job too. She had wired Pandit just before she had left for Agra, but had not updated him about Christopher's death.

The next morning, she left a note in the doctor's office thanking him for his help. When Rupali and Aktbar arrived, she left the children with them in the street while she went to the railway telegram office. She wired her father with the news telling him she was bringing the children home. She wired Pandit Wacha to let him know she would be coming to see him. She wanted to tell him in person that she would be leaving her work with him.

She went back to the bungalow where she organised the removal and transport of their belongings to her father's house in Kohampur. She watched as a row of porters placed her belongings on their backs, tables, chairs and beds, then trudge slowly to the station, placing them carefully onto the train.

She gathered up the children with Rupali and Aktbar and began the long journey to her Papa, via Allahabad. Another hot, squabbling journey ensued – the children were fractious and neither Rupali nor Aktbar could pacify them. Cecilia was so drained of all energy that she ignored them all, only feeding Alfie when she could stand his cries no more.

At Allahabad, she took them all to the riverside, the confluence of the Ganges, Yamuna and Saraswati rivers. It was a stunning setting, birds flying and swooping, the river so wide it almost looked like the sea. Ewing College was nearby, she showed them the building where she had studied. But they were not interested. The wide sloping beaches, miles of glorious white sand, hundreds of bobbing boats and sparkling waters entranced them. She left them to play under the watchful eyes of Rupali and Aktbar while she went to see Pandit.

He listened carefully to her plans, nodding his head occasionally and murmuring words of agreement. When she had finished, he said, 'You are a wise woman, Cecilia. Putting the needs of your children first. Moving back to your Papa's home will be the best thing for you all.' She breathed out and relaxed for the first time since she had received the telegram about Christopher.

He paused and smiled, 'But not for me, I fear. You are an excellent clerk, a hard worker and a highly intelligent woman. You have helped me enormously. I will miss you greatly.'

Pandit hadn't said anything to her about her work before, so it took her by surprise to know that he thought so well of her. He continued, 'I know you have been training while you have been working with me. I think you should continue that training. You have the potential to be a barrister. There will come a time when that will be possible for women in this country. Cornelia Sorabji is at the forefront of this. You should follow in her footsteps after it happens. You must fulfil your potential.'

'It is difficult for me - with five children to look after.'

He went on, 'Of course, it will not be not easy. But I believe in you, Cecilia. I know you will do it and be very successful indeed. I will contact solicitors I know in Karachi to help find you work. Those who are good enough for you.'

They both laughed at his comment. But she knew his words were more potent than just humour. They gave her a surge of pride and energy – a soothing balm covering the tumultuous worries of her life. They gave her hope. Basking in his words, she felt light and free.

Chapter Eight

She breathed a long sigh, deep with relief, when the train pulled into its final stop. Perhaps the children would stop arguing and crying now the journey was over. Their whining and whingeing had been lacerating her brain for hours.

Papa was waiting for them. She was shocked to see how he had aged since they had last seen each other, four years earlier. He had shrunk, his hair was white and his air was sad. 'Oh Papa, Papa,' she said, throwing herself into his thin arms, 'I have missed you so much.'

He wiped his eyes, 'I have missed you too, bette.' He hugged her tight before turning to the children. Rupali was carrying baby Alfie, the others were hiding behind her yellow sari and Aktbar's dhoti. Richard and John had only vague memories of their Papaji, but the younger children had never met him. Papa smiled at them and took baby Alfie from Rupali. 'Hello, little ones,' he said, 'I am your Papaji. You are coming to live with me.'

Richard was indignant, 'I am not a little one, Papaji, I am ten-years-old.'

John, following his brother's lead, 'And me, Papaji. I am not a little one, I am seven now.'

Papa laughed and ruffled their hair, 'You are right, my boys. I was wrong. You are not little. The others are.'

138

Cecilia smiled. Trust her boys to be cheeky and correct their Papaji.

Richard and John started chasing each other around with cries of excitement, enjoying the freedom from the confines of the train. They were as lively and happy as ever and did not seem to be affected by the events in Mahoba. All she needed to do was settle the children with Papa, then start to work at the new solicitor's office in Karachi. They would be back to normal quickly.

'We need to find a school for Richard and John,' she said to Papa while they were eating their dhal and rice the next evening.

'Well, Harold attends the local Catholic school. It is not too far away.'

She smiled at him, with thanks, 'I want them to go to a Catholic school. They have all been baptised.'

'Well, you are Catholic now. I am used to that now. Parsee schools are hard to find.'

She nodded.

Papa added, 'The school has a hockey team. They employ a hockey specialist from the North West Frontier Railway to come and teach the boys once a week. He takes them to the station hockey club to practise. Harold loves it, he is quite a good player.'

'Hockey? Why hockey? Surely it should be cricket or polo?'

Papa laughed. Laughter punctuated by pain, 'Oh, bette. Your children are Anglo-Indians. They will never play cricket or polo. Those are games played by British Officers and top colonials, not people of mixed race. Your children will never be allowed. But Anglo-Indians have many good hockey teams around India. They are a rising force in the game. Mark my words, there will be Anglo-Indian hockey players in the Olympics soon.'

'I think any sport will be good for them. It will teach them to abide by rules.'

'I have noticed how the boys never stop moving or being cheeky. They are certainly a handful.'

'I like them being lively. Still, I think hockey will do them good.'

'*Acha*,' said Papa, using the cover-all Hindi word, and tipping his hand in the manner of a Hindu. 'Let's go to the school tomorrow and enrol them. We can find out about the hockey when we are there.'

The school was in a large bungalow near the railway station. There was a garden outside with large banyan trees and benches underneath, providing shade. They were greeted by a young nun who had a wide, welcoming smile and curly brown hair escaping her wimple. She bent down to shake hands with the boys, smiling up at Cecilia and Papa. 'Good morning. I am Sister Anne. Of course, Mr Chattergee, you already know us.' She turned to Cecilia, 'I am the head teacher. Come into my office please.'

In the office there was a wooden jigsaw to play with and some slate for the children to write on. The boys occupied themselves while Cecilia and Papa spoke to Sister Anne. Cecilia explained that the boys' father had died in the Boer War and their stepfather had died suddenly. They had come back from Agra to be with her Papa.

Sister Anne nodded in sympathy. 'I am very sorry to hear this Mrs Keating. Life is full of many such trials, yes? We will make Richard and John happy here, I am sure. They appear to be bright boys, like their cousin, Harold,' she looked over to where all three were playing quietly for once. 'And polite boys too.'

She was not keen to disavow the nun of that notion so she changed the subject.

'Thank you. I understand that the pupils learn hockey here?'

'Yes, they do. It is a very popular game. We have a hockey teacher, Mr New, who gives his time free once a week. He is a guard on the trains and travels from Multan each Friday. He takes them to the Kohampur club near the station. There they can play on a proper pitch. We think it is a good thing for the children to do.'

Papa said, 'I agree, Sister Anne. Anglo-Indians will be the dominant force in Indian hockey in the future.'

Cecilia smiled to herself. Her Papa liked to tell everyone his hockey theory and she loved him for his enthusiasm and for wanting his grandchildren to be a part of it.

Papa added, 'I have watched Mr New teach the boys. I think he was a fine player himself?'

'I believe so, Mr Chattergee. I understand he played for many years. Like you, Mrs Keating, he is widowed. And sometimes he brings his little girl, Helen, with him. She is a lovely child, about three years old, I would say. But I do think she gets bored when he is teaching.'

'She is the same age as Cissy, Papa. Perhaps they could play together.'

'If it helps him teach our boys better, we will look after this little Helen for him.'

The nun nodded, 'That is kind of you, Mr Chattergee, I will tell Mr New. I am sure he will be very pleased to take up your offer.' She called over to Richard and John, 'Young men. I will see you at school tomorrow. We look forward to having you join us here. You will be with Harold and make lots of other friends.'

The following Friday, Cecilia went to the club by the station with Papa to watch the boys at hockey lesson and speak to Mr New about his daughter playing with Cissy.

141

They stood for a while on the edge of the pitch watching. Cecilia's heart was nearly bursting with pride as she saw her little men running around the pitch, not always with the idea of hitting the ball. Sometimes they just ran aimlessly round in circles, waving their sticks in a dangerous manner. She loved their unbounded enthusiasm. On the other side of the pitch, Mr New blew the whistle frequently, running up and down the side lines, shouting instructions. He was a tall man, with receding light-coloured hair and a muscular body. He looked older than her, about forty, she thought.

She saw his little girl sitting on the dry red mud behind him. A pretty child, with dark ringlets, wearing a pale blue gingham dress. She was scuffing her pink shoes in the red dirt, looking bored.

Mr New blew the whistle and shouted, 'Break now, boys. Have a rest. I have some mango slices and water for you.' Cecilia and Papa walked round the pitch to talk to him. Richard, John and Harold waved to them and they waved back. She could see that the boys were sweating and breathing hard. Good, perhaps they would sleep soundly tonight. But she knew they wouldn't. Nothing seemed to tire them. She was always hopeful, though.

Papa started the conversation, 'Good day, Mr New. I am Harold's father.'

Mr New wiping his forehead as he nodded a reply, 'Ah yes, I know. I think Harold has potential now he is learning more about following the rules of the game.'

Papa said proudly, 'I am sure he will play for India one day.'

Mr New smiled, the smile of a teacher who must indulge a parent's dreams. 'You never know, Mr Chattergee, you never know.' Cecilia noticed he had green eyes, which were kind and piercing at the same time. Mr New was certainly very attractive. His voice had the same lilt as both Maurice and Christopher, so she guessed he was Irish like them.

'But we have not come here to talk to you about Harold,' Papa said as he stood aside and gestured towards Cecilia, 'this is my daughter Cecilia.' George looked at Cecilia properly for the first time. She saw admiration in his eyes, a look that she had seen from other men on many occasions.

'Cecilia is the mother of those two boys, Richard and John,' Papa nodded towards the group of boys who were gobbling slices of mango and drinking from small glass water bottles.

Mr New brightened, 'They are both doing well for their first time.'

Papa continued, 'We notice you bring your little girl to these training sessions.'

The air seeped out of Mr New like a slowly deflating balloon. His shoulder sagged with the burden of the memories he was carrying, 'My little Helen Josephine, yes. She is motherless. Her Mama died the day she was born.'

'I am very sorry to hear this, Mr New. Did Sister Anne mention that we would be happy to look after Helen while you teach the boys?'

He frowned as if trying to recall. After a pause, he said, 'No. I don't think she did,' and shaking his head he confirmed, 'I don't remember anything.'

'No matter,' said Papa, 'we are hoping your daughter will play with Cecilia's other children while you are here. We do not live too far away. Cecilia has a three-year-old girl called Cissy and I am sure they would play together nicely.'

Mr New smiled, a wide, open smile showing a perfect set of teeth. Cecilia was even more attracted. His smile was dazzling.

'That is a very kind idea, Mr Chattergee. Helen tells me she is bored when we come here. But I bring her with me so her ayah can have a break. I am sure Helen will love to play with your children.'

Papa nodded, 'Then it is agreed. I know you must get back to teaching them now. Perhaps, after the session today, we can all go to my house for some dinner? That way, Helen can meet Cissy, Michael and baby Alfie.'

Mr New looked both pleased and relieved, 'It would be an honour Mr Chattergee, thank you. I would like to know your family more.' He emphasised the point with a slightly raised eyebrow in Cecilia's direction. She felt a frisson of excitement flow through her, unexpected and unbidden.

He ran back to the field, blowing his whistle and calling to the boys to start the game again. The clattering of the sticks and the shouts of the boys as they tried to reach the ball drowned any conversation Cecilia and Papa might have had.

Papa watched the game with the intensity of a man wanting his family to be future hockey champions. He paced up and down, stretching his neck to get a good view of whichever boy was nearer the ball. He called out to them and muttered under his breath when he saw a poor tackle or a rule broken. His son and grandsons could do no wrong though and he clapped loudly every time their sticks touched the ball, regardless of how effective their moves were.

Cecilia passed the time watching Mr New as he ran up and down the pitch, teaching the boys. He cut a fine, healthy figure. The boys were eager to please, trying hard to channel their energy into the game. Sometimes their keenness spilled into arguments and she was pleased to see that, in resolving the disputes, Mr New was both calm and fair. He looked like a good man. She was intrigued by him.

'Well, Mr New,' said Papa that evening, as they finished their vegetable jalfrezi and dhal, 'May I call you by your first name?'

'Of course. It is George.'

'Thank you. Mine is John, so we can both use first names from now on. And this is Cecilia.'

'Hello John,' he said with a smile, 'Hello Cecilia. We mustn't forget you are at the table too.'

'Indeed,' she replied, her tone crisp, 'I may be a woman, but I shouldn't be ignored.'

They all laughed.

Papa began a volley of questions, 'Where do you live, George?'

'I live in Multan, John. Helen and I live in a bungalow owned by the North West Railway. I work for them. I joined the company nearly two years ago. Before that I worked in the port in Karachi. After I met my late wife, Gertrude, we moved to Multan because there are more opportunities on the railways. It is a very busy time.'

'You are right. The railways are the future. Soon, we will all be able to travel more easily. Now, how did you come to be playing hockey?'

'I joined the Karachi team at the dockyard. I love playing. It is fast and keeps me healthy. The school asked if I would teach the boys and use the club pitch at Kohampur, so I agreed.'

'That is a very kind thing to do,' Papa said with a nod.

'I enjoy it. The boys are keen. It helps with their discipline. To play in a team and observe the rules.'

'Why did you continue to teach here when you moved to Multan?'

Cecilia cringed, papa was certainly asking a lot more questions than was necessary on a first meeting, she thought.

'After Gertrude died, I carried on as it gave me a distraction. I think we have enough talent among the boys to get some of them into the Indian team.'

Papa's smile was broad. He nodded with vigour, 'I agree, George, I agree. We will get them into the Indian team and then we will make sure the team can take part in the Olympics.'

'You have ambitions, John. I like it,' laughed George, his wide smile enveloping the room.

Standing, George made to go, 'We have to leave now, as we need to sleep on the train. It is a long trip.'

'Of course, George,' agreed Papa. 'But next time, perhaps you can both sleep in our house and travel back the next day? We have room here for everyone,' and glancing over to where the children were playing he added, 'They all seemed to like each other. I think they will be good friends.'

George looked at Cecilia. She gave him a tiny nod of acknowledgement. He turned to Papa.

'Thank you so much for offering your home to us, John. Helen and I will be very happy to stay with you next week.'

Papa and George shook hands. George turned to Cecilia and shook her hand too. 'I am very much looking forward to next week already.' Another raise of his appraising eyebrow.

So that she didn't show how attracted she was to him, she said, 'I think it will help us all if Helen comes here and play.'

George scooped Helen into his strong arms, 'Come along, little one. Time to go.' Helen wriggled but soon calmed down with the promise of a sleep on the train.

As the front door closed behind them, Cecilia turned to Papa with a frown, 'You were very forward with him, Papa. Asking him to stay next week.'

Papa threw his head back and laughed, 'Oh, bette, don't you see?'

'What, Papa, what should I see?'

'Oh bette. He seems like a kind man. And he is a free man – he is a widower. I liked him and think he might make an excellent husband for you.'

'Papa!' she admonished him, 'You are very naughty. I might not like him.'

Papa laughed again, 'I saw the way he looked at you, bette. And the way you looked at him too. You both want time together, that was clear. He lives so far away that he will have to stay here or you will never see each other properly.'

Cecilia laughed too. She pecked his cheek and danced away to play with the children. She was excited and happy. It would be fun getting to know George.

The next Friday, she made her way home from work early. She decided she would help Aktbar cook the meal so she could show George that she had some feminine skills. Also, she needed time to get ready and look her best for him.

'Aktbar, could you please teach me how to make chapattis?'

'*Acha*, Memsa'ab. They can be difficult.'

Cecilia knew that chapattis were just flour and water. She had watched Aktbar make them many times before. She wondered just how difficult they would be to make and cook, it looked easy to her.

Under Aktbar's direction, she started kneading the dough. The more you knead it, he said, the softer the chapattis will become. She was determined to make them beautifully soft. But the dough just wouldn't be kneaded. It clung to her fingers, stretching into thick spider webs between them. The more she tried to remove it, the more it stayed. Every time she pushed her knuckles in the dough, flurries of flour flew up over her face and sari. Watching her, the usually solemn Aktbar laughed.

147

'Let me, Memsa'ab. Perhaps you would be better rolling them out. Rub your hands together quickly and the dough will come off.'

'I agree, Aktbar. I will watch you knead them. Then I will roll them into rounds. It looks simple when you do it.'

Aktbar's eyes were smiling. He said nothing as he started to knead the dough that Cecilia had released from her fingers. She watched, fascinated as he expertly pushed and pummelled it into a smooth round lump with a soft sheen. She marvelled at his skill, something she had never even thought about before.

'Now, Memsa'ab. Before you roll out a chapatti, I will show you how I do it.'

Keen to redeem herself, she decided to keep quiet and not say what she was thinking, which was that she would be fine without a lesson. It was only rolling some dough into a circle shape after all. Aktbar took a lump of the dough and flattened it with a wooden rolling pin. Then, very fast, he rolled and turned the dough, and rolled and turned it until it was a completely flat and perfect circle shape. Smiling, he broke off a piece of rough dough, handing her the rolling pin.

Brimming with confidence, she tried to flatten the dough with a firm roll. It stuck to the rolling pin. She pulled it off and flattened it again. It stuck again. And again. And then it stuck to her hands. Again and again.

Aktbar eventually took it off her and flattened it into a small circle that needed more rolling. She started anew, rolling and turning the dough in the way she had seen Aktbar do. But the dough did not stay in shape and she could not roll it flat enough. She added flour but it just puffed into her face again.

'I had no idea, Aktbar, how hard it would be. I am covered in flour, it is even in my hair and over my face. And all I have made is this.' The mottled dough hung from her hand like a torn piece of dirty fabric.

They heard voices at the kitchen door. George walked in, holding Helen. He was followed by Papa, Harold, Richard and John. They stopped still at scene that greeted them.

Cecilia was mortified. She had wanted to get ready and look her best for George and now he was seeing her like this: a complete floury mess holding an unidentifiable piece of gunk.

Papa broke the astonished silence, 'What is happening here?'

Cecilia knew she must explain. She wasn't going to admit that she was cooking to try and impress George.

'Well as we are having guests, I thought I would help Aktbar make some extra chapattis.'

Papa burst out laughing, 'You, bette? Make chapattis? I never thought I would see such a thing. You have never cooked in your life.'

Peeved that she had been found out, she tried to make light of it, 'Well, I will not be doing it again. I do not suit cooking. I think I will stick to being a lawyer.' She swept passed them, without a glance, in a desperate attempt to maintain her dignity.

She cleaned herself up in her bedroom, changing into a lavender coloured sari and pink satin choli. Even after six children, her body was still thin and childlike. She brushed the flour out of her thick hair and smoothed it down as much as she could. Satisfied that she looked vaguely presentable, she walked back into the kitchen where the whole family was sitting down to eat.

'Ah, bette, you look lovely now,' said Papa.

'Thank you.' She turned to George, 'I am sorry you saw me like that.'

149

George replied, 'We were a bit earlier than planned. I am sorry. I thought you looked lovely.'

Cecilia laughed. George, Papa and the children joined in.

'While you were getting changed, I was telling George about your career. He was very impressed.'

Papa, matchmaking for her again, she thought.

'You are an intelligent woman, Cecilia,' said George, looking at her with renewed admiration.

'Thank you. I have transferred my work from Mahoba where I used to live. I am now working in Karachi. I am still training as well. As women have yet to be allowed to practise. But it will happen soon, I am sure. I plan to be a barrister when it is allowed.'

'And ambitious. I like that too,' he said. Looking at Papa he asked, 'I would like to take Cecilia out for a walk tonight after dinner, John. Would that be possible?'

'I do not mind this, George. But you must ask Cecilia, not me. I do not speak on her behalf.' His eyes were alive in triumph. His plan was working.

Cecilia was pleased. George wanted to get to know her better. An exciting prospect. And, at last, Papa seemed to be learning that she wanted to make her own decisions.

'That I can, Papa,' Cecilia agreed, 'Thank you, George. I would like to walk out with you. Now let's eat some of these delicious chapattis,' she paused, 'That I didn't make.'

They all laughed again.

In the evening, when the children were all settled, Cecilia and George walked to the nearby public gardens. It was hot and the streets were still crowded with people buying, selling and shouting and chatting. Animals wandered around, braying and neighing, children were running and shrieking. Vultures sat together in the trees, waiting expectantly for a carcass to emerge. As usual, dust, dirt and detritus were everywhere.

They picked their way slowly through the paths, avoiding as much of it as they could. They sat on a bench in the park, watching the antics of the animals and the people.

He told her about Gertrude's death and how it had left him bereft. He had a newborn to look after and a wife to mourn at the same time. She gently squeezed his arm as his eyes welled. He told her that he had chosen an older ayah, someone with experience. Helen was growing up nicely so was happy with his decision. He said he used hockey to help him with his grief and had had no thoughts of having another woman. Until now, that is.

He looked at her and smiled his dazzling smile, 'You are the first woman who has attracted me since then. You are very beautiful. You are good company too. You have lovely eyes, they sparkle with life. Your children are delightful and your Papa is a good man. I really like you, Cecilia.'

She told him about Maurice and mentioned Bridget. She told him that her marriage to Christopher was troubled. She didn't tell him why.

George nodded as she spoke, making noises of sympathy.

'So,' he said when she had finished, 'We have both had some sad times. Now we need happy times.'

'I would certainly like to see you more,' she said ignoring the social conventions that it was a man's role to ask a woman to continue a relationship.

He laughed, 'Your Papa said you were bold, Cecilia. He was right. I like it!'

'I am glad of that, George. I am also independent and want to make sure that whatever I do next, I will still work and train to be a barrister.'

'Yes, I understand.'

After they had returned home and George had settled into the lounge area to sleep on the chair, Papa gestured Cecilia to join him in the kitchen.

'How did it go with George, bette? Do you like him?'

'Oh, Papa, you are keen that I like him. But I do, so we agree.'

'He needs a wife too, to be a mother for his little girl.'

'Oh Papa. When I married Christopher, I was a widow, as I am now. I thought it would solve my problems. But it didn't. I don't want to make the same mistake again.' She realised that she had said too much to her father about Christopher, she had wanted to keep it a secret from him.

'Mistake?' he asked concern lacing his voice, 'What do you mean?'

'I didn't mean 'mistake' really. It is just that he was ill and I was a long way from home. From you.'

'Oh, I understand. I didn't know how ill he was. You did not say in your letters.'

'I didn't want to worry you.' She placed her hand over his, 'Never mind now. I am back and we will not be parted again. Besides, you are looking too old for me to move away.'

They both laughed. 'Yes, I think that is right. Susan feels that I am ageing quickly. She is so much younger than me.'

'But she has brought you much happiness. Harold has too.'

The next morning, they all gathered for breakfast, just like a normal family it seemed to Cecilia. Helen and the other children were playing agreeably with Rupali at the table, Papa was bouncing Alfie on his knee. George was cutting up fruit while Aktbar was stirring some chai on the stove. A peaceful, happy scene. A glimpse of what the future could hold.

When George had handed out the fruit, Papa said, 'You are welcome to come and stay again next week, if you would like to, George.'

Papa winked at Cecilia.

'That is very kind of you, John, I think we will.'

George looked at Cecilia and winked too. Embarrassed, she busied herself taking Alfie from her Papa and walking him up and down.

George stood up and said to Helen, 'Come on, little one. We have to go home now.'

Helen protested noisily as her Papa scooped her up. Cecilia gave her one of Aktbar's chapattis. 'Here you are, bette. You can have this to eat on the train.' Her tears drying up, Helen looked at it with suspicion, her bottom lip pouting. Cecilia said to her, 'Don't worry. I didn't make it. Aktbar did. So, it will taste lovely.'

Helen looked relieved and took the chapatti. Everyone else laughed.

'Mama, that is funny,' said Richard, 'You can't cook, we know that!'

'You are so right, Richard. I will not try again. Ever.'

George said his goodbyes with a wide smile, 'I will see you boys at hockey next week. Don't forget to practise with your ball and sticks, the way I showed you.' He turned to Papa, 'I look forward to staying with you again next week.' He blew a kiss to Cecilia and left.

Her heart fluttered as she hugged the excitement to herself. George was very attractive. And she liked him. She was falling in love.

'I think we should get married,' George said some weeks later, on one of their regular evening walks, 'we like each other's company. Our children like each other.'

She had grown fond of this man over the last few weeks. He was gentle and kind.

'I agree, George. We will make a good marriage. But for me it is too soon. Christopher only died six months ago.'

'Yes, but if we marry in another six months, that should be enough time, no?'

She nodded, 'Enough time will have passed by then, yes. But we need to think about some things.'

'Yes, I know. You will need to move to Multan.'

'But what about my work? I have only just joined the practice in Karachi. If I move to Multan, I will have to start again.'

'Come to Multan soon. You can see if there is a solicitor's office you can join where you will not have to start again.'

They looked at each other, each knew what the other was thinking. 'You want me to sleep with you there, don't you?'

'Of course, you are a beautiful woman. I have wanted you in my bed for a very long time.'

'Well, I want to be in bed with you too. I must arrange to visit you in Multan as soon as possible.'

'What else do we need to think about when we are married?' asked George, turning to practicalities.

'It's Papa. He is older now and I do not want to leave him. I left him when we went to Mahoba. It was not good.'

'But he has Susan, Harold, and your brothers and sisters.'

'Yes, but the older ones are married now with families of their own. Susan looks after him and Harold is a joy. But he is my Papa.'

'Perhaps they could move to Multan with us?' suggested George.

'I am not sure,' she said with a sigh, 'it is a lot to ask of him.'

When they suggested it to Papa, he was taken aback.

But he became philosophical once he had thought about it. 'Well, I worked hard to bring you two together. I wanted you to get married from the beginning. It would be wrong to stand in your way.'

'That is sorted then,' said George.

'We do not want to marry until Christopher has been passed for a year. The wedding will be in October. But I have to be sure I can get work in Multan first,' Cecilia looked at George with determination, 'Or else I will not be getting married at all.'

There was a silence as both men absorbed her words. 'Well,' declared Papa eventually, 'work must be secured first. You must go to Multan as soon as possible to find it.'

George nodded, 'Yes, that is very important, I agree. Perhaps we could leave for Multan today. May we leave Helen with you? Is it possible that Rupali can look after her along with the other children? That would make everything easier for us.'

'Of course, of course.'

Cecilia and George exchanged glances. This way, she could look for work during the day and they could make love in the evenings without being disturbed.

Their trip to Multan was a success, mostly. They consummated their relationship with gentle lovemaking which Cecilia treasured after her experiences with Christopher. And, armed with two letters of recommendation, one from Pandit Wacha and one from the law firm in Karachi, she secured work with a Parsee law practice. But the lead barrister there, Pandit Wadia, wanted her to start straight away. She explained that she would prefer a later start, after October.

'Mrs Keating,' he said, 'we have a lot of work to do. Here the INC is gaining ground and is taking up much of our time, as it did in the practice you worked for in Allahabad. We need someone as soon as possible. We cannot wait until you marry Mr New.'

'Which side of the debate are you working for?' she asked, once again being bolder than a woman should.

'Independence, of course. We believe India can survive well without the British. We just need to work for a peaceful break.'

'I agree,' she replied without giving away her concerns about her children being Anglo-Indians. 'I would like to join you. May I go back to Karachi and make arrangements? It may take me a week or so. But I will send you a wire to let you know the date I can start.'

'That would be very good, Mrs Keating. But please ensure it's as soon as possible.'

They shook hands. She left, elated that she had secured work but worried about the practice's support of independence and their need to have her join them sooner than was convenient.

At George's house, she explained to him, 'I think India should be an independent country. The British have abused their power here but I do not know what it will mean for my children. It is clear that they are rejected by Indian society and the British do not like them either. But at least the British give them work on the railways and the ports and in the police. I fear life will be even more difficult for them without the British providing some level of protection.'

George nodded, 'I know, I know. Little Helen is white because Gertrude was English. She will be alright in British circles. But all your children are Anglo-Indians, they will have problems. If we have children of our own, they will be Anglo-Indians too and face the same problems. Once you start working here in Multan you may be able to transfer to another, more suitable, practice.'

'I like that idea.'

They made love again. Afterwards they lay in each other's arms. As the evening sun glittered through the shutters on their naked bodies, they discussed their wedding and decided to organise it for October 1907. She would move to Multan earlier than planned to start work. They discussed what to do with the children.

'I am going to miss them if we leave them with Papa so they can finish school,' she said, her voice laden with sorrow.

'I do understand. Perhaps we can bring them with us straight away.'

She sighed and kissed his shoulder, 'But I will be disrupting them again. They have not long started the school they are attending now.'

'Then it is best if we leave them until the end of the year. Once they come here, I will transfer my hockey teaching to their new school.'

'I will go back to talk to Papa.'

At the station, they parted without showing affection. It would be frowned upon by the people around them. She boarded the train and leaned out to wave to him. George blew her a kiss. They both laughed at the boldness of his action as the train drew away. This time, all the usual discomfort of the train journey didn't bother her, she was so flooded with excitement and happiness.

On arrival at her Papa's Kohampur home, she told him her news and asked him to look after the children while she moved to Multan and started work there.

As ever, her Papa was worried for her and the children, 'Bette, this will be a difficult time for you and them. You won't like to be separated from them and they will miss you.'

'I know, Papa. But I need the work and Pandit Wadia needs me to start now. Very few law practices will employ me as I am an Indian woman. I have no choice. I will come back every week to be with them. It is only for a few months. We will still get married in October and then they will move to Multan to start the new school year there.'

Papa was not convinced, 'I know Pandit Wadia. He is a fine man and a respected Parsee. I would like to telephone him to ask if he will delay your start date.'

Cecilia's heart sank. She was nearly thirty years old, a mother of five and an articled clerk. Yet her Papa was wanting to act on her behalf. As ever, it rankled with her, especially as she also knew that it was a good idea. Papa was likely to make headway with Pandit Wadia in a way she couldn't. Which was the most important issue at stake.

'Very well, Papa,' she said as she stood to leave the room. 'Please see what Pandit Wadia says about it.'

She heard her Papa leave the house to go to the telegraph office and make the call. She felt anxious while he was gone and tried to concentrate on playing tag with the children in the yard. But she kept on listening out for him coming back through the door, wondering what the outcome would be. When, at last, he returned he called her into the kitchen, 'Bette. I spoke to Pandit Wadia. He remembered me from when your Mama was alive. Parsees are such a small community.'

Cecilia rolled her eyes, 'Yes Papa, I know, I know. But what did he say?'

'He agreed to delay your start but only until August. Not October. He said there was too much work to delay any more. It is not exactly what we wanted but it is something better than the deal you agreed with him.'

'It is better than before,' she replied.

Papa carried on talking, 'Pandit told me he is working for the INC to make India a country independent of British control. What do you think of that, bette?'

'I think it is a good idea for some, Papa. I worry what the future will hold for the children without British rule.'

'You will be working to bring that situation about. Not a comfortable position for you.'

'I need to work Papa. George and I agreed that I would look to work in a different practice once I am married to him and living in Multan properly.'

'It is a compromise, bette, much of life is.' Papa sighed, 'Now, we must tell the children of our plans.'

Papa's talk of 'our' plans irritated her. She forced herself not to start an argument. It wouldn't change anything, anyway, she decided.

So, as Papa and Pandit had agreed, Cecilia arrived in Multan in August to start her new job and move in with George. Pandit welcomed her with relief. He was a small man who sustained a permanently worried look. While he was kind, he seemed too intense to have a sense of humour.

'I will take you to your desk,' he said scuttling down the corridor. She followed him into a nearby room, where he gestured nervously to a table which was covered in haphazard piles of files. Next to it was a chair which was also covered in heaps of papers.

'We have been waiting a long time for you,' he said, by way of explanation. 'All these files need reading as soon as possible and then you can put them away in the cupboard. Then you will be able to sit on your chair and work at your desk.'

'Well, it is nine o'clock now. What shall I do after ten o'clock?' she quipped.

There was a pause while he worked out she was joking. Then he laughed. 'I like it, Mrs Keating. That is very funny.' And he left the room with a smile – it seemed his face was not used to such movement.

She scanned the files, coughing as fluffs of dust puffed up when she turned a page. She noticed a recent copy of *The Times of India* on top of one of the piles. She picked it up. It was dated 24 August 1907. The main headline ran across the front page:

Madam Cama unfurls the new Indian flag in Germany.

She read the article, which detailed how her acquaintance, Bhikaiji Cama, who was at her birthday party when she met Maurice all those years ago, had attended a conference in Stuttgart. She had unfurled the flag of independent India, insisting the whole conference salute it. According to the paper, the event had caused a sensation, not least because she was a woman. And it was the first time the newly designed flag of India was raised on foreign soil.

Pandit Wadia returned to find her reading the newspaper. 'I read that article. Interesting. We Parsees breed strong, brave intelligent women,' he said with a smile. 'Madam Cama is one of them. And you are another, I know. Your references are impeccable.'

'Thank you, Pandit Wadia.'

Cecilia hugged a feeling of pleasure secretly to herself. It felt good to know he thought well of her so soon into their working relationship. She would review his position on the independence movement in a few months, she decided.

The next day, she and George went to the church of Christ the Holy Redeemer in the east of the city to apply for their wedding licence. As they picked their way through the streets towards the cream-coloured building, Cecilia had a growing sense of foreboding. She was worried about telling the priest the truth that she was living with George. She knew he might refuse to marry them as he would view them as living in sin.

By the time they reached the church entrance, she had decided to lie about their status. There was no time to tell

George as the priest welcomed them just as they walked through the gate. He was a tiny, wizened white man. His clothes were shapeless and dirty. Only a grubby dog collar identified him as the priest. He introduced himself as Father Theodore and took them to his office, gesturing for them to sit down.

'You are here for a marriage licence?' he asked.

'Yes, Father,' said George, 'We would like to get married in October.'

'Very well,' said the priest. He opened a wooden cupboard in the corner of the room taking out a large, leather-bound book and a quill pen.

He sat back down and opened the book, carefully finding a blank page, 'Now,' he said with a smile, 'I need your details.' He turned to George, 'Your name please.'

'George Henry New.'

He wrote it slowly with exacting precision. His neat handwriting was at odds with his scruffy appearance, she thought.

'Where do you live?'

'Multan.'

'How long have you lived in Multan? It is important for the granting of the licence.'

'Over five years, Father.'

'Very good. The minimum time is four weeks. And what is your occupation?'

'I am a guard on the North West Railway.'

'And your condition?'

'I am a widower, Father.'

The priest nodded in a sympathy, 'And what is your father's name?'

'It is George Henry New also.'

'Thank you.' He turned to Cecilia, 'Name?'

'Cecilia Keating.'

'Where do you live?'

'Kohampur, Karachi,' she could feel George stiffen with surprise beside her.

The priest raised his eyes, 'This is most unusual. The bride normally marries in her own parish. Why are you not marrying in Kohampur? Or St Patrick's church in Karachi?'

Cecilia felt herself redden as both men looked at her, waiting for an answer.

'Well,' she paused as she tried to think of something plausible.

'The churches in Kohampur and Karachi are busy,' she heard herself say. George was looking at her startled. 'Besides,' she added, 'we love this church and our friends have said that you are very good, Father Theodore.'

This flattery seemed to satisfy the priest and he carried on with his task, 'What is your condition?'

'I am a widow, Father.'

'Very well,' and then he laughed, 'No need to ask if you have an occupation, Mrs Keating. Of course you don't. You are a woman.' He laughed out loud at the prospect.

She could feel her body tense. But decided, as she invariably did, not to say anything to correct him. She didn't want to cause trouble and risk him not granting them a licence.

He moved on with his questions, 'What is your father's name?'

'John Chattergee.'

'A Hindu?'

'No, Father, he is a Parsee.'

'A Parsee? Are you a Parsee, then? Is this a mixed marriage?'

'Oh no, Father. I converted to Catholicism before my first marriage.'

He nodded, '*Acha*,' he said, tipping his hand.

'Right,' he stood up and went to another corner of the room. To a desk with drawers. He pulled out the top drawer and took out a parchment certificate.

As he sat back down, he explained, 'I have all the information I need. I now have to issue your marriage licence. You will need this when you come back to book your nuptial mass.'

He slowly transferred the written information onto the parchment in his cursive script. It took him a long time. They watched in silence, fascinated.

When he finished, he blotted the certificate and, once sure it was dry, he handed it to George. 'Here you are, Mr New. Your wedding licence. I hope you have a long and happy life together.' Turning to Cecilia, he added with a knowing look, 'Blessed with many children.'

Again, she swallowed her annoyance. It was nothing to do with him. He should not make such comments. She walked out of the room without another word, leaving George to deal with the protocols of saying goodbye to the priest.

Outside, in the heat of the day, George joined her.

'Why didn't you say goodbye to him? It was rude to leave like that.'

'He was rude to me. Assuming I would have lots of children with you.'

George laughed, 'I love your frankness. Yes, he was rude. Thank goodness I had hold of the licence before you left, else he might have changed his mind and not given it to us.'

'That's true. I am sorry. I am so hot-tempered by nature. But I keep it to myself. It spills out sometimes.'

'I didn't know you were going to tell him lies too. Saying you live in Kohampur when you live with me in Multan. And you didn't correct him when he assumed you didn't work.'

'I know he would not like us living together before we are married. So, I thought it would be best to lie. As for my work,

I have met many men like him. They do not like women who work and they make our lives difficult. I thought if I said nothing, we would get the licence. If I told him he was wrong, he may not have issued it.'

'I understand.'

She smiled at him.

'But I hope we do have more children.' He said, looking at her in a questioning manner.

She softened, 'I would like to have more children. I would like to bring up a family where there is a father present. Maurice had to go to war so quickly after we married, the boys don't remember him. And poor little Bridget never even met him. Christopher was too ill. I would like my children to have a proper father.'

'I feel that way about Helen. She never knew her mother. I want her to have a mother and brothers and sisters. When we marry, she will have all of those things.'

They bought some brinjal bhajis from one of the many food stalls that lined their route home. They enjoyed the freshly cooked taste, while they walked and talked about their wedding and how excited they were to be planning a future together.

The Church of Christ the Holy Redeemer was nearly blotted out by the blinding midday sun as Cecilia and her father walked towards it. A small crowd had assembled outside, waiting to greet her. As they neared the door the crowd parted, letting her and Papa enter the imposing building.

The group followed them into the church lobby. They all stopped to greet her and wish her well. The auntijis, Bala and Bhakti, kissed her and whispered that George was a much better prospect than Christopher. They had never liked that second husband of hers. Cecilia's sister and brothers with husband, wives and children, kissed her in turn and murmured words of love and support. Channa and Veena were there too, smiling with their husbands and families beside them. Cecilia soaked up their loving wishes. She straightened her pink floral dress and took a deep breath. Taking Papa's arm, she nodded that she was ready to walk up the aisle with him to her wedding ceremony. For the third time.

George was standing at the altar in his guard's uniform. He looked smart and handsome, smiling broadly at her as she walked towards him. As she drew level, her heart quickened with excitement. This attractive man would soon be her husband. Together they would make a happy family. This time it would work, she was sure.

The children were in the pews with Rupali and Chetna, Helen's ayah. She could hear them fidgeting as the nuptial mass unfolded. She turned and waved at them and they all waved back, much to the disgust of Father Theodore, who was just as rumpled as he had between when they first met him. He frowned at her, making it clear he thought her behaviour was unseemly. She didn't care, she just smiled at the priest in defiance. Scruffy old man, she thought.

The wedding breakfast, at their house, was a happy affair with all the children running and chasing each other in the large back yard. Cecilia looked at her family. Her sister and brothers, all now in their early twenties, were married to lovely people. Her younger brother Harold was lively and happy. He was playing with her children and Helen in the yard. Papa was talking to the auntijis and managing to circulate around all the guests being the genial host, as ever.

George's family were in Ireland so couldn't come to the wedding. Some of his former hockey team were there as well a number of his railway colleagues. She thought fleetingly of the wedding breakfast when she married Christopher. What a difference between this one and that one. With Christopher, the reception was full of tension and descended into belligerent drunkenness. With George, the atmosphere in the room was friendly and celebratory.

At last, at last, she thought. There will be happy times ahead for us all.

When the party was over and all the guests had left, Cecilia, Papa, Susan and George helped Aktbar and George's cook, Ravi, to clean and tidy up.

As they finished Papa said, 'It was a lovely day. I am happy to have you as a son-in-law, George. And we are happy with our new bungalow next door aren't we, Susan?'

Susan nodded saying nothing. Cecilia wondered why she was always so quiet. Susan was a woman who rarely voiced an opinion. She liked her but found her company somewhat tedious.

Cecilia was happy in her married life. The children were settled in their new home and schools. She kept the two ayahs as there were so many children to look after. Both ayahs seemed to like each other and the two other servants, Aktbar and Ravi, managed the cooking and cleaning between them with no noticeable tension.

She enjoyed working for Pandit. He was impressed with her, telling her that he was glad she was working in his Chambers.

'A good lawyer or barrister needs a sharp brain, a quick grasp of issues and a phenomenal memory, Cecilia,' he told her one day, 'you have all of them. You are warm and kind. People respond to you and trust you. You will make an excellent barrister one day. I hope you will consider training for the bar.'

After so many years of studying and working, Cecilia was delighted to hear his encouraging words. He thought she could be a barrister. So had Pandit Wacha. She must be good enough.

'Yes, I am waiting for Cornelia Sorabji to get there first,' she told him with a smile.

Pandit replied, 'Miss Sorabji will get there quicker if she has more help. You should join her campaign? You will make a difference, I am sure.'

'There are many Parsee women fighting for our rights. I would like to join them, Pandit. But my children are young and need me more. They have had a lot of upheaval in their lives. I have to have priorities and my children are my priority.'

'Very well. I understand. But as your children get older, you may have more time and you can probably help then,' he gave her a sardonic glance, 'I don't think the fight will be over by then.'

'You are right, of course, Pandit Wadia. We have a long way to go.'

Waking one morning, Cecilia felt nauseous. Her stomach was cramping, her throat was dry, her head was aching. George was already at work and she was due into Chambers a little later. She felt so ill she could hardly move.

The bedroom door opened a little and through the gap she saw a timid Rupali.

'Memsa'ab. The children are missing you. Are you well?'

'I am ill, Rupali. But I must get up and see the children before I go to work.'

'Oh Memsa'ab. I am not sure that is a good idea. How may I help you?'

'Please bring me the chamber pot, Rupali. I need to be sick. Then I will be alright, I am sure.'

Rupali disappeared from the door and emerged a few minutes later with a chamber pot. She placed it by the bed and discreetly left the room.

Cecilia retched uselessly. She knew with certainty that she was pregnant again.

She lay back with bittersweet thoughts. She did want another baby, she wanted to share parenthood with her new husband and for them to enjoy their baby together. But being pregnant was so tiring. She wondered how she would manage to carry on working with seven children.

The bedroom door burst open and the children ran in shouting. Richard and John were chasing each other, Michael and Cissy were following them, aimlessly sucking their thumbs. Helen was carrying baby Alfie.

Richard shouted, 'Mama, Mama. Rupali says you are not well. We have come to cheer you up.' He climbed onto the bed and started jumping as high as he could.

Cecilia groaned as the mattress heaved. 'Please Richard, please stop. It is making me worse.'

Richard stopped in astonishment, 'Why, Mama? I thought it would be good for you.'

'Well, it is not. But thank you for trying.' She decided to get up and carry on the day as normal. She just didn't have the time to be ill.

Richard looked crestfallen, she hugged him tight. 'You are such a good boy. I am very lucky to have all of you. Now, you big boys need to get ready for school. Where is Rupali? She should be here, helping.'

'She was, Mama,' said Richard, with his usual earnestness, 'But we said she wasn't to come into your bedroom with us. We wanted to cheer you up by ourselves.'

She ruffled his hair and John's too, 'Rupali is in charge, you know. You must do as she says. Not the other way round.'

She could hear Rupali outside the door, 'Come, Rupali, come.'

The ayah entered the room slowly with her eyes downcast, 'I apologise Memsa'ab. I could not stop the children running in.'

'Never mind,' Cecilia smiled, 'Richard and John must get to school now. Please take them all back to the bedroom and sort them out. Chetna can help you.'

After the older boys had left for school, the house was a little quieter. Still feeling queasy, Cecilia was preparing to go to work when Chetna came into the room. The older ayah moved slowly, her ample body clearly a hinderance.

'You are not well, Memsa'ab?' she asked.

'I am a little better now, thank you, Chetna.'

The ayah gave her a knowing look, 'I think you may be having another baby, Memsa'ab.'

Cecilia could only agree, 'I think you are right'.

'Please lie on the bed, Memsa'ab. I will see how far along you are.'

Cecilia did as she was told and Chetna felt her stomach gently. Eventually, she pronounced, 'I think you have another six months. The baby will come around August.'

Taking a deep breath, swallowing the nausea, she went to work.

That evening, once the older children were settled in bed, while she was rocking little Alfie to sleep, she told George the news.

He was delighted, 'This is wonderful, Cecilia. Having our own little baby will be so exciting.'

Cecilia kept her true feelings to herself. Being pregnant again would not be easy. Another child would be another expense for school and food. Her work and studies would be interrupted – once more. She wanted to enjoy the moment and be happy with George, so she said nothing. Little Alfie was fussing in her arms, wriggling and crying. She tried to placate him, singing and chatting to him, cuddling him and stroking his face. Nothing would settle him, as ever.

'Let me walk up and down with him for a while,' suggested George, 'I am going to need the practise again with a new baby on the way.'

But Alfie was not going to sleep easily. 'He's a funny one,' said George, 'Always likes to be heard and have attention.'

'Yes, he does. He has been the most demanding of all the babies. Let's hope the new one is easier.'

It was a hard pregnancy with many days when she felt too tired to move, but every one of those days she carried on regardless. There was never any time to attend to herself. The demands of her work and the children took up every moment of every day, relentlessly needing her time and attention.

On 18th August, with some relief, she gave birth to a little girl. Chetna attended her. The birth was without incident and Cecilia was glad to have the baby out of her body, knowing that the ayahs could help her now.

Once the sheets were changed, the baby wrapped and the room swept, George brought the older children into the bedroom to see their new sister. Rupali followed him with Alfie in her arms. Richard, John and Michael looked at the baby. They weren't interested. They left the room quickly to go back to practising hockey in the yard. Rupali, still with Alfie, followed them to make sure they didn't get up to too much mischief.

Helen and Cissy were fascinated. They climbed on the bed and clucked over their sister. Cecilia let them hold her in turn while she taught them to support the baby's head. They kissed her and Helen asked, 'What is her name, Mama?'

Before Cecilia could explain that they had not chosen a name yet, George said, 'Gertrude. Her name is Gertrude Rosanna.'

Cecilia looked at him in surprise. 'Gertrude?'

George shrugged, 'It is a nice name.'

'But it is the name of your first wife.'

Helen and Cissy looked up with curiosity as they heard their parents' voices tighten.

'Well, I thought it would be a nice way to remember her.'

'But, I...' she paused as the new baby began to cry. She lifted her out of Helen's arms and said with a sigh, 'She needs me to feed her now. I don't have time to argue with you, George.'

'If it makes you happier, we can call her Gertie. Gertrude never liked that nickname, so we never used it.'

'Very well. I will call her Gertie.' Turning to Helen and Cissy, she said, 'Her name is Gertie. Now, off you go, she needs a feed.'

The girls scampered away, chattering excitedly to each other, talking about all the games they would play with their little sister when she grew older.

Cecilia marvelled at how easy it all was – or at least easier than she had expected. Chetna and Rupali proved their worth by looking after all the children with their usual kindness and patience. Aktbar brought his young son to the bungalow on many days to help him and Ravi with the cooking and cleaning.

Little Gertie proved to be a placid baby. Richard and John soon overcame their initial disinterest, amusing her with antics that she seemed to know were meant to entertain her. Helen and Cissy were always fussing around her and cuddling her. Even Alfie, only sixteen-months-old, seemed to recognise he was no longer the youngest. He was still demanding, more so than Gertie, but he didn't seem to resent his new baby sister.

When Gertie was about a month old, Cecilia went back to work. Pandit Wadia was pleased to see her, 'We have missed you, Mrs New. There is so much work and we need your brain. I hope the baby is well but I hope you do not have another one soon.'

'So do I, Pandit.'

Pandit started talking about work, 'We have an appeals case that will be heard in London and I have to leave tomorrow for the High Court there. I will be meeting Sir Dadabhai Naoroji Dordi there. He is a Member of Parliament, and a man I greatly admire. He is working very hard for independence.' He smiled, 'I have to use my time wisely there, as it will be a costly trip. And us Parsees getting together to help make reforms is a very good use of my time. Now, I need all the papers in order and the case bundles made ready for the journey. All the documents must be sent to the port today. I need your opinion on the arguments we can put forward. This is an important case for the INC and we need to win it. We want the British Government to agree to leave a founding member of the INC to continue his activities. They are peaceful activities after all.'

'Certainly Pandit. I will start straight away.'

She worked through the day, sorting the documents and reading through them at the same time. A name caught her eye, Bal Gangadhar Tilak. She paused while she tried to remember where she had heard the name. She couldn't at first. She decided to read a little more about him and then it dawned on her, of course, he was the man speaking at the barrage on the day out with Christopher, years ago, the day that had led to the evening when Michael was conceived. Yes, Bal Gangadhar Tilak. From the INC. She remembered his passionate speech, a large flabby man exhorting everyone to join the movement that would bring India out of British Rule. She remembered saying to Christopher that he was in danger of being charged with sedition. She was interested to see that it had already happened:

> The continued activities of Bal Gangadhar Tilak have come to light and the Government of India regards such activities as seditious. The government has contacted Bal Gangadhar Tilak and asked him to cease and desist these activities with immediate effect. We have already imprisoned him once on such matters, in 1897, and will not hesitate to do so again.

Cecilia felt it was unlikely that he would stop. It was more likely he would be tried for sedition again in the next few years. As she read on, she began to feel uneasy. The more she read, the more she became unhappy about the background of Bal Gangadhar Tilak. The unease grew into anger. She needed to speak to Pandit Wadia about it now.

She stormed into Pandit's office and sat down with a bump, dust rising from the cushion as she seated herself. He looked up, surprised, 'What is it? I am very busy at the moment. I have all these papers to read before I leave.' He gestured to files on his desk and floor.

'I will not keep you long, Pandit. I think you should not defend Bal Gangadhar Tilak. It is not right.'

'What is not right, Mrs New?'

'He is not a reformer. He wants *swaraj*, which might be good. But he does not support women's rights.'

'Not everyone does.'

'But we Parsees do. He is a Hindu, Pandit, he does not have the Parsee view of women. He has said some terrible things about women and girls and he wants to deny us our rights.' She was aware that her voice was becoming more urgent and was rising in line with her emotions.

'But I repeat, he has not committed a crime. At least, not since he was freed after being incarcerated for sedition some years ago.'

'His words and writings have influence, Pandit. A lot of influence.'

The passion rose in her voice as she explained to him: 'He supported the husband when that eleven-year-old died during sexual intercourse. He said that the husband was doing a harmless act and that little girl was a dangerous freak of nature. She was eleven-years-old, eleven, Pandit. He raped her.' She almost spat the words as images of her own rape by Christopher flew back into her head.

'I know. His views are not always palatable.'

'They most certainly are not. And he supports the caste system. We Parsees are working to change it as we want a fair system. How can you be representing him? It is not right.'

'I don't think any situation is clear cut, Cecilia. I can see why you do not like this. But he has not committed a crime and he is entitled to his opinion. He believes in *swaraj* and is a founder of the INC. We work for the INC, so we have to represent him. If we only represented people we liked, or agreed with, we would soon be out of work.' He laughed an empty laugh. Then, 'I will not enter into more discussion on this subject. You have work to finish today. As do I.' With that, he went back to reading the papers on his desk.

Cecilia stomped out of his office. She was ablaze with fury. Not just because of her anger about Bal Gangadhar Tilak. Also, Pandit had not given any credence to her thoughts. He was prepared to defend a man with views that were detrimental to women and girls. He had always been so proud of being a Parsee and what their community stood for, but was

174

willing to undermine it all for money. She sat at her desk and fumed. And fumed.

She jumped up again, marching into Pandit's office for the second time that afternoon.

'I can no longer work here, Pandit. I am going home.'

'But you have work to do today. And you have only just returned.'

'Then find someone else to do it. You have disappointed me, Pandit. I cannot work in Chambers that undermine the cause of women and girls.'

He opened his mouth to respond. But she had already left.

'But we need the money,' said George, bewildered, when she told him what had happened. 'And you've only just gone back to work.'

'I know. But it is a matter of principle. I cannot work for a firm that defends such a man. And besides, I am not comfortable with the thought of working for *swaraj*. My children might suffer because of it.'

There was a pause while George thought about what she had said.

'We have two boys at school. That costs enough. And soon Michael, Alfie and the girls will go, and that will be more expense.'

'I will just have to find another job at a different practice.'

'That will not be easy, if rumours get around about you walking out of Pandit's Chambers.'

'I know, but I will find Chambers that have the same principles as me.'

'Another way to save money would be not to send the girls to school. I think it might be a waste of money, educating girls.'

175

Her eyes blazed, 'The girls are going to school whatever happens. They must have the same chances as the boys.' Her voice was firm enough for George to counter no argument.

'Very well. But what will we do? Your principles are certainly expensive. I am not sure we can afford them.'

'Well, we will have to. There is no point in standing for something if you only stand for it in the good times. We will find a way, I am sure.'

George looked at her, 'I love you Cecilia, I really do. But this will not be easy. For any of us. You have such a short fuse.'

She thought of all the times she had hidden her feelings, all the times she would like to have lost her temper and hadn't. She sighed, 'I will get a new job as soon as possible. But I also want to spend a bit of time with the children. Alfie needs me, I think, he is so much more demanding than the others. And Gertie is so tiny, I would like to be with her more.'

George, with a change of heart, said, 'You are right about Alfie. He is not yet two but is a real handful. And Gertie needs to know her Mama too. Why don't you start looking for work in a few weeks' time? I have some savings and I know you do too. Let's use them and give you a break from work.'

Cecilia kissed him, 'Thank you, I would feel better if that happened. Life is so busy, this would let me rest a little.' Then whispering, 'And we can make love again, as I will not be so tired.'

A grin spread across George's face, 'Now, that is good thinking, I like it.' And he kissed her firmly on the lips, signalling his intentions for that night.

Cecilia spent the next six weeks at home with the children, helped by Chetna and Rupali. Life was chaotic but fun. Every day, her heart swelled with pride for her children, her love for them burst from her soul. Richard was growing fast, both he and John looked like Maurice. They had his easy nature and ready smile. They practised hockey every day after school, then with George when he came home from work.

Michael was gravitating towards playing with his older brothers, spending a lot of time watching them in the yard. He was a little lost when they were at school but Cecilia worked out a way of amusing him. She chalked out puzzles on stones and asked him to solve them. He had a sharp brain, so she had to make them more difficult for him every day. They both really enjoyed the process and the time together.

Helen and Cissy played games that were full of imagination. They pretended to be other people, created dances and made little figures with sticks and scraps of fabric. They spent a lot of time with little Gertie, who fascinated them with the way she would grasp their fingers as soon as they touched her tiny palm.

Alfie cried a lot, he was loud and demanding of everyone's time. Nothing seemed to be right for him and he was too little to tell them what was wrong. Cecilia tried all sorts of diversions but nothing seemed to quieten him. Until she thought of giving him some pebbles to build structures. Alfie played with them for hours, making shapes and buildings and working out how they could be stacked safely. Cecilia, Chetna and Rupali watched him with relief. A level of quiet had descended the house when Alfie was preoccupied. They all enjoyed the peace, even if it was temporary.

There was a knock on the door. Aktbar answered it and came into the kitchen, saying, 'There is a gentleman asking to see you, Memsa'ab.'

'Did he say his name?'

Before Aktbar could respond, Pandit walked into the room.

'Pandit Wadia is my name,' he said with one of his rare smiles.

Cecilia stood up quickly, handing Gertie to Rupali. 'Pandit. Welcome.'

'May I sit down?' he asked, sitting down.

'Would you like some chai? Aktbar has some on the stove.'

He nodded, 'It smells delicious. Yes, please.'

Aktbar placed a glass of chai on the table for him and then left.

Pandit watched the steam rise from the chai for a few moments before saying, 'Mrs New, I owe you an apology.'

She raised her eyebrows.

'I got back from London yesterday. It is a cold rainy city. Very grey indeed. Not a place to live, I fear.'

'And...'

'I met with Sir Dadabhai Naoroji Dordi there. And Cornelia Sorabji. Also, her sister Susie. The campaigner for girls' education. I think you know the Sorabjis.'

'A little. My mother knew their mother.'

'Well, I had a meeting with them all and I told them about our, er, discussion on the subject of Tilak. They were shocked I was defending him. They said you were right to take such a principled stand.'

She looked at him in surprise. He looked even more intense than usual, worried and concerned about her reaction.

'I had to continue to defend him when I was there. I won the case. But they persuaded me to no longer act for him. You were right and I was wrong. I apologise.'

Cecilia was stunned, unsure of what to say. After a lengthy silence punctuated only by the noise of the children playing in the yard, she nodded, 'I appreciate you saying that, Pandit. It is not easy to come here and apologise. Thank you.'

'Well, when I realised how wrong I was, it was easy. I believe we must recognise our mistakes and responsibilities. And learn from them. With that in mind, Mrs New, I have come to offer you your job back. I promise that I will check the background of every new client and will not act for them unless we are happy with their values.'

As he spoke, she could barely contain her smile, 'This is excellent news, Pandit, I would love to come back. Your promise means a lot.'

Pandit stood up, 'So tomorrow, then? I will see you in Chambers. Welcome back.'

'Yes, I will see you there. And thank you again.'

She plucked up the courage to ask Pandit Wadia how he managed to finish compiling the documents on the day she walked out on him.

'Hmmm, that day,' he said with a steely note in his voice as he remembered, 'it so happened that a young lawyer visited me and I asked him to help me.'

'That was kind of him.'

'Yes it was. He is a very talented young Muslim lawyer with strong feelings about *swaraj*. While we worked we exchanged views. He is convinced that Muslims need a separate country. I am not sure I agree, but I could see his point. He is a charismatic young man and will go far.'

'What is his name?'

'Mohammed Ali Jinnah. He will make his mark on this country one day.'

'I am sorry I left you with work to do that day, but at least you had time to speak with such an impressive man.'

'My Chambers seem to be a place where many people gather. People who want to change things. I like it that people come to talk and air their views. We look at points of law which may or may not help our cause and work to change them accordingly. Important work.'

Cecilia decided to tell him of the concerns she had been keeping to herself since she joined his Chambers, 'Pandit. I worry about self-rule. I do not think it will work for my children. They are Anglo-Indians and I don't think they will have a role here if the British leave. They certainly will have no protection.'

'We do not know that, Mrs New, we cannot predict anything. But we can ensure rights for Anglo-Indians are built into any agreement that all the parties sign. That is something we should work towards.'

'That is a good idea, Pandit. That may be the only way my children will have opportunities.'

'I have had a letter from a friend, Annie Besant. She will be coming to Chambers next week. I suggest we talk to her about it. She is influential. I think she will be empathetic.'

Annie Besant arrived a few days later, with a young Indian boy in tow. She was a white woman in her fifties with short wiry grey hair. She wore a plain grey sari with a long-sleeved grey choli. She had kindly blue eyes and a soft intelligent voice.

She introduced the young boy to Cecilia and Pandit, 'This is my adopted son, Jiddu Krishnamurti. He already has a great interest in human life and politics. I believe he will become a famous thinker one day,' she said with a mother's pride. He was a serious boy who barely acknowledged her words. He seemed to be deep in thought, as though he were in a world of his own.

They sat at Pandit's table and began a long conversation about Indian home rule. Mrs Besant was an intellectual, 'I search for truth, Pandit. We must always seek the truth. And the truth is India is not being ruled for the profit of its own people. It is being ruled in the interests of the British.'

'I totally agree, Mrs Besant, India must rule itself. We need the INC to be successful.'

Cecilia asked, 'Mrs Besant, what do you see as the role of the mixed-race community, the Anglo-Indians, if the British leave?'

Mrs Besant looked surprised, as if the question had not crossed her mind. She thought for a moment before replying. 'Well, we must fight for what is right. I have spent much of my life fighting for women's rights and equality for poorer people because I believe it is right to do so. Therefore, it would be right to advocate for the rights of Anglo-Indians, although I have not thought about them before.'

Cecilia explained, 'Anglo-Indians work on the railways here. And in the ports, sometimes the police service. I feel they should have more opportunities to move into law, teaching, politics and medicine. They should not be restricted because they are mixed-race. And the girls too – they should have the same opportunities as boys.'

Mrs Besant smiled, her face lit up as if she had found a kindred spirit, 'I like you, Mrs New. I agree with you. We must work for the rights of everyone, including mixed-races and girls. I would like to keep in contact with you as we grow the India independence movement. It will take a while to build it to something credible. But we will make it happen and India will have self-rule one day. Mark my words.'

After Mrs Besant left, the young Jiddu Krishnamurti trailing behind her having not uttered a word, Pandit said to Cecilia, 'You have impressed Mrs Besant. She will be an ally for Anglo-Indians when we take our demands to the British.'

'I have been thinking for some time that we must show a lead on this issue, Pandit. No one else seems to have thought about it. I will do the work on it. I will construct an argument that compels the British.'

'Of course, but we must not let it distract us when we are working on other business.'

She nodded, 'I know. I will be very intent on all my work. I promise.' She felt a burst of happy energy at the thought of being able to make a difference for her children.

When she told George later that day, he agreed that it was a something to aim for, something that would help their children, especially his little Gertie.

'But,' he sounded a note of caution, 'what will happen to me? To us? I am British and you are Indian. Where will we go?'

'I assume that we will have a choice because we both work already. It will not be a problem.'

George shrugged, 'I do not know politics like you do. But I do not think the British will give up ruling India easily. They are making too much money. I think it will be a long time before they agree to withdraw.'

'You are probably right. But the home rule people are a powerful lobby. They will negotiate hard. But then, some Indians want separate countries for Muslims and Hindus, which will need to be negotiated too. It is very complex.'

'And the British will want the best deal for themselves, that's certain.'

'Yes, that's very true. The British will stop at nothing to get their way. They have proved that many times in the past.'

Cecilia knew she was pregnant again as she sat at her desk and started to feel queasy. She tried to concentrate on the publication she was reading, *Hind Swaraj*. It had been translated from Gujarati into English, making it easier for her to read. But waves of sickness kept washing over her, she felt wan and weak. She was determined to carry on as she had in previous pregnancies. The article, by a lawyer called Mohandas Gandhi, was a call to action for Indian independence. He argued for non-violent resistance – something he had learned from the suffragettes in the UK. He was writing from South Africa, where he lived. She shivered because reading about South Africa reminded her of Maurice. His terrible death and her terrible loss. She fixed her mind on the pamphlet.

Well Mohandas Gandhi, she thought as she finished reading it, you have some very good ideas but what about Anglo-Indians? Have you thought of them? I don't have the time to write to you. I have work to do, seven children and another on the way. If you want to make changes to India, you will have to come back here. You can do nothing from South Africa. I will write to you when you are here.

Chapter Nine

Red hot tears rolled down Cecilia's cheeks. Her knees were shaking, buckling under the weight of her grief. Unsteadily, she picked up a handful of the hard red earth and threw it over little George's coffin. Another baby buried – it was not fair.

George, tearless and cold, stood away from the grave. Immediately it was over, he turned and walked away, leaving her with the priest. Father Theodore touched Cecilia's arm, trying to guide her to the chapel and saying, 'I think your husband is very upset. Come to the church and pray with me'.

'Why should I?' she sobbed, shoving his gentle hand aside. 'It won't bring my baby back. Go and pray by yourself, it won't do me any good. This is my second child to die, you know – how is there a God? How can there be?' She stamped away.

Later, she sobbed uncontrollably in her bed. 'I want my baby,' she cried over and over. Her curled up body, still battered from the birth, her breasts achingly full of milk that would never be suckled. She was bereft. George seemed unable to console her, too wrapped in his own grief. Their dead son had started to tear them in two.

Richard, Maurice, Cissy, Michael, Alfred, Helen and Gertrude stood by her bed, bewildered. They weren't used to the loud noises of despair that their mother was making. After a while, Gertie climbed onto the bed and stroked her mother's arm. Cecilia recognised that her little girl was trying to comfort her. She smiled through her tears, gathering Gertie in her arms. She reached for the others, they climbed onto the bed too. Her children, as ever, giving her comfort and strength. Cecilia slowly stopped crying and wiped her eyes and nose with the edge of her sari.

'I am sorry, sorry to keep on crying. Your baby brother George has gone to heaven. We will not see him again. It makes me so upset.'

'Is he with Bridget?' asked Richard, the only one old enough to remember she had gone to heaven too.

Cecilia nodded, 'Yes, they are. Bridget is looking after him, I am sure.'

'Why did the baby die, Mama?' asked John, 'Why did God want him in heaven? He was only just born.'

Tears started to close her throat but she answered her earnest little eleven-year-old as best she could, knowing the younger children were listening.

'I don't know, John. He was born a little early. He had a disease called jaundice. It meant his body was not working properly when he came out of my tummy. He tried to live for three days, but God wanted him back.'

An uneasy silence descended as the children tried to absorb this information. She hoped she had explained it in a way they could understand. But she was struggling to understand it herself.

She added, 'We will never forget him, he was your brother. A part of our family, a very important part. We loved him, so much, didn't we?'

'Yes Mama,' they chorused.

'Where's Papa?' asked four-year-old Alfie, his ever-lit curiosity on alert.

'Papa has gone for a walk. He is very upset about the baby. He wants to spend time alone to pray for him.'

The truth was George was not out walking. He was lying in Richard's bed, unable to talk or walk, flattened by the tragedy. He had opted out of everything. He had even left her when the baby became ill. She had been alone when his tiny, yellow body had given up. George had let her arrange the funeral without his help. He had only just made it to the Mass on time.

She was crushed too. Yet she had no choice but to pick herself up and carry on, keeping the family together. A kernel of resentment took hold inside her. Why should he indulge his grief when she had to continue as if nothing had happened? She wanted to stay in her room and cry until the tears could no longer flow. She wanted her baby back. She wanted to love him and hug him, nurture him and watch him grow. She had carried him inside her, loved him every day and looked forward to being with him when he was born. But now these things could never be, however much she cried or prayed otherwise. She felt alone for the first time since she had met George.

She decided to try and comfort her husband, to make things better for him if she could. He was lying on Richard's bed with his back to her. She sat on the edge, stroking his arm. He was awake but he didn't say anything. Nor did she. Eventually, he turned and gave her a weak smile. He squeezed her hand. His eyes were wet, his face stained with tears. He turned his back again. Sobbing, she left.

Aktbar was in the kitchen, he was sad too. The death of baby George had affected everyone. He put some chai on the table in front of her. He took some halva from a tin and placed that by her too.

'Halva is very sweet, Memsa'ab. It gives strength'

'Thank you Aktbar. I am sure it is not strength in my body that I need. It is strength in my soul. And I do not know how to get that.'

She went back to work two weeks after baby George's death to try to forget her sadness and to set about achieving her new goal. It was easier to be at work than at home. Her children were a stark reminder of losing Bridget and George.

Pandit was right when he said that his Chambers were a gathering place for people who wanted to change the country. Visitors came without notice and stayed to talk for hours about the political and social issues of the day.

She had not been back long when a woman entered the office. From her face, she looked to be around forty but her gait was slow, her body was frail and her eyes were sightless. She felt her way into the chair opposite Cecilia and asked to speak to Pandit.

'Certainly,' Cecilia jumped up, deciding to bring Pandit into her office to save this woman from navigating the corridors, which were piled high with files, 'who may I say is calling?'

'Susie Sorabji.'

Cecilia smiled at her, but was not sure if she could see it, 'Oh, my mother was a friend of your mother, Miss Sorabji.'

'What is your name?'

'It was Cecilia Chattergee, before I married. My mother was Susan Chattergee.'

'Of course, I knew your mother too. She passed away quite young, I was sorry to hear.'

'Yes, I miss her very much. How is your sister?'

'Ah, but which one? I have six sisters.'

'I had forgotten, but I shouldn't have, as all the Sorabji sisters are making a difference in their own fields.'

Susie smiled, a small sad smile, 'I would do more if I had better health.'

'That must be very frustrating for you.'

'Yes I am passionate about education for girls. I cannot be in a school anymore because of my poor sight. Now I teach kindergarten teachers and fundraise for girls' education.' She leaned back in her chair, exhausted from the effort of talking.

'I will fetch Pandit. He will be pleased to meet you. He met your sister, Cornelia, in London recently.'

Pandit entered the room smiling broadly as he shook Susie's hand. 'It is wonderful to meet you – another Sorabji sister. What an influential family.'

'Thanks to our parents, Pandit, they encouraged us girls to be independent. Especially our mother. She was very forward thinking.'

'Indeed. I knew your parents a little. What brings you here today?'

'Well, Pandit, I need to discuss your work for the INC. I am worried by it.'

His eyebrows rose, 'Really? Why is that?' Cecilia could detect a note of irritation in his voice. Pandit did not like to be questioned.

'My family is not convinced the British leaving India is a good thing.'

'Why so?'

'They have done many helpful things here. They have built the railways, a civil service, a free press and universities.'

Pandit showed no surprise, Cecilia knew he had heard these arguments before. Nevertheless, his reply was as fresh as if he were saying it for the first time, 'I understand your point, Miss Sorabji. But for the good the British have done, it is all to support their own activities. The railways were built to exploit trade, as was the administration system, universities and the press, which is not always free. India itself is not becoming richer as a result. It is becoming poorer, in fact.'

'Jobs are created for Indians in all the developments.'

'Only menial jobs, though. If the British don't like something, they will stop it. Look how they behaved in the Sepoy Uprising and the partitioning of Bengal. And,' he said to drive his point home, 'they do not educate girls.'

'If the British leave, India will be worse off.'

'I would like to see the British withdraw in a peaceful manner. The passive resistance, which is advocated by the lawyer, Mohandas Gandhi, would be the best route.'

Cecilia was listening to their discussion. It felt quite different from so many other discussions in Chambers because most visitors were keen for Indian independence. She was intrigued that the Sorabji family were not convinced by the arguments.

'Well, I must admit that Cornelia believes independence is a good thing, but the rest of us don't,' she laughed as she continued, 'but we will change her mind, I am sure. She cannot fight her six sisters forever.'

Pandit nodded. 'One thing that does concern me, though,' he said, bringing back seriousness to the conversation, 'the idea that Muslims and Hindus must have different countries. This is an idea that does not sound right.'

'I agree with you, Pandit. Hindus and Muslims live together now. Everything is in harmony.'

'Mohammed Ali Jinnah is the main proponent of this idea. He is charismatic and is likely to convince others.'

'Well if he does convince people, let us hope he can find a peaceful way.'

Cecilia decided to ask the question which was bubbling up inside her, 'Miss Sorabji. What do you think will happen to Anglo-Indians if the British leave?'

Susie frowned, 'Anglo-Indians? The mixed-race people, the Eurasians?'

Cecilia forced down the irritable words rising in her mouth. She said in a calm tone, 'They are called many names. Anglo-Indian is the most respectful.'

'Oh, I see. I hadn't really given them a thought. They run the railways, don't they?'

'That and the police service and the ports. But they can do other things too. They just need opportunities.'

Susie shrugged, 'They are a very small minority, aren't they?'

'Yes,' replied Cecilia an increasing crispness in her voice, 'But I have given birth to eight of them.'

Susie's unseeing eyes flickered in surprise, 'Oh, I didn't know you had married an Englishmen?'

Cecilia didn't mention she had married three Englishmen, 'I am worried that Anglo-Indians will not have opportunities for work and education when the British leave. They will be stranded in a sort of limbo. Pandit thinks we can build in protection for them in an independence agreement. What do you think?'

'Well, I do not want the British to leave. If they do, that does sound like a good idea. Mrs? I forgot to ask your name.'

'It is Cecilia New.'

'Well Mrs New, you give me lot to think about.'

Pandit stood up, bringing the conversation to an end, 'Thank you so much for visiting, Miss Sorabji. I admire your work promoting the education of women and girls. I remain unconvinced that British rule is a good thing for this country.'

Susie stood up slowly feeling her way to the doorway of the room, 'I don't think I will change my mind, Pandit, but thanking you for hearing me.'

'I hope we can find a peaceful way to stop the British from continuing to drain this country of its riches.'

Making no reply to Pandit's remark, Susie left, carefully picking her way out using her stick to identify anything in her way.

Cecilia looked at Pandit, 'This move for independence will not be easy will it?'

'No, not easy at all. There are many vested interests.'

'Many activists haven't even thought about Anglo-Indians, as we know.'

'You are already working on this, Mrs New. You must make sure you create a solid case. One that will oblige the British to take action.'

'I'm pregnant,' Cecilia said to George.

'Again?'

'Yes, I am sure of it.'

'Oh. I just hope this one is born healthy. I don't want to lose another baby.'

She quelled the bitterness inside her. He was speaking as if only he had lost a baby, only he felt the sadness, not her. Well little George was the second baby she had borne and lost, her second baby to die in her arms. He didn't even comfort her. He had spent the last few months having little to do with them all. She had spent the time trying to be both parents and doing a good job for Pandit.

She said none of this, but reassured him that it would be fine, 'I feel well with this one – not quite as sick as the others. I am sure that is a good sign. Richard and John are much older now, they are no trouble. Papa is here and Susan is always helpful. Rupali and Chetna too. Helen and Cissy are at school most of the day, so everything will be much easier this time around.'

He shrugged and left for work without another word.

Watching him, she sighed. Once again, she had mixed feelings about this pregnancy. She was scared, so scared of losing another baby. The fear threatened to stop her functioning, but she knew she couldn't afford to let it control her – she had to control it. It took a massive physical effort to create the happy thoughts that she needed every day. But she was determined.

At work, she spoke to Pandit.

'I understand the problem, Mrs New. It would be a terrible tragedy if you lost this baby too. You must take care of yourself. But there is work to be done here. Might I suggest that you take files home and work there? I can pick up anything you have worked on and drop off new files for you, so that you do not have to travel into the office or carry anything too heavy.'

'Oh, Pandit. That is an excellent idea. That would really make a difference, I could rest a lot more if we work that way. Thank you so much.'

The pregnancy was smooth and she enjoyed it, to her surprise. It was less awkward than any of her previous pregnancies. Her body swelling with this new life was exciting and she treasured the moments when she was alone and touching her belly, talking to her baby.

Lying on the bed, with George pacing the floor outside, Cecilia gave birth to another boy, he was pink, healthy and crying loudly. The contractions had come quickly and the labour was swift. Chetna attended the birth, as she had done with Gertie and baby George.

Cecilia was euphoric. Her baby was healthy. She started to feed him. He quietened down. She wrapped him up, lying him next to her, stroking his cheek in a daze of happiness.

Chetna cleaned the bedroom and left to tell George.

He burst into the bedroom and picked up his new-born son with a huge sigh of relief, 'He looks fine, so healthy. Such good news.' He kissed Cecilia's cheek and walked up and down, cooing at his new son.

Rupali brought three-year-old Gertie in to see her brother, 'What is his name?' she asked, her big brown eyes looking at him with curiosity.

'Oh, I am not sure,' Cecilia said, 'We haven't decided yet.'

'Christopher,' said George.

Cecilia looked at him, confused. He had chosen the baby's name without asking her. Again. He had chosen Christopher. Why Christopher? She did not want to be reminded of her second husband.

George saw her questioning face, 'It is in honour of your late husband. We named Gertie after my late wife, so we should do the same to honour him.'

She remembered George didn't know how her life had really been with Christopher. She would have to agree to the name Christopher or explain why she did not want it. She smiled at Gertie, 'Yes, his name is Christopher.'

Gertie climbed onto the bed and kissed him, 'I like him,' she declared, before climbing down again and running off to play in the yard.

When Christopher was four-days-old, he became unsettled and started crying constantly.

Chetna looked at him and said, 'I think he looks a little yellow. Perhaps we should get a doctor to look at him.'

The doctor, a nervous Hindu man in his forties, examined the baby saying, 'I think he has jaundice.'

Cecilia gasped as if someone had punched her in the stomach, 'Not jaundice, please, no.'

The doctor looked at her.

'I had a baby boy last year. He was three-days-old when he died of jaundice.'

'I am sorry to hear that, Memsa'ab. It looks as if this baby has only a small amount, he needs to drink lots of boiled water and have lots of your milk to flush it out of his system. He should be well after that.'

But he wasn't.

He died in her arms, just six-days-old.

Baby Christopher's death cleaved yet another fissure in their relationship. They were both blindsided by grief. There was so little time in the day to think about it because of their work and the demands of the children. It was in the quiet of the night that this latest loss came to the fore of their minds.

She cried every night, George's back was turned every night. She knew he was crying too, engulfed in his own grief. They were two people next to each other, miles apart.

Once again, Cecilia had to carry the burden of dealing with the children. George had no life, no energy, no interest in anything. She had to pretend nothing had happened. She was weary by having to be strong, drained by being both parents. Her grief was an unbearable maelstrom. Every day and night.

Only Aktbar, with his wise elderly eyes, seemed to have any understanding. In his quiet way, he worked harder around the house to help make her life easier. He and his son, Salim, along with Ravi, did extra jobs without being asked. She knew they were supporting her in the only way they could. She couldn't acknowledge it, she was too busy and too weary to say anything.

Over the next few months, Cecilia noticed slow changes in George. He started to talk to the children again and seemed interested in her too. His changes grew until he was nearly his old self. Nearly but not quite. He never spoke about his feelings. He moved away from his sadness in his own time, in his own way. She wanted to talk to him about the loss of Christopher, the children's reactions and how she had been their mother and father all those weeks. But he would not be drawn into any sort of conversation. He either ignored her or changed the subject.

Still, he was nearly back to his old self. She felt she should be grateful for that, at least.

Back at work, they had another visitor. A short, rotund man with matching round glasses strolled into her room as if he were in charge. He seemed to assume she was a servant.

'I know Pandit Wadia, from when we both lived in Karachi some years ago,' he told her. 'He is someone whose views I value and I would like to talk to him now.'

Saying nothing, she showed the man into the office. Pandit looked delighted to see his visitor and greeted him warmly, 'Sultan,' he said excitedly, 'It is good to see you. It has been a long time.'

'Yes, a very long time. I am here to discuss matters of great importance.' He looked at Cecilia with an expression which told her to leave the room.

'Is it about self-rule in India? *Swaraj*?' asked Pandit.

The man nodded.

'Please, Mrs New will be a good contributor to our discussion. She is highly intelligent. And a Parsee too.'

There was a pause, while the man looked closely at Cecilia as if he were trying to see any sign of intelligence.

'Very well,' agreed the man eventually with an air of both surprise and reluctance.

They all sat round the table in Pandit's office.

'You will be aware,' he said addressing Pandit alone, 'that I was a founder of the All India Muslim League around six years ago?'

195

'Of course, of course,' replied Pandit. He nodded towards Cecilia in an effort to bring her into the conversation, 'we have been reading about its activities in pamphlets and newspapers since then. Very impressive.'

'Well, it is time for me to resign my presidency. Time to allow someone else to take over.' He still addressed Pandit, 'There is a young man, Mohammed Ali Jinnah who is willing.'

'We know him. He is impressive. He comes here to Chambers to discuss his ideas frequently.'

'He will do a good job, I know. And I need to release time for my horse racing activities and improving education for other Muslims. That is my duty.'

'Of course, of course, we have huge respect for your role, don't we Cecilia?'

Cecilia watched on, amused. Pandit was treating this man with great deference. Yet, at the same time, he was challenging him by trying to bring her into the conversation.

'Oh yes,' she agreed, having no idea who this man was and or what role they were talking about.

'So, Pandit,' the man continued, 'I am here to ask your opinion on one matter before I leave the organisation. You know I have good relations with the British?'

Pandit nodded, 'I have been following your progress in the newspapers. They have made you a Knight of the Realm, I know. Three times, I think?'

The man laughed, 'The British are very odd. Three Knight Commanders they have given me. How many does a man need?' He slapped his thigh at his own joke. Pandit followed his lead and began laughing too. Cecilia was silent.

'Three Knight Commanders surely gives you influence?'

'Of course. You know my goal is to advance Muslims in this country.'

'You have founded many educational institutions, I know.'

'Now it is time for Muslims to enter politics, that is my belief.'

There was a pause before the man continued, 'I wish to present my two-nation theory to the British and thought I would ask your opinion first. Parsees are fair and insightful.'

Pandit nodded, 'Thank you. I will try and so will Mrs New.' He nodded to her, trying to bring her into the conversation again.

The man continued, addressing Pandit only. 'My two-nation theory is that Muslims must live in their own state within India. The British will not rule this state, nor will Hindus or Sikhs. It will be a separate state ruled by Muslims alone. I think that is the best way to advance Muslims and ensure they are protected.'

'Do you think Muslims are at risk at the moment, then?'

'Yes. But I think the threat will be greater in the future. And I want to make sure it is dissipated now.'

Pandit had made a steeple with his hands and was rubbing his chin with it as he thought. Then he said, 'Sultan, I do not believe people give up power easily. The British may not like this, nor will the Hindu and Sikh leaders.'

'Islam is a peaceful religion, Pandit. I will work towards this solution only in a peaceful way.'

'That is good news. I think that is a message that all the others must hear. We want to come to a solution through dialogue, not dissent.'

Cecilia decided to interrupt the conversation, 'What will be the place of the Eurasians in this strategy, please.'

'Eurasians?' said the man in surprise.

'Or mixed-race people? Or Anglo-Indians? There are many names for them,' she paused and then added, 'including *chi-chis*.'

She saw understanding dawn on him.

'I had not thought about them, I will admit. They are a small community, are they not? And the Muslims among them will be smaller still.'

She felt herself getting annoyed again, 'They are still important people.'

'Of course, of course,' he said, 'What do you think should happen?'

'At the moment, these people have no official nationality, which leaves them in a difficult situation. They will not know which is their nation in the two-nation state you describe.'

He seemed to be warming to her.

'I see your point, Mrs New. So, the British must legislate on their nationality? Do you agree that is the first step?'

'Yes.'

He stood up and shook hands with Pandit. Then he turned to Cecilia and bowed a gentle bow. 'You have given me much food for thought, Mrs New. I shall not forget what you have said. I will begin that discussion with the British. I am pleased that you joined our conversation. You are an impressive woman. And beautiful too.' He bowed again and left.

Pandit turned to Cecilia, 'Do you know who that was?'

'No. You didn't introduce us. You called him Sultan, so he must be someone important.'

'Yes, very important. He is the Aga Khan.'

'The Aga Khan?'

'Yes, the Imam of Shia Muslims around the world.'

Cecilia sat down, stunned, 'I have heard of him but have never seen a photograph of him. I did not know what he looked like.'

'He is also a good man. Very wise. But I fear for his idea of a two-nation state. I cannot see it as a good thing, separating people by faith.'

'I agree. And it doesn't allow for mixed marriages and mixed-race people.'

Pandit was thinking hard, 'Your thoughts on mixed-race people were well-raised, once again. I hope your work in that regard is progressing well.'

He looked at the pile of papers on his desk. 'Back to work now.'

As she stood up to leave, he opened a letter and laughed out loud. It was rare that he laughed, he was such a serious man.

'What is funny?' she asked.

'What I just said has come true,' he waved the letter in the air as he said to her, 'we have just seen the Aga Khan. Now this letter is from a Madras lawyer, Eardley Norton. He wants to visit us next week, with his client, Regina Guha.'

'I have heard a little of Mr Norton, but not of Regina Guha.'

'He is a famous lawyer, wanting the British to value Indians and give them full rights. He is a very important man but was involved in a scandal I believe. It led to him having lower responsibilities. He was an early member of the INC as well. I have not heard of Regina Guha myself.'

'I wonder what they want to talk about?'

'If I were to guess, I would say that this Regina Guha, may be like you. Trying to make change for women. Since you joined us, we have had many women to come and talk about their ideas for the future of women and girls.'

'I do not think it is to do with me. More to do with the women's activity going on all around the country in many spheres. It is gaining momentum, I think.'

'Let's hope so. I do not believe that we can have an equal society without the full participation of women.'

Cecilia once again marvelled at the man. He not only spoke wise words, but he lived them too. She knew she would forever be grateful to him for letting her work with him and study law too, even when she was pregnant or nursing young children. Or mourning them, she thought as another wave of sadness washed over her.

Eardley Norton was tall and slender. He had clear eyes and angular features, which gave him an air of authority mingled with grace. He spoke with the measured tones of the well-educated Englishman. Cecilia guessed he was aged around sixty, his hair was grey, his gait a little slow. He must have been a very handsome man in his youth, she thought. She wondered if the scandal, the one that Pandit had mentioned, had involved a woman. Very probably, she decided.

Regina Guha was young, barely twenty, Cecilia thought. Her dark hair was tied back in a severe bun. She wore a dull brown sari with no trim or decoration. She had an intense expression which didn't change even into the ghost of a smile when Mr Norton introduced her.

'Miss Guha is studying law at Calcutta University.'

Cecilia looked at her with fresh interest. They had something in common. Miss Guha said nothing.

'When she matriculates, in 1916, she intends to submit an application to be enrolled as a pleader.'

Cecilia gasped and they all turned to look at her. She addressed Miss Guha with a wide smile. 'That will be a brave challenge to the courts.'

Now Miss Guha's expression changed. Her face lit up as she spoke for the first time. 'I am not sure that I am brave. But I want to be a pleader and work in the law, just as men do. It is ridiculous that women can study law yet not practise it. I am not the first person to challenge this, there is a case already going through the courts. But Mr Norton and I think we have a very strong case if that challenge is unsuccessful.'

Pandit asked, 'What is your case, Miss Guha?'

'Well,' she said, taking a deep breath, 'the legislation is written to say that "persons" may practise law. We believe the definition of "person" does not exclude women. This means that, as it is drafted, it is legal for women to practise law.'

Pandit looked concerned, 'They will have to decide that in the High Court,' he advised.

'Of course,' replied Mr Norton, 'We would like to work with you on drafting the case. You have an excellent reputation for good drafting of civil rights law.' He looked at Cecilia, his eyes clearly enjoying what he saw, 'Your Chamber employs Mrs New. We have heard of her, she wants to practise law too, I understand.'

'Indeed I do,' Cecilia replied as she ignored his gaze and focussed her attention on Miss Guha, 'I have been studying and training for years, but I have children and it has been a protracted process. I would really like to help Pandit with your case. It seems that it is very strong indeed.'

Pandit was more cautious, 'We will certainly work with you, Mr Norton. But the High Court is made up of men. A lot of men do not view women as equals.'

'Maybe so, Pandit, maybe so. But they cannot say women are not "persons" can they? That would be completely wrong.'

'It will be interesting to hear the outcome of the current case and then we can make a plan, Mr Norton.'

Cecilia knew she could not let them go without raising the issue of mixed-race people. 'Mr Norton, Miss Guha, have you considered that the Act should also include a "person" as a definition of a mixed-race person? A woman or man from the Eurasian people.'

Mr Norton frowned as she went on, 'Lawyers in India are mainly British or perhaps Indian. I do not know of any from the Anglo-Indian community. I wonder if we can work on legislation that specifically includes Eurasians?'

'I hadn't thought about it like that,' he said, 'But now you mention it, specifying a definition of "person" would be a good thing. What do you think, Miss Guha?'

'I think it is an excellent idea. I am a Bengali Jew, so I believe mixed-races should be able to participate in society at every level.' Cecilia felt a strong connection between them. If only they lived nearer each other, she would have a friend.

Cecilia walked home with a light step. In Miss Guha she had found a kindred spirit. Her view that Eurasians should be included in legislation and women could become lawyers gave Cecilia hope.

Her mood evaporated as soon as she arrived. The children were in the yard, not playing as they usually did. They looked sullen and sad, sitting around saying nothing. George was at the kitchen table, his head in his hands.

'What has happened?' she asked, 'The children are not happy.'

His voice was low with anger and despair as he answered, 'It is Alfie. The school said he started a fight today and they asked me to collect him. He is not allowed back there for the rest of the week.'

She sat down with a thump. Oh Alfie, she thought, it is always you, isn't it?

George looked at her, waiting for a response.

'Why did the school contact you, not me?'

'They tried to contact you first. They did not know where you worked. They sent an older pupil to the station to find me. I had to collect him.'

After a pause, George went on, 'Alfie is the wildest of all of them. He is always fighting about something. He is out of control.'

She had no reply.

'It seems that all your children with Christopher are difficult, Cecilia. Michael and Cissy are argumentative. Not as much as Alfie. And all the other children are not nearly as bad tempered as those three.'

She knew he was right. The Keating children seemed to have inherited a wild streak from their father. She had been sure they would calm down under George's influence as they grew up. It didn't seem to be working yet.

George was still talking, 'I thought the hockey would help discipline him, but it didn't. He doesn't understand teams and rules.'

'He is young for a game like hockey,' she soothed, 'he is only six.'

George snorted, 'I have taught children as young as four. They understand the basic game. Alfie just kept trying to hit everyone with his stick. He refuses to understand.'

Cecilia knew it wasn't funny but had trouble stifling a laugh at the thought of little Alfie trying to whack everyone. She changed the subject, 'What was he fighting about, do you know?'

'I didn't ask. I just marched him home and left him sulking in the yard.'

Cecilia called Alfie. He sidled into the kitchen with little Gertie following behind him.

As she knelt down to talk to him, she noticed he was holding Gertie's hand tightly.

'Alfie, my boy, why did you start a fight today?'

George shouted, 'Today? Today? He starts a fight every day.'

'Shh, you are not helping. Now, Alfie, please can you tell me what happened.'

Almost in a whisper he said, 'A big boy said my Papa was dead. I said no, my Papa is alive and works on the railways. Then he started to pull my hair and kick me. I hit him back.'

George looked on with interest at this news.

'Did Sister Anne tell the big boy off too?' she asked.

'No,' Alfie started to cry and little Gertie stroked his arm to cheer him up. 'He told her it was my fault and I started it. She believed him. But I didn't start it, Mama, I promise I didn't.'

'I believe you, Alfie. I believe you.'

She scooped them both into her arms. She set Gertie on George's lap as she cuddled the distraught Alfie on hers.

'Mama, Mama,' he said between his sobs, 'My Papa isn't dead, is he?'

She made a quick decision to tell him the truth as a lie might make the bullying at school worse.

'Well, yes,' she said gently, 'your Papa is dead. He was called Christopher and he died because he was ill. You didn't know because you were only a tiny baby when it happened.'

Alfie pointed to George and said, 'But he is my Papa.' His tone had an edge of belligerence to it.

'Of course, he is your Papa.' She locked eyes with George as she said, 'This Papa saw you and he said to me he wanted to be your new Papa. So, we got married. That means you have had two Papas! When the big boys tease you, tell them you have two Papas and you are lucky. I bet they do not have two Papas. It shows you are very special.'

Gertie wriggled down from her father's lap. And ran to her big brother, 'Alfie,' she said, in her little four-year-old voice, 'I huff you, Alfie.'

They all smiled at her. Alfie, sniffling up his snivels replied, 'I love you too Gertie.'

The two children hugged each other. Holding hands, they went back to the yard to play.

George was staring at her, waiting for an explanation.

She shrugged, 'I didn't know what else to say. How else to explain it.'

'I hope it makes him feel better. Then he might not fight so much.'

They looked at each other for a moment, knowing what each other was thinking. Then they both laughed and agreed it would not make any difference at all to Alfie. Cecilia was grateful for the moment of harmony. But she knew even though George was nearly back to normal, nothing was really the same.

As a husband, George was not like Christopher. He did not take his anger out on her. He just became more unhappy and withdrawn. He almost seemed to take his anger out on himself. Yet his melancholy affected everyone, making them all sad. She was grateful he was not violent. She could live in relative peace with him. She resolved to make him happy again so that they could be a proper family once more.

That night they made love with a tenderness that had been missing over the last few months. After, they lay in each other's arms, sated and content.

But life was not to give her the chance to rest. Soon she was pregnant again. The child would be due in October, Chetna estimated.

Not again, not again, she thought. She didn't want to tell George as things were a little better between them now. She knew he would dread another baby too. They were still grieving for their dead children. Another loss would surely ruin them forever.

At work, Pandit was reading *The Hindu*, a paper founded by a friend of Mr Norton's. It covered progress made on social issues, particularly women's issues.

Pandit closed and folded the paper in his usual slow manner. He looked thoughtful. She waited for him to say something, knowing that he was thinking about his words.

'I have been reading more and more about the growing town of Quetta. I have read about its expansion in *The Times of India* and now, in this,' he gestured to *The Hindu*. 'The British are building Quetta into a city of national importance because it has good routes into Afghanistan. I am wondering if we should open a branch of Chambers there. There is bound to be a lot of legal work. We could be the first practice to establish a base in there if we are quick enough.'

She wondered why he was consulting her as she had very little knowledge of Quetta, only that it was in the hills in the north of the country. She soon found out.

'Cecilia, I want you to visit Quetta and give me your opinion on whether we should do this.'

At once, she saw a way to delay telling George about the new baby. She knew the trip to Quetta would take a few days, putting off the moment. However, she thought it would be best to seem reluctant or else Pandit might guess something was amiss.

'But surely, Pandit, you must go? I cannot make the decision, only you can. You must see the town for yourself.'

'I am too old for such travels, Mrs New. I value your judgement. You will be my eyes and ears. If you think it is a good idea, then we will set up an office there.'

'That is a lot of responsibility, Pandit. I am honoured that you think so highly of me.'

'It is a long train journey. I think you should go later today. Stay as long as necessary and write me a report on the train journey back. So that I have it as soon as you return.'

She went home to pack. The older children were at school and the littles ones were playing with Rupali in the yard. No one noticed her arrive or leave. She would see George at the station. She would tell him about the trip. But not about the baby.

She knew George would not be concerned about her visit to Quetta – the ayahs would look after the children. He could play cards with his friends every evening.

At the station, George ensured she had a seat on the train, near the shutters for some cooler air when it was moving. He kissed her goodbye, 'Good luck. We will miss you, come back soon.'

She settled into her seat, excited to be going away and avoiding telling him her news for a bit longer. Excited to be entrusted with such a big responsibility. The train steamed its way across the country, rising into the hills of Balochistan state. She was entranced by the lush greenery and dramatic slopes. The views were breath taking. It was so very different from arid Multan.

She fell in love with Quetta. Its elevation gave it the temperate climate she preferred. There were fruit trees and plants everywhere, not struggling as they did in Multan. This abundance brought vitality to the town. It was enchanting. She was staying with friends of Pandit, who were Parsees too. An older married couple whose children had grown and flown. Peter, a sprightly man of about 60, was a doctor. Lucia, a woman of gentle wisdom, was a nurse. They had lived in Quetta for many years.

'We have seen much investment by the British,' said Lucia, 'they are using the town as a trading route to Afghanistan and the rest of Asia.'

'They are building such a lot here, that we have begun to call it Little London,' laughed Peter.

'But the weather is better than London, I think,' said Cecilia.

They walked her around the town. There were wide boulevards lined with British-built bungalows with large, well-tended opulent gardens. It was bustling with energy, people moving fast in all directions. Wherever she looked, buildings were being erected, horses with carts clipped and clopped, donkeys strolled aimlessly, cows wandered everywhere. She thought that her family would thrive in this happy environment.

'They are building a big railway station, so that they can move goods more quickly,' Peter told her. She nodded, but said nothing out loud. Inwardly she was thinking that if George could find new work here, it might help his melancholy.

'Quite a few people seem to be working at the station,' she said to Peter, 'do they need more staff?'

'Oh yes. They keep asking for more people. Of all ages and experiences.'

'Do the workers have a hockey club?'

'They have a small club but it is not very good because it is quite new. I think it needs someone who is good at the game to lead it.'

Cecilia saw that there would be a role for George in that – it would be something that he would enjoy. And the boys too.

'I was just thinking about my husband and children and whether they would like it here. They play hockey.'

'I see, well they could be important to growing the club. I understand that Pandit is wondering if he should open a branch of Chambers here?'

'Yes, he is wondering if there is a role for his work. Whether there are people here who are working with the INC.'

Lucia joined in, 'A number of people who would like self-rule. There is a young man who is making a name for himself. His name is called Labh Singh Saini. He is leading the charge.'

Cecilia told them, 'We are keen to make changes peace-fully. And we are looking for the British to legislate on the citizenship of Eurasians.'

'Eurasians?'

'Some people say Anglo-Indians, some say mixed-race. Legislation seems to have passed them by. It is not clear what rights they have. If we are to have self-rule, we should know who we are ruling.'

'I hadn't thought of the Eurasians. A small group, no?' asked Peter.

'Very small. But they should be recognised and have rights.'

'You are passionate about this cause, Mrs New. Why so?'

She did not feel she could tell these people that her children were Anglo-Indians. There was too much stigma attached.

'I see Anglo-Indians working on the railways and in ports. And sometimes in the police. But nowhere else. That can't be right.' And to change the subject, she added, 'We want to see equal rights for women too.'

Lucia agreed, 'Yes, it is time.'

Peter nodded, 'There are many women making progress in the medical and educations spheres and some in law too. We will support them.'

'I intend to be a barrister, but at the moment I am happy working with Pandit. He is a kind and wise man.'

'He is indeed. I think he would do well to open a branch here. There will no doubt a lot of work.'

'I like Quetta, it is busy but has a good mild climate compared to Multan. It also seems like a fruit garden, there is fruit growing everywhere,'

Lucia said, 'It rains a lot here, so it is not always as good as you think!'

They all laughed.

On a serious note, Cecilia asked, 'What are the medical facilities like?'

Lucia replied, 'They are the best in the region.'

Peter smiled, 'It is the best clinic – in the whole of North India I believe. We work there so we are biased, maybe. We are also specialists in treating children and babies.'

Cecilia felt a stab in her heart and tears prickling her eyes at the memory of her lost babies. The baby she was carrying seemed to move too, as if he or she knew what Mama was thinking. With the certain knowledge that her unborn baby would be safer in Quetta than Multan, she resolved to ask George about moving the family here, if Pandit agreed to start a branch in the town.

Later that day, she began the long trip back to Multan. She wrote her report leaning on her lap, as the train shook and shuddered its way from the mountains to the plains and across to Multan and its barren landscape. Her pregnancy made the journey even more uncomfortable. She could feel the train's judders shake the baby inside her. She had to keep quelling that nausea rising in her throat.

She tried to keep any bias out of her report. She recommended that Pandit open an office in Quetta. It was a growing city with an increasing profile in the INC. Pandit would see the sense in what she said, she was sure.

'No,' said George when she told him, 'we are not moving.'

'The climate will be better for everyone. There will be more opportunities for you at the station there.'

'I don't want more opportunities. I am happy with the job I have got.' His voice was stubborn.

'But you will be able to have more senior jobs and earn more money.'

'I am not interested.'

'There is a hockey club of railway workers. It needs someone to build it up.'

'I don't want to build another one.'

'I think the children will thrive in the climate, it is milder than here.'

'I like the climate here.'

'There is an excellent children's hospital there. If we have more children, they will be safer than here. We don't want to lose another one.'

'We are not having another child.'

She said nothing for what seemed a very long time.

'Are we?' he asked.

She said nothing.

'Are we?' he shouted.

She nodded, 'In October.'

'No! What happens if it dies too? I cannot lose another baby.'

Nor can I, she thought but said nothing. George, as usual, was thinking only about himself.

He stood up, pushing his chair over, and left the house.

She went to bed. Tears fell over her cheeks, making the pillow either side wet with her sadness.

She was happier at work, where she seemed to be appreciated more than at home.

'I have read your report,' Pandit said, 'it makes sense. There will be a lot of work there, from what you say.'

She nodded.

'I had thought I was too old to set up the office myself. I was going to ask you. But I have read what you had said about the climate.' He gestured to her report, 'I think it will suit me better as I get older. Mrs New, we have established an excellent working relationship. I respect and admire your work. I feel we should find a way of working in more of a partnership style.'

Her curiosity was piqued. 'Yes, Pandit?'

'I could open the branch in Quetta and move there. Then we could find a way of sharing the work in each office.'

'I like your idea, Pandit, thank you.'

He said, 'I will take a trip to Quetta myself, probably leaving next week. I will find office premises and somewhere to live, so I may be some time.'

'I will look after the office here for you Pandit.'

'I trust you to do that, Mrs New. When I return, we will discuss how we make this work.'

She enjoyed running the office in Pandit's absence. She would contact him by wire and telephone when she needed him. But mainly she made the decisions herself. She met clients, doing the work in a calm, efficient manner. She thrived on the responsibility. She was almost disappointed when he returned five weeks later. Almost. But not quite. The extra work was making her tired and taking its toll on her pregnant body.

When he came back to the office, Pandit saw the weariness on her face, 'Mrs New, I have had a full and thorough visit to Quetta. I have ideas how it can work. But you look very tired and I suggest you go home and rest for a few days. We can have the conversation when you are feeling better.'

A rest was exactly what she needed. She thanked him profusely and set off for home with as much relief in her step as her pregnancy would allow. She stayed in bed for the next few days. The children came in to see her to chat or have her tell them stories. They were little bundles of joy and warmth who kept her happy.

But the peaceful time was short-lived. A knock at the door the next week delivered a letter addressed to her. It was from Sister Anne, head teacher at the children's school. Cecilia read it and let it drop to the floor beside the bed. Oh, Alfie, Alfie. Why are you so naughty? she thought, for the umpteenth time.

She called Chetna and Rupali into the bedroom.

'How does Alfie behave for you both?' she asked them.

'Well,' started Rupali, clearly reluctant to go on and say anything. Chetna had no such reservations.

'He is a very naughty boy, Memsa'ab. He never does as he is told. He starts fights with the other children all the time and he has a very bad temper.'

'Oh dear,' said Cecilia for want of anything else to say.

Chetna warmed to her theme, 'I find him the naughtiest child I have ever looked after. I despair of him. He will come to no good.'

'Is he a bad influence on the other children?'

'Mostly he is. He seems to love little Gertie more than the others. He upsets the Roche children and fights with all their friends.'

'Do you agree with Chetna, Rupali?'

213

Rupali nodded saying nothing while she looked at the floor.

'Thank you both. I now have decisions to make.'

When George returned, she showed him the letter. 'It doesn't surprise me,' he said, 'Alfie is too wild for his own good.'

'We have to find him another school now they have expelled him.'

'We should send him to a boarding school. The discipline will do him good.'

'I would miss him. He is a real little character. I love him.'

'We have to think of the other children, Cecilia. They will be better off without his influence.'

She didn't tell him what Chetna had said. She didn't want to add fuel to his fire. But she knew he was right. There were no other Catholic schools nearby, so a boarding school was the only choice.

'It will be expensive,' she warned George. 'How will we pay for it?'

'We can stop employing two ayahs, for a start. And I will work more hours. Whatever we pay, it will be worth it. Alfie is nothing but a nuisance.'

She felt her stomach contract on hearing such a description of her precious Alfie. He was naughty, she agreed, to the point of being infuriating on many occasions. But she loved him so much and he had a kind side, hidden somewhat, but it was there. She could see his rampaging life force and was convinced that it could be shaped if he had the right influences. The priests who ran St Joseph's boarding school in Karachi had a good reputation, so it could be the best place for him.

Alfie was not convinced. 'I don't want to go, Mama,' he screamed, 'I like being with you and Gertie.'

214

She put her arm around him, 'I know bette. We like being with you. But the school has said you can't go back. You are too naughty to be there, they told me.'

'But I am not naughty, Mama. I only fight when the children are nasty to me.' His voice was loud and indignant. His big brown eyes wide with innocence.

'That is not what your teachers say. They say you always start the fights.'

Tears rolled down Alfie's face, he stuck his bottom lip out in a sulk. His head bowed, his shoulders slumped. Even his big ears were drooping. She could see his resistance had crumbled.

Only Gertie was sorry when Alfie left. She hugged him and cried, trying not to let him go. He hugged her back with a sad smile. Cecilia watched the two of them and her heart swelled with pride. It was a joy to see the love they shared. And she was happy that Alfie was loved by at least one of his siblings. The others were watching them while they stood at the back of the yard, not feeling the need to say goodbye or feel sad.

After George had left to take Alfie to his new school, a relieved silence descended on the house. Instantly it became a peaceful place. It was surprising the impact just one person – and a child at that – could have on a whole house, Cecilia reflected.

George returned, smiling widely at everyone, 'I think it is best he has gone, Cecilia. The school seemed nice and they were friendly to him.'

She was already missing her little lively boy.

George went on, 'And I have more news. I heard from my colleagues at the station that there is apprentice work at Howrah. I think it will be a good job for Richard.'

'Howrah? That is too far away.'

'It will be good for him to get away from here. Be independent.'

'But Howrah? It's near Calcutta? Miles away.'

George shrugged and repeated, 'It will do him good.'

'But I don't want him to go. With Alfie gone – the family will be breaking up.'

George sighed, 'The family has to break up sometime. There will be more opportunities for him at Howrah. The British are still building a huge railway junction there. It is taking trains from Calcutta all over the country.'

'But what if he doesn't want to work on the railways?'

'Once he gets to Howrah, he will find more choices in the city there, it is a major port too.'

'But we could move to Quetta, there will be lots of opportunities there for him, I told you before. More choices for all of us.'

'I said before, I am not moving to Quetta.'

'But we could all go together and Richard wouldn't need to leave us.'

George sighed loudly, 'I am not moving to Quetta. And it will be no good for Richard. It is too backward still. Howrah has already grown, it is a developed city and the opportunities are there now. He needs opportunities now. Not in years to come.'

'But where will he live? He is only fifteen-years-old. We do not know anyone in Howrah.'

George smiled, 'I have friends there, through the railways and hockey. I have already sent a letter to my friend, Andrew, who lives in Kharagpur, which is nearby.'

Cecilia was annoyed. George had made another major decision without bothering to consult her. Richard was her son, not his.

She turned to leave the room saying, 'Let us see what your friend says before we do anything about it. Let us not say anything to Richard.'

'Andrew rang the station today. He is very happy to have Richard staying with them.'

She spun round in fury, 'You didn't say this before. Why?'

George shrugged and picked up the newspaper and started to read it. She stomped over to him and snatched the paper, throwing it onto the floor.

'How dare you? How dare you?'

Picking it up, and smoothing it out George made out he was reading the newspaper but carried on talking to her, 'I am in charge of these decisions. I am the man of the house. They cannot be children all their lives. They have to grow up and fend for themselves at some time or another. You cannot keep them with you. That is something you need to learn. We need more room in the house with the new baby on the way. So, you need to let him go.'

'But I have already lost three children. Alfie has just gone. I don't want to let Richard go before I have to.' Her voice was soft and full of stifled tears.

George didn't look up. 'You have to, whether you like it or not.'

In that moment, she could almost see the rest of their relationship collapse in front of her eyes. Her heart pierced with a hatred of him. Again.

'I will miss you so much,' she told Richard as he prepared to leave a few days later. 'You are such a good son and a lovely big brother to the little ones. They will miss you too.'

He had packed a small trunk and was wearing his best clothes. Cecilia hugged him hard. The children lined up to follow suit. George stood by watching the scene unfold. Richard was moved by the affection shown to him, particularly by Helen and Gertie, who were wailing at the prospect of not seeing their big brother for a long time.

'Don't cry,' he reassured them, 'I will be back soon, as I want to see the new baby. It is due in two months, so I will see you all then.'

Cecilia told him, 'We will send you a wire when the baby is born. It will be lovely to see you, then. I love you, Richard, with all my heart.'

He smiled as tears welled in his eyes, 'Bye, bye, Mama. I love you too.'

George picked up Richard's suitcase, 'Time to go, young man, or we will miss the train.' He nodded at the family. They left for the long journey to Howrah.

If Alfie's absence had brought peace to the family, Richard's departure left a gap that was hard to fill. All the children looked up to him. He showed them love and patience. John and Michael still played hockey in the yard, but some of their passion for the game had left along with their brother. Helen and Cissy seemed lost as they played make-believe games without him to listen to their stories. It was little Gertie, at four-years-old, who seemed to inhabit the role of the wise sibling. She became the peacemaker and dispenser of advice and care. As Cecilia watched them, she knew Alfie's absence lessened the numbers of squabbles that the children had, but that Gertie was still needed most days to calm quarrels down.

She looked up at the sound of Richard bursting through the door, 'Mama, I have come to see baby Joseph Edward, I can't wait to see...' She saw him stop still and take in the scene as he looked around the room, 'What has happened?'

'Mama? Mama? What happened?' his voice rising in panic.

Cecilia couldn't bring herself to say anything as she sat on the bed, her eyes swollen and her body still bloated from the confinement. Her throat contracted as her words shrivelled there.

George was sitting in a chair, his head down. Without raising it, he said, 'We lost him. He died this morning.'

'No, no, that cannot be. We cannot lose another brother. Why?'

'He was born early, as you know, a month early. He had jaundice like his brothers and was too fragile to fight it,' said George as he left the room. Richard stood in shock for a few seconds before walking over to her.

'Oh Mama,' he said, as he sat next to her on the bed and pulled her into his chest for their mutual comfort. 'Another little brother, gone. This is so sad, Mama, so sad. I cannot believe it. I cannot bear it.'

Still too distraught to speak, silent tears flowed like rivers down her cheeks and pooled on her son's chest, soaking his clothes. After a while, she wiped her eyes and told him the story.

'He died in the early hours. Of jaundice. We couldn't get you a message, as we knew you would be travelling here. We had his funeral mass this morning. I am sorry another of your brothers has died. I loved him so much. And all my children who have passed. I loved them all.'

'Oh, Mama, you do not deserve this – you are such a good Mama. It is not fair.'

Cecilia bowed her head, 'I am lucky to have all of you, I know. I ache so much for my lost babies.'

They stayed in their embrace until little Gertie burst into the room. She squealed with delight to see her big brother.

Cecilia and Richard moved apart, smiling at her joyful innocence. Richard picked her up and cuddled her hard, 'My little Gertie.'

'Richard, I love you. I want to pick up this house and move it next to you.'

They both laughed, 'But it would be very heavy, bette.'

Little Gertie pushed out her bottom lip in a pretend sulking gesture, 'I am going to grow big and strong enough to lift it myself.'

She paused and then said suddenly, 'Come and see the house I built with Helen in the yard. We found some twigs and string and made a house for us to play with. Come come.' She jumped out of his arms and dragged him out of the room.

She watched them as they left, Richard shrugging his shoulders in resignation as he looked back at his mother. She smiled at him, indicating she was fine with him playing with Gertie.

She wasn't fine in herself. Not at all. She lay back in the bed, exhausted from her tears and another loss of a precious child. She wanted someone to hold her, to tell her that she would feel better one day. George had been elated when this baby was born. But when they realised they would lose this one, in the same way they had lost his brothers, George had walked away, leaving her to hold Joseph Edward as he took his final breath.

She felt a failure. Her body hadn't produced a healthy baby for the last three years. As a mother, she had been unable to save her children. She had failed at the most important things in life. She had alienated her husband by being so useless.

She thought of Bridget, George, Christopher and now Joseph. Her lost babies. Darkness crowded her mind as she wondered where they were now, whether they knew each other and whether they were healthy in their next lives.

The shadows of her dead babies pinned her to the bed. She couldn't move.

Aktbar and Rupali checked on her every day, bringing her food which she did not eat. They also brought news of the children. She couldn't move or react. When Richard left for Howrah a few days later, she barely acknowledged his goodbye. She just touched his arm with a weakness that worried him enough to speak to George.

As her husband and son stood outside the bedroom door. she could hear them talking.

'Mama needs you. She is so melancholy.'

'I am melancholy too, you know.'

'I understand, Papa,' he replied in a soft voice, 'But Mama carried those babies in her belly. She knew them before they were born. And she lost Bridget too.'

She heard a long silence, then a sigh from George. 'I will talk to Mama, as you suggest. It is hard to find the words to talk about the babies. I don't know what to say, I am so sad. We are both wretched.'

Richard, with the wisdom of youth, answered, 'Perhaps you do not need to say much. Just hug her. I am sure she will be pleased to just be with you.'

Cecilia heard them say goodbye and waited for George to come into the bedroom. He lay on the bed beside her and he touched her back. She sighed and turned towards him.

'I am so sorry,' he whispered, 'I do love you.'

She felt a sudden need to unburden herself. A need for his support and his understanding. 'I cannot move for the weight of emptiness on my mind and body.' She told him and waited for his sympathy. But she was shocked at his burst of reply.

'You cannot stay in bed forever, Cecilia. The children need you – they are missing you. You are needed at work too. Pandit sent a letter asking when you would be coming back. And we need the money. You are not the only one who is sad, you know. Stop being so selfish.'

George was back to being distant, his fleeting tender tone had turned crisp and sharp.

Her hatred resurfaced with a vengeance that propelled her weak body. She pushed him away, getting out of bed without a word.

Her children were the only source of happiness now. She had missed them during her melancholy and she realised she needed them as much as they needed her. She spoke to the children about the death of Joseph. They did not seem unhappy about it – they seemed used to it. It had happened to George and Christopher. It had become normal for them.

She needed to return to work, it would stop her thinking too much about her sadness. Pandit was kind, but she could see he was unnerved by her losing another baby and he did not know what to say. In fact, he said nothing, and she was grateful to him. She did not want to mention Joseph Edward again. She had decided to keep his brief life a memory that she treasured to herself and not to share it with anyone. He was her treasure, her secret and her precious angel.

Pandit delayed opening a branch of Chambers in Quetta. He told her it was a plan for the future, but for now, he would stay in Multan. She was relieved, because she knew it would be too much work for her while she was still reeling with grief. Besides, George was still set against the idea. So she carried on as if nothing much had happened.

A semblance of normality settled on the family. She and George were working. Rupali dealt with the children, taking the older ones to school and playing with them all at home. Aktbar cooked and bought food from the traders who called at the door. Even Chetna, who had left to save them money, came to help out on occasion.

But, then, she realised she was pregnant again. Her body and mind almost closed down in shock. The fear she felt when she was carrying Joseph seemed to double. She could not think about this baby without a feeling of panic coursing through her already ravaged body. She just couldn't lose another baby, she had to make sure this one survived.

Once again, she did not want to tell George.

As she retched uselessly over the chamber pot, she thought about what to do. She would need to spend a lot of time resting, in bed for the most part. But, if Pandit brought the legal bundles to her house, as he had done before, it would be possible to work. The children could play in her room and she would read to them and help them with their homework.

She wrote a note to Pandit, asking John to take it to his office.

'Yes, Mama,' he said, pleased to be entrusted with this responsible job. 'I will take Michael with me for company.'

'Of course, bette, of course. Please could you wait until Pandit writes a reply and then bring it back to me.'

'Yes, Mama, I will.'

She heard John explaining the task to Michael, a heady excitement in his voice. Michael replied. She couldn't hear what he said, it sounded as if he were excited too. A little adventure for them both.

They returned sometime later, with the reply and the happy looks of having successfully accomplished a task. She opened it and smiled. Pandit had agreed to her working at home. He was happy with how it worked for them before. Once again, she felt a surge of love for him.

George sighed when she told him about the new baby and he left a long pause before he said, 'You are right to rest every day. That may prevent this one from dying too. I could not bear to lose another one. You have disappointed me enough in that regard.'

She was so floored, she could not react to his cruel words.

She changed the subject, 'Now Alfie is away, the other children will enjoy playing hockey more and you could take them all to the club to practise. It will give me a rest.'

'Michael and John enjoy it. But would the girls be interested?'

'Yes. Why not? Just because they are girls, we should not deprive them of the chance. We should not choose for them. They should choose for themselves.'

'Right, I will take them to the club and teach them. Even Little Gertie can learn too.'

'I am sure she will enjoy it.'

He seemed invigorated by the thought, which was a relief for her. Perhaps he didn't mean those cruel words, it was just the heat of the moment after all.

When her time came, she gave birth very quickly. The new baby once again seemed healthy. They called him Joseph. She felt she needed another son called Joseph, as it would help her deal with the emptiness of losing the first one. But to show he was a different child the baby's middle name was Thomas, not Edward.

Cecilia only relaxed when Joseph was a month old and thriving. He had lived longer than his three older brothers. She was delirious with happiness.

George, too, seemed relieved. He had started smiling a little again. He was taking notice of the new baby and paying attention to the older children. The children were wary of the new baby. As if he might die like the others. And their parents might cry every day again. But gradually, as he grew, they started to play with him and cuddle him.

Life was becoming happy again.

One day, early in 1915, Cecilia was at work and overheard a conversation taking place in the lobby. A man's voice, quiet and insistent, was saying, 'But I have been told she works here.'

Kiran, who answered the door for them, replied, 'I have not heard of her.'

The voice persisted, 'Mrs Roche. Mrs Cecilia Roche, wife of Maurice Roche. I am sure they said she was here.'

Cecilia jumped on hearing her old name and rushed to the lobby, her heart pounding. Was it Maurice? Was he alive after all? Was he at the door?

She stopped short as she saw the man who had been speaking. Not Maurice after all. He looked about fifty-years-old. He was an Indian, short, thin, bald and wearing a dhoti. He had small round, frameless glasses and was leaning on the stick in his right hand.

Feeling irrationally disappointed, she nodded to the man and said, 'My name is Cecilia New. But I used to be Cecilia Roche. I was married to Maurice Roche.'

The man's face broke into a wide smile lighting up his very being, 'Then you must be the right person. I took a chance by knocking after someone told me a Cecilia worked here.'

'Please come in. Come.'

He followed her into the office. She gestured for him to sit down. He refused, 'I am happy to stand, Mrs New.'

Her heart was beating fast. What did this man want with her? Was he bringing news of Maurice? Was Maurice alive, after all? Had the British army made a terrible mistake, as she had long hoped? How many nights had she laid in bed, praying that he was alive and would one day come to find her.

She placed a glass of water on the table beside him, her heart still beating hard. He cleared his throat and said, 'My name is Mohandas Gandhi.'

She felt herself take a sharp breath inwards as she now realised who this man was, 'Aah. I have read your publication *Hind Swaraj*. It was, er, interesting.'

He nodded. 'Thank you, thank you.' He smiled at her, 'They started calling me Mahatma after that – but I have yet to earn the title. I have come back to India to work for self-rule. Before I start, I have to deliver a promise I made, many years ago.'

'I don't understand.'

'Mrs New, I have been living and working in South Africa for many years. During the Boer war at the turn of the century, I volunteered with the medical corps. I was a stretcher bearer.'

'I didn't know.'

'I met your husband, Mrs Roche. An impressive man. We struck up a friendship in the Army Hospital while he was visiting his soldiers. After a number of them died, he wanted to give me a message for you. In case he didn't survive, you see.'

She felt tears in her throat and forced them to stay there while he continued.

'He asked me to tell you that he loved you. And your children. You have three, I believe?'

She winced but said nothing.

'He said he would always love you, wherever he was. And wherever you were, I promised him I would find you and tell you.'

Through all these past years, she had held out a tiny glimmer of hope that Maurice was still alive. Now that hope was stamped out. She felt his loss all over again. And nausea as she remembered his dreadful death and the agony he suffered.

'Mrs New. Your husband radiated love for you and your children. I wish I could have known him better.'

'You know about the manner of his death?'

'Yes. It was a terrible thing. The whole Regiment was in shock. When I heard how that good man died, I became even firmer in my belief that violence only leads to more violence. We cannot make violence our means of change.'

He paused then went on, 'So, here I am. I have found you. It is a privilege to give you this message, though I know it is laden with sadness for you.'

'Our third baby died,' she said softly, more to herself as her memories resurfaced, not really to him. 'She was born early with the shock of the news of his death. Her name was Bridget. She never grew strong. She died just before her first birthday.' She looked at Gandhi more directly now, 'She never knew her father, but she is with him now, I am sure.'

'I am sorry for your double loss, Mrs New. War has many casualties, more than just soldiers. That we both know. I will spend the rest of my life working for peace. I have seen the worst of man.'

Another silence followed. Neither of them seemed comfortable or to know what to say. Suddenly, Pandit entered the room saying, 'Mrs New, I need you to...' he stopped as he saw the visitor standing by the door. He looked at them both in turn, taking in the scene.

'Mahatma Gandhi?' he asked, in a bewildered voice.

'I am,' he replied.

Pandit's brow creased in curiosity, 'What are you...?'

Gandhi smiled, 'What am I doing here? Is that what you are asking?'

'Well,' conceded Pandit, 'it is most unexpected.'

227

'I had a message for Mrs New, from her husband who died in the war in South Africa. Finding her was the first thing I have done since my arrival back in India. I have delivered the message. Now, I must start my own work which is why I returned. I will take my leave.'

He turned to open the door but stopped when he heard Pandit's voice.

'Please do stay awhile. Many others, other people of importance, come here to talk about *swaraj*. We are a part of the movement. I would appreciate spending time with you and learning your ideas.'

Cecilia held her breath, unsure how he would reply. To her relief, he turned back to the room, sitting down on the chair she had offered him a few minutes earlier. Pandit would have a debate with him, she was sure. She would use this opportunity as she had used others in the past.

Pandit and Gandhi entered into a long discussion about the merits of self-rule, a two-nation state and passive resistance. It was clear they had forgotten her.

She found herself itching to join in, but knew her interjections would not be welcome. However sensitive Pandit was to the rights of women, he was still a man. And men always felt their own opinions were more important, more measured and more rational than women's. She had learnt that very early in life and, yet again, she was watching it playing out in front of her.

Eventually, she could bear it no longer and burst out, 'What about mixed-race people?'

They both looked at her, astonished that she was still in the room with them.

'Well,' she said, emboldened by the fact she had their attention. 'Mixed-race people will be a problem if you do not include them in *swaraj* legislation.

After a shocked silence, the men recovered themselves. Pandit gave her a little nod of approval and Gandhi looked at her expectantly.

'There are many people of mixed heritage who have no formal recognition or citizenship. They are neither Indian nor British. If there is self-rule, they must surely need to have citizenship of one of the countries, or they will have no rights.'

She and Pandit watched Gandhi carefully while he pondered a reply.

He broke the silence. 'There are so few mixed-race people, we cannot account for them. There are millions of Hindus and Muslims. We must legislate for them.'

She was annoyed by the way he dismissed her views, so she continued, 'But my children are mixed-race, they will suffer with no formal citizenship.' She could see he was taken aback by her pushing her case. But she didn't care.

'You felt respect for my husband, didn't you? You have told me already?'

He nodded, 'Indeed I did. He was an honourable man.' Gandhi's glasses glinted as the sun shone through the window on them.

'Well, his children, my children, are mixed-race. Surely the best way to honour him would be to ensure they have their proper rights?' She knew she had found an irrefutable argument.

'You make a very good point Mrs New,' he said and fell into another pause, his head bowed. When he finished thinking, he looked up saying, 'I believe that this is a matter for the British to decide. I will ensure that any *swaraj* discussions include the British legislating on the status of mixed-race people, in honour of your husband.'

'Thank you.'

Christmas was drawing near. Cecilia was heavily pregnant again. This time, she was nearly at full term with no problems. She had confidence now, as little Joseph had been fine. She was sure this baby would follow suit. Even George was looking forward to the birth.

He announced the railway had given him time off over the Christmas period.

Cecilia was excited and said, 'Quetta will be a good place for us to spend Christmas. It will make a nice break for us all and I can have this new baby near a hospital.'

He laughed, 'I have just told you that the railway is giving me a holiday for Christmas. Straight away you bring Quetta into it. You never give up, do you?'

Cecilia smiled at him, 'It is a nice place, George, and the baby is due just before Christmas. There is a good hospital there. I would feel better knowing that there is a doctor nearby.'

'But Joseph Thomas is fine. I have already said you do not need to worry this time.'

She replied, 'I still think it would be good for all of us. Richard can come too. You can see Quetta for yourself. If you don't like it, I will stop asking to move there.'

He nodded with little enthusiasm, 'It will be worth it just to keep you quiet.'

The train journey from Multan to Quetta was, as usual, overcrowded, hot and smelly. George found them seats. She was grateful to sit down. Alfie was welcomed back into the fold for the holiday, the children having forgotten how argumentative he could be, for the moment anyway. They squealed with delight as they all played together.

She watched them together as she bounced Joseph Thomas on the edge of her knees. Her pregnant belly stopping her from hugging him closer.

'Papa,' said Richard as he cuddled Gertie and Helen to him, 'I still play hockey in Howrah. There is a very good club at the railway yard. And, I must tell you, Papa, there are two excellent brothers who play sometimes in Jhansi. They are about Alfie's age. I think they will play for India one day, they are so much better than the rest of us.'

'It would be good to see them play one day soon. What are their names?'

'Dyhan Singh and Roop Singh. Perhaps you can come to Howrah when we play their team? We only play friendlies at the moment. But I think you would enjoy it very much.'

Cecilia was pleased George was so interested. After Christmas and when she had had the baby, she would encourage George to stay awhile with Richard. They would both like that, she knew. And it would give her a break from George's moods, which still ebbed and flowed without prediction.

They had only been in Quetta a few days when, on 22 December, Cecilia gave birth to a boy. He was, to their relief, healthy. George suggested that his name would be George Henry.

'Like you and his older brother?' Cecilia asked him.

'Yes. I would like to call him after me. Our other baby George died and I would love a son with my name. I think it will help me get fully better.'

It was the first time he acknowledged that he was still suffering in his mind. She was glad he had. So, it was easy to agree. Cecilia took baby George to the hospital to be checked when he was two-days-old. She was delighted Peter was the on-duty doctor and pronounced him in robust health. She carried him home with joy.

When she got back, she put him in a little basket and decorated it with ribbons.

'Here is your Christmas present,' she told the children. 'A lovely brother for you all.'

Richard played with the new baby and cuddled him for hours. John, Michael and Alfie were less interested. Helen and Gertie were fascinated, as they had been with Joseph. They held the new baby and with Cecilia's encouragement they made sure Joseph, who was only fifteen-months-old, did not feel left out. Cecilia treasured those moments in her heart. Her children were her inspiration. Her love for them filled her life and drove every decision that she made.

George had not been in a low mood so often since they had arrived Quetta. He could be a good companion when he made the effort. All things considered, life was agreeable, if not perfect.

They held baby George's christening on New Year's Day at the Holy Rosary Church in Quetta. It was a small, family affair, and Cecilia was proud of how the children behaved. Even the baby only squealed a little when the water was poured on his head. But he soon settled back to sleep. The impressive red sandstone church, with its twin towers and rose window, seemed to mark a new start for them.

When they got back to Multan, Richard travelled on to Howrah and George took Alfie back to his boarding school.

On the evening George returned, over dinner of vegetables and dahl, he said, 'I liked Quetta, Cecilia. It is a city that is growing fast. It will have many opportunities for the children when they grow up. I think I could get work there. The North Western Railway will give me a transfer, I am sure.' He was talking as if it were his idea, not hers. Again, she bit her words down. Getting to Quetta was the most important thing, she decided. Not getting into an argument.

She smiled at him, 'I will talk to Pandit about setting up an office there.'

But other events delayed the move.

The telegram boy, Javed, stood at the door saying, 'This is urgent – they said to run and give it to you.'

Cecilia tore it open and read:

> Please ring St Joseph's boarding school as soon as you read this telegram.

'When did this message come in?' she quizzed the boy sharply.

'Just now Memsa'ab. Just now. Office *chalega*?' He asked if she was going to the telegraph office.

She nodded, '*Acha.*' She looked back and saw that Rupali was playing with the children and called, 'I am going out, Rupali, I will be back soon.'

Taking her purse, she ran to the office, her mind full of foreboding. It was not far, in a railway building in the British section. The run was easy as the boulevards, of course, cleaner and quieter than in the Indian part of the town.

What had Alfie done? Had he started a fight? Been rude to a teacher? Perhaps he was ill – he had to be seriously ill or they wouldn't have contacted her. Oh, Alfie, what has happened? We sent you to the school to control you and your bad behaviour.

Javed ran with her, sometimes circling her, sometimes beside her, sometimes jumping in front of her, always feigning concern. She knew he was wrapped up in the excitement of the moment, hoping for a drama he could relate to his friends later.

She burst into the telegraph office where, as usual, Sahib Joshi was sitting behind the desk with an air of over-inflated importance. His greying moustache was so large it looked ridiculous. She was sure he thought it made him look dashing. It didn't.

'I need to use the telephone, Sahib. I need to phone my son's school. Here is the money.'

He nodded, outwardly showing no interest.

She grabbed the handset and rang the number on the telegram. Joshi was pretending not to be interested by studying files, but Cecilia noticed they were upside down and he was listening eagerly. Javed had no such scruples. He stood close to her bouncing up and down on tiptoes, hoping to hear the voice at the other end.

Trying not to snap when the call was answered she said, 'This is Mrs New, Alfred Keating's mother. I had a telegram telling me to ring the school.'

A slight hesitation at the other end before, 'I will find the Abbot, Mrs New.'

The wait seemed interminable as Cecilia rifled through all the possibilities in her mind, settling in the potential news that Alfie was very ill or dying. Her heart was beating fast, her throat was dry, her breathing shallow.

'Mrs New,' a stern voice suddenly said, 'I am the Abbott, Father Peter. Alfred has run away, I am afraid. Well, we think that is the case.'

Recovering quickly from the wave of relief that flooded through her because he was not ill or dead, she said, 'I don't understand, Father. Run away? How has this happened?'

He paused, 'We don't know, Mrs New. His bed was still made this morning, so he hadn't slept in it. That's why we think he ran away last night. We had to reprimand him for his appalling behaviour yesterday. He cannot be far. He only has his uniform to wear so everyone will know he is a pupil here.'

'But we sent him to your school to be safe. You should be looking after him.'

'Alfred is a wilful child, Mrs New. He is uncontrollable. When we find him, we will send him back to you. He is expelled.' The voice was curt.

'Let's find him first,' said Cecilia in an equally crisp tone. 'Where are you looking?'

'We have contacted the polis, Mrs New. They are looking for him now in the town. He cannot have gone far, as I have said. He will be found easily, I am sure.'

'Please send me a wire as soon as you have found him.' She put the receiver down with a thump.

Joshi watched her as she left with a swirl of her sari, without a goodbye. She knew he wanted to know what was happening – but she wasn't going to tell him. Alfie was known in Multan as a naughty boy and she didn't want to underline it. The name of her family was very important.

Javed followed her, running, and jumping up and down. 'Memsa'ab, Memsa'ab, where are you going *now*? How can I help you? What has happened, Memsa'ab? Tell me Memsa'ab, tell me.'

She stopped. For the first time, she looked properly at the boy. He was very dark with hopeful, intelligent eyes and an earnest manner. She decided to use him and get rid of him at the same time.

'Javed. Go to the rail yard and get Mr New, my husband. Ask him to come home, *kripaya*. Please.' She handed him a few coins.

Alight with excitement, Javed ran off to the rail yard.

George arrived not long after she got home. 'What has happened?'

Cecilia looked at Javed, who was still hovering in the background, agog with energy and curiosity.

235

'Go back to the telegraph office, Javed. *Is dam.* Now,' she snapped.

Javed turned and fled.

'George. Alfie has run away from school. They do not know where he is.'

'That boy of yours is a nuisance, Cecilia. I am sure he will be fine – I need to get back to work. I didn't need to come home for this.' His voice was quiet and held a controlled anger.

'But I am worried about him. Anything could have happened to him, George, anything.'

'He will be fine. Any trouble he gets into will be of his own making and he will be able to sort it out. And be back in school in no time.'

'The school has expelled him. He will be coming back home after they find him.'

'I don't want him back here. He is trouble.'

'We have to have him back. He is only 12-years-old. Perhaps if we can find him a job, he will calm down.'

'He is your son. I am fed up with him. He causes destruction wherever he goes. No good will come of that boy, I tell you this.' He walked out.

Once again, he had left her alone to sort out a family problem.

She sat at the kitchen table thinking. Aktbar silently placed a mug of frothing chai in front of her. As she sipped its sweet wetness, there was a knock at the door.

Javed had returned, once again he held out a telegram. 'For you Memsa'ab, for you,' he was jumping up and down again in excitement.

Cecilia, gasping for air, ripped the telegram seal. It was from Richard:

Alfie at my house. Bringing him back to you tomorrow.

The relief that washed over her was all-encompassing. She pushed the telegram to her forehead as if trying to cool down. She had no idea how Alfie had got to Richard's house, it was miles away from his school, but that didn't matter at the moment. Alfie was alive and well.

Javed was asking, 'What is happening, Memsa'ab? What is happening, please?'

Fishing more coins out of her skirt pocket, she ruffled his thick dark hair and smiled, 'Everything is fine, Javed. You must leave now.'

Javed look crushed but, although somewhat mollified by the money, he left with the bounce drained out of him, along with the realisation that he wasn't going find out what had happened.

She sat on the sofa. Her other children came running in, oblivious to all the drama that had been going on, followed by a dishevelled Rupali. Dishevelment was her default state these days, it seemed.

She heard sounds of 'Mama!' 'Hug me!' 'Mama, he pulled my hair', 'Mama, she kicked me!' 'Mama, he broke my toy,' but she couldn't tell who had said what.

She just hugged and kissed them, holding them tight as her tears of relief fell on their hair.

Wiping her eyes, Cecilia smiled. 'I can hear the fruit wallah's bike. Shall we have some? Last time he was here, he had some lovely mangoes and bananas. Alfie will be back tomorrow. Isn't that good news?'

There were shrieks of happiness. Despite the calm his absence had brought to the house, the children had missed him. They delighted in his naughtiness – a vicarious pleasure, she knew.

The next afternoon, Richard and Alfie appeared at the doorway. Richard's arm was over Alfie's shoulder. Alfie, dressed in clothes that were too big for him, a pair of dark trousers and military jacket, looked slightly abashed but also carried his usual air of defiance.

'Alfie! Alfie!' The children circled him, jumping up to get his attention. He smiled at them, no doubt concocting a great story in his head to tell them.

Cecilia skipped into the kitchen – Richard and Alfie followed. She ladled them each a cup of chai from the dekshi.

'What happened?' said Cecilia her voice trembling with nervous anger.

'Be kind to him, Mama,' said Richard, 'He was very unhappy at the school.'

'You ran away, Alfie. Why did you do it why? I was so worried about you. We sent you to that school because you didn't like the one in Multan. It has cost us a lot of money. Why weren't you happy there?'

Alfie's bravado seeped out of him as he looked at the floor, 'I didn't like it Mama. The priests and bigger boys were not very nice to me. They did horrible things.'

'What did they do?'

'I can't tell you, Mama. They weren't very nice. They hurt me. I didn't like it, so I ran away.'

'How did you do it? I don't understand.'

'He sold his school uniform, Mama,' said Richard. 'To a family who wanted it for their own son. He got these clothes from them too.' He gestured to the ill-fitting clothes, 'And he bought the train ticket to my house with the money. It took him two days – I don't know how he found us. He is very clever indeed.'

'Mama.' Alfie looked up at her, his large brown eyes filled with pleading tears, 'I am sorry, Mama. I didn't mean to worry you. I had to leave that place. Please don't make me go back. I don't want to go back. Please, please, don't make me.' Alfie's unbroken voice was rising higher and higher as he began to panic. Tears spilled over his cheeks. 'I will be good from now on, Mama. If you do not send me back there, I will be good always.' He flung his arms around her waist and hugged her hard.

She moved his arms away and bent down to look at him with serious eyes and a stern voice.

'Alfie Keating, if I do not send you back to that school, do you promise me you will be a good boy from now on. Forever?'

'Yes, Mama, yes I do.'

'So, you will not be naughty?'

'No, Mama, I promise.'

'You will make us proud?'

'Yes Mama, I will do everything to please you and Papa. I will never be naughty again. Ever.'

'You promise me.'

'Yes, I promise.' He sounded so earnest in his anxiety.

There was a long pause while Cecilia made her son wait for an answer.

'Very well then, I will not send you back.'

Alfie hugged his mother harder than ever, 'Thank you Mama, thank you, thank you. You are the best Mama in the world. I love you.'

Over his head, she smiled at Richard and winked. Richard frowned, puzzled. Looking back at her wayward son, she said, 'Well, Alfie Keating, I am glad you have promised to be good and will never be naughty again. That will make things easier for this family. You cannot go back to the school anyway. They have expelled you. They don't want you back.' And she laughed out loud. Richard joined her as the realisation dawned on him.

Alfie was affronted. 'Mama, you tricked me!'

'I had to find a way to make you be a good boy – and you have promised me now.'

'But Mama, it was a trick.'

'Yes, but you have promised to be good – so now you must be.'

Then Alfie laughed as he saw the funny side – and because he didn't have to go back to that school.

'Oh Alfie, what are we going to do with you?'

'He cannot live with me, Mama. That is why I bought him back. He is uncontrollable.'

'You are right, Richard,' she turned to Alfie, 'I don't think school suits you, my boy. We must find you some work.'

'I would work very hard and show you that I am not so bad, Mama.'

'Papa says you were a nuisance to him when you were living with us before. Things will be better if you can show him you are growing up and you are not naughty anymore. He needs to know that you can be a hard worker. Shall we ask him to find you work in the railway yard? But do not let us down. You must keep the good name of the family.'

'Oh, Mama, thank you. I will be a good train driver.'

'You are a bit young for that, Alfie. You have to be a cleaner first, then a fireman. Then you take examinations before you become a driver. You could probably work in the sheds for now.'

Richard stood up, 'I have to get back to Howrah, Mama. It is a long journey and there is a train that leaves soon.' He looked at Alfie, 'You have to be a grown-up now, Alfie. I know you were unhappy at school. But you cannot run away from work like you ran away from school. You must keep trying, even if you don't like it. You have lost your education now. Working hard is the only thing you can do get make your life better. And Mama's.'

He hugged his brother and then held Cecilia in his big arms. She felt comforted.

'Mama,' whispered Richard, 'He will always be trouble. He will never change. But perhaps work will help him grow up a little.'

'I hope so,' she replied.

With a stab of fear and a final, almighty push, Cecilia gave birth again.

'She's beautiful,' she said to Chetna as she cradled her baby girl. She stroked the baby's pink cheek and felt an envelope of love surround them both. The baby was breathing gently.

'A baby girl, I am so lucky.' She lay back and closed her eyes with joy and thanks.

George ran into the bedroom and knelt at her bedside, looking happier than he had looked for years. 'A girl! Cecilia, thank you.' He kissed the baby's head announcing, 'We shall call her Victoria. I have always wanted a girl called Victoria. I am going to tell the children.' He bounced out of the room.

Again, he had chosen a baby's name without asking her. She sighed. She was disappointed he didn't mention how healthy the baby looked, how this one would thrive and survive.

She focused on the baby to forget her husband. Having a girl would surely mean happiness. Her brothers would protect her, her sisters would mother her. The whole family would unite over this precious new baby, she was sure. George bought the children into the bedroom.

'Come, come,' Cecilia beckoned them. 'This is your new sister, Victoria.'

They crowded round. Helen, Gertie and Cissy were once again entranced. They stroked her arms and kissed her. They squealed with excitement at the baby's every unconscious move. The boys wanted the reassurance this baby was well and would grow strong. When they saw their parents' happiness and their sister's rosy cheeks, they left.

But about two weeks later, the nightmare began again. Little Victoria started to vomit, unable to keep her milk down. She would not be comforted. Cecilia, panic settling in her stomach, dread settling over her mind, called to George. 'She isn't well. I need to get her into hospital.'

George picked up his baby and rocked her gently, 'She does not look too bad to me, Cecilia. I think you are overreacting.'

Hatred of him flared up again, 'I am not overreacting,' she snapped, 'I am her mother. I have seen four of my babies die. I know the signs. It will not happen again.'

George rolled his eyes, 'Look, Bridget died of the plague. That has gone now. The boys all died of jaundice, this baby has no signs of that. She just has a little fever. She will be fine.'

She decided to ignore George. She would not lose this child too.

'I will not take that chance. I am going to the hospital in Quetta, where they have the best children's ward. I want Peter to see her and make her well. I have to go today in case she gets worse.'

'It is a very long way to go. I don't understand why.'

'I will not lose another child. George was born in Quetta. He had good care. He is a healthy baby now. I am sure Peter and Lucia will make a special effort to make sure Victoria is alright too.'

George shrugged, 'I don't think it is a good idea. She will get better soon, I am sure.'

Cecilia voice was full of steel, 'I need you to get me a seat on the next train. After I leave, please ring Peter at the hospital and tell him I am on my way. Let him know what time I will be arriving.' She looked down at Victoria who was crying in pain and bringing her tiny knees up to her tummy. Her little pink faced had turned red. 'We need to go now.'

Without a reply, George left the house. She walked behind him, also in silence. At the station, George pushed his way through the crowds. He was wearing his railway uniform, forging a way through the crowds on its authority. Cecilia followed in his wake, carrying the wailing Victoria. As usual the train was packed and people were standing in all the corridors. George found a seat occupied by a young man.

'You must give this lady your seat, her baby is not well,' he commanded, with the mandate his attire bestowed.

The man jumped up and moved away. George made sure Cecilia and Victoria were settled.

He said, 'I am sure she will be alright. There is no need to do this. You are taking a risk with her.'

Cecilia didn't answer. She was still too annoyed with him and too worried about the baby who seemed to be getting worse by the hour. She looked out of the window, rocking Victoria distractedly, until she heard George leave.

The journey was a nightmare. Victoria was hot, then cold, then hot again. She cried in pain the whole way and nothing Cecilia did comforted her. Unbearably agonising thoughts flew unbidden into her mind. What if the baby died? What if she died before they got to Quetta? Had she done the right thing taking her on such a journey? Holding Victoria to her body, she leaned back and prayed. And prayed. Never had her belief in God mattered so much. He would surely help her. God would never let her lose a fifth baby.

She scanned the heaving masses as the train pulled into Quetta station. With relief, she spotted Peter who was looking for her through the throng of people and animals. As they found each other, they dispensed with any pleasantries. She gave him the baby and said through breathless gulps, 'She has been getting worse, going hot and cold and vomiting.'

With a quick glance at Victoria, Peter said, 'We need to get her to the hospital. Now.'

He made his way through the heaving noisy crowds. Once out of the station, Peter started running as fast as he could with the baby in his arms. Time slowed for Cecilia even though she kept pace with him. She was swallowing her dread and praying.

Peter burst through the hospital doors shouting, 'Find a bed for this baby. I need cool boiled water. Now.'

Nurses scurried about. Soon one appeared at her side saying, 'Follow me.'

The bed was in the children's ward. For a moment, Victoria stopped struggling and opened her tiny three-week-old eyes. She seemed to know that there were other babies in the room.

Peter laid her in the bed and waited until another nurse arrived with some cooled, boiled water. 'Here,' he said to Cecilia, 'give her this by teaspoon. She needs to have fluids in her, she has lost too much with the vomiting. I will get some gripe water to settle her stomach too.'

Gratefully, Cecilia gently spooned tiny sips of the water into Victoria's mouth. The baby seemed calmed by it, a little. She knelt by her baby's tiny cot. Peter had placed it next to the nurses' desk. Cecilia stroked Victoria's arm and sang her gentle lullabies. She whispered to her and encouraged her to get better so that she could play with her big brothers and sisters.

She spent hours nursing her baby. But it didn't seem to be working. With increasing fright, she saw Victoria weaken, her cries turning to whimpering mewls. Cecilia looked around the ward. There were no nurses at the desk. She ran to find Peter.

He was in the main office and looked alarmed when he saw her face.

'Come, come now,' she ordered.

She turned and ran back to the cot. 'See, see, the diarrhoea. And she is still vomiting.'

Peter listened to Victoria's heart through his stethoscope and he felt for her pulse. Cecilia watched him, hoping that he would say that they could make her better. But deep inside her, she knew. Peter put his stethoscope away slowly and placed a gentle hand on her shaking arm, 'I am afraid you need to prepare for the worst. We cannot do any more for her, we are losing her.'

Cecilia lifted Victoria out of her cot. The practical side of her rising to the fore. She should baptise Victoria now. In the corner she found a bucket of clean water and used it to anoint her baby, saying the words of baptism that she had heard so many times before.

Then she kissed her baby, saying into her ear, 'Now you are baptised – you will be stronger. I love you.'

She paced her up and down the ward, never wanting to let her baby go, in any sense of the word. She wanted to walk life into this baby. The nurses watched her, worried. They let her carry on, as they looked after other young patients.

After many hours, Lucia appeared at her elbow, walking in step with her, providing her silent comfort.

Peter arrived soon after, 'Let me see her now, please.'

Too scared to speak, she handed Victoria to him. He carried her tiny form into the hospital garden. Cecilia followed him. They sat on a bench under the shade of a banyan tree.

Silent tears streaked Cecilia's cheeks as she prepared for the news that she already knew.

'She has gone,' said Peter, 'but she died in your loving arms.'

Like all the others, she thought. Now five babies had died in her arms. There was no comfort in that, whatever Peter thought. Cecilia took Victoria's lifeless body from him and held her with a tenderness only a mother could know and show.

'Please leave us alone.'

Peter nodded. 'Lucia will come back in a while. There are arrangements to be made and we will help.'

She felt worse than when all the other babies had died. She had taken Victoria on a long journey. She had done it to save her – but it hadn't worked. Did it make her worse? She started to feel guilty, she had made the wrong choice.

Lucia returned, 'I have spoken to Father Bucher. He will say the funeral mass this afternoon.'

'I should never have brought her here. The journey made her worse.'

'Please don't think that. You did your best for her. That is all anyone could do. I think she lived longer because you brought her here.'

'But you don't know that. What will George think?'

'I don't know. You will need to let him know. But first, we must have her funeral.'

It was held in the same church as baby George was christened. Back then, this magnificent church had held the promise of a new beginning. Now the very same building marked an end, to Victoria's life and surely her marriage too.

Father Bucher remembered her. He had been the curate when George was christened. He was as sad as the rest of them as he performed his most solemn duty. He didn't speak to her but smiled a sad smile – his whole demeanour flat and empathetic.

Throughout the funeral mass, she held Victoria's shrouded body on her lap, wanting to keep her until the very last minute.

She had bathed her dead daughter and wrapped her in the fine white shawl that Lucia had given her. Just Peter and Lucia attended the Mass with her. Father Bucher's voice, loud and deep, echoed through the vastness of the empty church, vibrating in her empty heart. At the end, Cecilia placed Victoria's body in its small casket and carried it to her grave, surrounded by a force field of loneliness. Peter and Lucia followed at a respectful distance. Father Bucher walked behind carrying a stoup of holy water. The cemetery caretaker had dug a small hole, just big enough for the casket. They stood beside it, waiting for the priest to catch up with them to say the blessing.

Father Bucher gestured to the caretaker to take the casket from Cecilia and lay it in the ground. But she couldn't let it go. They looked alarmed, so she reassured them, 'She is my baby. I want to lay her in her grave. It is the last thing I will ever do for her. My final kiss.'

Tenderly and tearfully, she knelt and placed her baby's coffin its resting place. She stayed kneeling beside it. A broken woman.

The priest gave the blessing, the caretaker started to fill the grave, with Lucia and Peter throwing in a handful of soil each. When it was full, they all looked at Cecilia.

'Please leave. I want to be alone with her.'

They hesitated.

'I will be fine. Please go.'

After they left, she lay face down on the ground beside her daughter's grave and cried. All the tears in the world seemed to pour out of her until she had no more. She stayed there until darkness fell along with the temperature. Then she stood, dusting her sari, still stained by Victoria's vomit and faeces.

She knew she must tell George. She could avoid it no longer.

She used the hospital phone to call Multan station. When he came to the phone, she blurted out the news. She had planned to tell him gently, but the words flew out of her mouth before she could think.

She heard his agonised groan. Then, 'It's your fault. You killed her.'

It was as if he had kicked her, she felt so shocked. 'I wanted her to get the best treatment.'

'You took her on a long journey when she was ill. She didn't need to go. You killed my daughter. I didn't even get to say goodbye to her.'

'She was my daughter too. Not just yours. I was doing what I thought was best,' she was crying again.

His voice grew louder and angrier, 'You are always talking about you. You. You. What about me? You never think of me, do you? She was my little girl. My baby. I loved her. I can't believe I have lost four babies now.'

Once again words flew out of her mouth unbidden, 'Stop it, stop it,' she shouted, 'I loved her too. I thought I was giving her the best chance. Stop blaming me. It's not my fault. I hate you.'

She threw the phone into its receiver bolting out of the room, her yellow sari swaying angrily in her wake. Yet, she couldn't shake the feeling that George was right. That she had caused Victoria's death. She was eager to see her other children, to be a mother to them. She had to get home and hug them. But she did not want to see George.

Her head down, her tears fell on the street all the way to the railway station. She elbowed her way to a seat on the train. Other passengers, seeing her anger and sensing her unhappiness, didn't protest.

After so many nights without sleep, she found the rocking of the train irresistibly soporific. When she woke, she couldn't

248

open her eyes. Her eyelids were dry and stuck together. She was all cried out. There were no rivers of tears left in her body. But there were waterfalls left in her soul.

She peered through her swollen eyelids and saw they were on the outskirts of Multan. She would soon be home. Feelings of love and dread battled inside her. The love was for her children, seeing them soon was making her feel happy. The dread was for seeing George, facing his anger because she felt it might be justified.

The bungalow was dark when she arrived. She visited the children's rooms. She could see by the light of the moon, they were all peacefully asleep. She looked everywhere in the house, but there was no sign of George. Glancing into the yard, she saw a small candle alight in Aktbar's quarters. He will know where George is, she reckoned.

She knocked on Aktbar's woodworm-ridden door. He answered quickly and his face was flooded with relief when he saw her, 'Memsa'ab,' he said as he opened the door wider. Behind him, slumped over a small table, was George. Asleep, with an empty bottle of whisky in his hand.

'How long has he been like this?' she asked.

Aktbar shrugged and tipped his hand left and right, in a gesture that meant he wasn't sure.

'I am going to leave him here until the morning, Aktbar. You can look after him.'

She went to bed, glad she was alone. Knowing George's drunkenness had only put off the moment when they would have to face each other.

In the morning, before George emerged from Aktbar's room, the children were awake and excited to see her. She was in the kitchen with Rupali and they were making breakfast when Gertie asked, 'Where is Victoria?'

'Yes, Mama,' added Helen. 'Where is the baby?'

Her stomach lurched with the realisation that George hadn't told them. He had left her to do it.

She forced some curiosity into her voice, 'Did Papa not tell you?'

'Tell us what, Mama?' asked Michael.

She sat at the table and gathered them to her.

'Victoria died, she got ill and didn't get better. I took her to the hospital but they couldn't save her. I am sorry.'

Helen, Cissy and Gertie started howling. John, Michael and Alfie sat on the floor, with their heads bowed. Christopher and George, too young to know what was going on started to cry too, copying their siblings.

John looked up and said, 'Papa didn't tell us. But he said you shouldn't have taken her to Quetta and that it would be bad for Victoria. So, it is your fault, Mama.'

'No, no. That is not true. I thought they could make her better. The doctor said she lived a little longer because of that. But she would have died wherever she was.'

'I don't believe you Mama. You took our sister away from us and she died.' John was adamant.

Michael, Gertie and Helen all agreed, 'Papa said that if she died it would be your fault.'

A knot of despair settled inside her as she tried to defend herself against the accusing faces of her children.

'I wanted her to live. The doctor told me I did the right thing.'

'How much did you pay him to say that?' The voice had an angry snarl to it. They looked to the source of the sound. George was leaning in the doorway, scruffy and stubbly.

Cecilia's heart started to hammer. She knew that they couldn't argue in front of the children. Fury was flaring inside her. She decided to pretend it was a joke.

Smiling, a little too wide and too forced, she said, 'Don't be silly, Papa, I didn't pay the doctor anything.'

He said nothing but stayed leaning in the doorway, arms folded, watching them.

'Come on, children, it is time to get ready for school. Rupali, please can you take Joseph and George to play in the yard.' She shushed the older ones out of the kitchen. She noticed the unhappy glares that they gave her as they left. Her heart sank. How was she going make the children believe the truth instead of the lies that George had told them. What could she say without being disloyal to their father?

After the children and Rupali had left, she stared at George with a defiance that she didn't feel.

'Why did you tell them I was wrong to take her to Quetta?'

'Because you were.'

'I did what I thought was best. You should have told them that. You didn't even think she was very ill. You told me I was overreacting.'

'I always said you were wrong to do it. From the beginning, I said that. I was right, wasn't I?'

'Why didn't you tell the children that she had died?'

'Because it was your fault. I decided you could tell them. You have to take responsibility for your actions. You killed my child.'

The simmering volcano of hate erupted inside her again. She felt it wash over her like molten lava. She said nothing, fearing that she would not be able to control herself. He turned away and she heard him shouting to Alfie, 'Get ready for work, boy, we should be leaving now.'

Chapter Ten

Over the next few weeks, an element of uneasy calm descended on the house. Mainly, she knew, because George was in the doldrums again. She was treading gently around his moods. She noticed Alfie was not so combative, at least with his siblings, since he had started going out to work. John was working on the railways too now. He was bringing in money, growing into a mature adult.

It had not been easy for George to find work for Alfie with the North West Railway. At twelve, his age was the problem. It had taken George some time to persuade his boss Alfie could run errands, shovel coal and make tea for a low wage. Eventually Mr Scott agreed to give him a trial for six months. It seemed to be working. Most days they came home in a companiable manner.

She noticed George was closer to the children than he had been for some months. She was uneasy. She knew this new bond was forged when he undermined her over Victoria's illness and death. The children were not willing to listen to her side of the story. Her heart ached with this new sadness.

George and Alfie arrived back from work one evening, laughing. George sat down and lightly cuffed Alfie around the head. 'He's getting better, this one, Mama. He works hard all day and makes us all laugh with his cheeky ways.'

'And I got some rupees, Mama,' added Alfie, excited.

'So, where are they, Alfie?'

'I bought some laddoos and halva on the way home, Mama. I don't have any left.'

'So, where are the laddoos and halva?'

Alfie looked astonished that she could ever ask such a question. 'I ate them, of course.'

George burst out laughing, 'Mama, he ate them so quickly, before I could stop him. He said he didn't want his brothers and sisters to have any.'

'Oh, Alfie, that is not fair. I told you that, now you are working, you have to give us some money to help run the house. It was naughty of you to spend it all. You should have saved some sweets for the others at least.'

Alfie tried, but couldn't quite manage, to look sorry. In an effort to emphasise his regret, he lowered his head.

'Alfie,' Cecilia's voice was sharp, 'you knew that you should have given me some rupees, so don't pretend otherwise. I will let it go this time. But it is important that you do not spend it again. Papa and John go to work to keep all the family – we have food and clothes to buy for everyone. I work to make sure that we have money to pay Aktbar and Rupali and school for the others. We work for our family. You must as well.'

George, who had been watching the exchange in an amused silence, added, 'It is true Alfie. You must be a grown-up now. And grown-ups pay for the house and family.'

'Yes, Papa. Yes, Mama. I will be a grown-up now.' But he didn't sound convincing.

Later that evening, in bed, Cecilia spoke in whispers to George. 'You must watch him. Alfie will always be naughty if he thinks no one is looking.'

'He has changed, Cecilia, I am sure of that. He will not give us trouble anymore. He is usually too tired after a day at work, for sure.'

They fell asleep, content for the first time in many months.

As the night turned to day, from the depths of her slumber, Cecilia stirred. She could smell something. The faint smell of burning wafted passed her nostrils. She jolted awake. Was the house on fire? Where were the children, were they safe? She looked around. She could see enough to know that there was no fire in the room. The faint acrid smell was not wood or flesh. It smelt like burnt hair. It seemed to be coming from near to her, from George. She looked at him and could just see that his moustache was half burnt, slightly fizzing as it melted.

'George, wake up,' she shook him by the shoulder, 'your moustache is on fire.'

George mumbled and groaned, 'What do you want? Leave me alone.' He was groggy with sleep.

'Wake up George, wake up,' she pushed him more urgently.

Suddenly Cecilia's voice penetrated his fog. He sat up, startled. 'What? What?'

'I think your moustache is burnt.'

He put his hand up to his face and felt above his lip. He took his hand away and saw ash and smudges on his fingers. 'What happened? How did this happen?'

'I don't know. It's looks as if half of your moustache has been burnt away. The other half is still there, though.'

Cecilia nearly laughed at George, with his half moustache and his whole indignation, but she decided not to give in to the mirth.

With a roar of realisation, George leapt out of bed in his grubby vest and leggings. 'It was your bloody Alfie, I know it was. He's set fire to my moustache, the little bleeder! I will sort him out,' he roared as he ran towards the children's room. Cecilia ran after him.

Hurtling into the boys' bedroom, George turfed Alfie out of bed. 'You. You,' he screamed. 'You set my moustache alight.'

'No Papa, no, I didn't. It wasn't me,' protested the sleepy Alfie.

Cecilia noticed that there was a box of matches under Alfie's bedcover. Evidence that George was right. Saying nothing, she slipped over to the bed and sat on it, moving the evidence into her pyjama pocket as deftly as possible.

John, Michael, Joseph, and little George all woke and sat up in bed, thrilled with the drama.

George raised his hand to hit Alfie who was cowering in the corner. 'You bad child, how dare you. I will teach you a lesson.'

'George, stop, stop,' shouted Cecilia. 'Don't hit him. He says he didn't do it.'

Pausing, his hand in the air, George lowered his voice but it was laced with threat and menace. 'He is lying. Of course, he did it. Who else would have? He is the naughty one here.'

'It wasn't me, it wasn't me,' came a frantic chorus of denial from John, Michael, Joseph, and little George.

'It wasn't me, I promise,' pleaded Alfie, all big eyes and big ears.

Cecilia looked at her son, who was lying so glibly. What would become of him, she wondered, someone so naughty and such a liar.

In the face of no evidence and Alfie's denial, the immediate red anger seeped out of George. He put his hand down. 'I thought you had grown up, Alfie. I thought you had changed.' He stomped out of the room and Cecilia could hear him in the next room, looking for a mirror.

Cecilia peered into the girls' bedroom, as she walked past. Cissy, Helen and Gertie were huddled on one bed, listening in fear. She smiled at them and nodded, indicating that every-thing was alright.

She took Alfie's hand and led him to the kitchen where she sat him down. She got out the dekshi, added milk, tea, sugar, cardamom and ginger. She started to brew the chai.

Alfie watched in silence.

George stamped into the kitchen, holding a small hand mirror. 'Look, I only have half a moustache.'

Stifling a laugh, she clucked soothingly, 'You will just have to shave off the rest. Then it will look fine.'

'It's taken me months to make it into a handlebar. Months.'

'I know, I know. But it will grow again quickly.'

George picked up his razor, steadied the mirror above the small sink and began to shave. He examined the burnt area for injuries. He found nothing but hurt pride. When he had fin-ished, he turned to them both.

'You look younger. It suits you.' Cecilia told him.

George harrumphed. He looked into the mirror again and had to agree, if somewhat grudgingly. He looked younger. A bare face suited him.

'I agree I look better. So, in the end, it hasn't turned out too bad. Alfie, I am going to work. You can make your own way there today.'

He kissed Cecilia on her forehead in a perfunctory manner, picked up his bag and left. Cecilia looked at Alfie with a hard stare.

'I didn't do it Mama, I didn't.'

She took out the box of matches and put them on the ta-ble. 'Well?'

'Not mine Mama. I don't know where they came from.'

'Alfie, they were in your bed. They came from you. Stop lying to me. We both know.'

Alfie shrugged. 'Yes Mama, I did do it.'

'But why, Alfie, why? It was a very dangerous thing to do. And it was not a nice thing to do either.'

'I am sorry Mama. I wanted to feel excited. I wanted to do something exciting.'

'But Alfie, it was wrong. You are old enough to know that. You do not have to do wrong things to feel excited.' She paused. 'I will not tell Papa this time. But if you are naughty again, I will not protect you. You must grow up and learn to be good.'

'Yes Mama,' said Alfie with as much sincerity as he could muster, which was very little.

At once, all the other children came rushing into the kitchen, eyes all wide with excitement and bouncing with a thrilled energy.

'Alfie, Alfie, did you do it? Did you set fire to Papa's moustache? Did you burn Papa?'

Alfie laughed at them, lapping up the role of the adulation due to him as the naughty brother. Cecilia saw that their hero-worshipping of Alfie was only going to make him naughtier.

Before he could answer them, she shooed Alfie to work and set about making breakfast for the other children.

'Mama, Mama, did Alfie do it?'

'He is very naughty isn't he, Mama?'

'Isn't he?'

Raising her voice above all the noise she shouted, 'Children be quiet!'

Once silence had descended, she told them, 'Alfie was very naughty. He did it. It was very dangerous. Alfie has been punished. Papa does not know. So, we must keep it a secret. It is very important not to mention it to anyone. Don't even say anything to Alfie. Can you keep it a secret?'

'Oh yes, we will Mama, yes we will.'

'Right, that is the end of the matter. Rupali will be here soon. You older ones have to get to school.'

The next day, George announced he would be working in Howrah for the time being.

'Howrah? You didn't mention it before.'

'No need until it was confirmed earlier today. They need more guards.'

'But it is so far away.'

'I have lost patience with Alfie now. I know he set fire to my moustache. You know too.'

She said nothing. George went on, 'Anyway, I hate being in Multan now. Since my children died. Since you killed Victoria.'

She winced, 'Victoria would have died anyway. Peter said. They were my children too. I don't see why you are finding it harder than me.'

'I have lost four children. Four. And I cannot understand why you took Victoria to Quetta. That is my biggest sadness. I cannot live with you at the moment. I have tried. But it is impossible.'

'But you have children here, they need you,' she hissed.

'I will only be gone a few months. I will ask the railway to send you my pay.'

'But the children will miss you.' She deliberately didn't say she would miss him.

'I will be lodging with Richard. We can ring the railway office to talk to them occasionally.'

'So, you have made up your mind?'

'Yes. I will come back when I feel better.'

If only she had the luxury of coming back when she felt better, she thought bitterly. His luxury was not afforded to her, as a woman and a mother.

'Very well,' she said in a sharp tone, 'you can tell the children when they come home. I am not saying anything.'

Later that evening, she watched as he carried his large bag to the door. He turned to say goodbye to the children. They were all crying, telling him they did not want him to go. He kissed them each in turn, telling them he would be back soon. Her eyes met his, in the mutual knowledge that he was lying. She knew he was desperate for the children to think well of him. He had had the upper hand on this since Victoria's death. He had continued to manipulate them, casting her as an uncaring mother.

At least his departure would give her the opportunity to right things now. She would never contradict what he said, she did not want her children to feel torn because their loyalty was conflicted. She would not undermine him as he had her. Instead, she would show the children how much she loved them by doing just that. Loving them.

Life was easier without George, without his constant mood fluctuations, self-absorption and accusations. While she got through the daytime without thinking about her lost babies too much, she cried herself to sleep every night without fail. In the dark, her dead babies competed for her attention, as her living children did in the light. And the shadow of her decision to take Victoria to Quetta became darker and heavier as each day and night passed.

Pandit was once again pleased to have her return to work. She was perpetually surprised that he welcomed her so warmly. On more than one occasion, she had expected him to tell her not to return as she was not reliable because of her pregnancies and lost babies.

'You are the fastest, quickest, most intelligent colleague I have ever had,' he told her. 'And you have a sense of fun that we need here.'

She was grateful for his kind words. But she was somewhat bemused. She felt her sense of fun had disappeared a long time ago. Life and tragedies seemed to have knocked it out of her. Nothing was fun anymore. Except possibly time with her youngest children whose antics were amusing when she was not too tired to appreciate them.

Emboldened by his comments, she plucked up the courage to ask him, 'Pandit, why do you keep welcoming me back? Even if I am all those things? It must be difficult for you to plan our work. You have been so good to me. I don't know why.'

She watched as a shadow darkened across his face and his body slumped in his chair. His eyes looked at the wall as he replied, 'My wife died in childbirth. I loved her so much. I still miss her. Our baby, Nadia, was born healthy. She was my world. She was beautiful, clever and quick witted. She wanted to be a lawyer, like you. I lost her when she was twenty-years-old. Her husband killed her. She died after he beat her with a stick and then strangled her. I didn't have the chance to save her. To protect her.' He paused, tears welling in his lonely eyes 'I was her father and I couldn't protect her.'

He looked at her now, the tears spilled down his cheeks, 'When Nadia died, I vowed that, through my work, I would support women to be independent. So that what happened to Nadia would never happen again. You remind me of her. I promised myself I would protect you in any way I could. In the way I couldn't protect Nadia.'

She felt a surge of love for this poor man. Like her, he seemed defeated by life.

Determined to show him that his effort had been worth-while, she said, 'I am sorry to hear your story, Pandit. I didn't know there had been such loss in your life. It is sad indeed. But your promise in Nadia's name has changed my life. Without your understanding, your kindness, your willingness to be flexible, I could not have kept this job. I could not be financially independent. My work has given me something to focus on, something other than my grief. You have made such a difference to my life. And my children's lives.'

He smiled, 'I am so glad, Mrs New. I see such promise in you. Life will be easier for you soon and our work will take on a new status. We will get you to the Bar, I know. And you will be able to clarify the position on your children's citizenship through your work. We have exciting times ahead.'

'Thank you, Pandit. I can feel a little lightness coming back to me because of your words.'

He nodded then turned away, blowing his nose. She realised that he was exhausted and a little embarrassed from telling her his story. She left him in his office, taking an even greater love and respect for him with her.

It was March 1919 and Pandit sighed as he read *The Times of India.*

'What is wrong, Pandit?'

'No good will come of this,' he said, 'It is bad. It will make *swaraj* much more difficult. I knew it was going through the legislature, but I hoped it wouldn't pass.'

He handed her the paper and pointed to the article. She noticed his hand was shaking a little but she decided that it was anger about the new Act, rather than infirmity.

The article outlined the Rowlatt Act, which had just been passed by the Imperial Council in Delhi. The police now had the powers to arrest anybody for any reason. The legislation was meant to curb the emerging nationalist movement.

'I see our friends are protesting,' she said.

'Yes. Mohammad Ali Jinnah has resigned from the Council in protest.'

'Yes, so it says. I wonder what he will do now. He will find other ways of making his voice heard, I am sure. It may even inspire him to work harder. That will upset the British.'

Pandit smiled at her, 'And your friend, Mahatma, is protesting too.'

She laughed, 'Not my friend, Pandit. I know you are joking with me. Yes, I see Gandhi is calling for a *hartal*. He thinks a mass strike is the best way of protesting.'

'He leads by example. Like us, he doesn't want violence. We need to follow the process and see what happens. We will need to stand ready with legal help. I will write to Jinnah and Mahatma and offer them our services.'

A few weeks later, Cecilia arrived early for work and picked up the newspaper before Pandit arrived. With increasing horror, she read the lead article. It was about a massacre at Amritsar carried out by the British. A general, Reginald Dyer, had given the order to open fire on a crowd of people who had gathered peacefully to protest against the Rowlatt Act in Jallianwala Bagh. They were also celebrating a Sikh festival. Hundreds of unarmed people, including women and children, had been killed. The event was causing political and social uproar.

Pandit arrived to see her tutting angrily over the newspaper.

'What has happened?' he asked, concerned, 'you have lost all colour from face, Mrs New.'

She handed him the paper, 'You were right, Pandit. The Rowlatt Act has caused this.'

He read it in a manner that grew more serious as he took in the implications of the massacre.

'This is terrible, Mrs New, truly terrible.'

'Yes. This will set the cause of *swaraj* back by years.'

'The British are blaming the Indians and the Indians are blaming the British. People will never forgive each other. Nor will their children. Violence solves nothing. This is a sad day.'

'All I can think about is my children, Pandit. This could make things a lot worse for them.'

'We must follow the same path as we have been, Mrs New. We must press the British to give citizenship to Anglo-Indians. We have to find a way of making the British see the value of your community.'

'We need to cost the value of our worth to them.' Suddenly she found an argument to back her cause, 'If we speak in terms of money, they will surely listen. Money motivates them, for sure.'

'Exactly right, Mrs New. I look forward to reading your arguments on this matter.' He walked into his office with renewed purpose.

The work was challenging, as far as she knew it had not been done before. Framing the research terms, carrying out the surveys and analysing the data were all new to her. She found it as exciting as it was difficult. She knew that this work would benefit her children and grandchildren and the whole Anglo-Indian community for years to come. It was of major importance both nationally and internationally. It stretched her mind and kept her thoughts focussed when they started to stray into her personal grief. She was finding some peace through her mission.

But that peace only lasted a few months.

In late November, George came home. When she took the children to meet him at the station, Cecilia saw why Richard had accompanied him. George had aged terribly and was deathly pale. He was 52-years-old, not a young man, but he looked so much older. He had lost weight and seemed to be made of just bones, his hair was all gone. He could barely walk, leaning on Richard for support.

A brief picture of the big handsome man she had fallen in love with came into her head. She felt a surge of love for that man and sorrow for the stranger in front of her. The hatred she had felt for him, which had been shrinking since he moved away, disappeared in that one moment.

The children didn't notice his frailty. They ran to him, throwing their arms around him, 'Papa, Papa, you are home!' they chorused as they rushed to cuddle him, nearly knocking him off his feet. Richard managed to steady him before he fell. George did not seem to know where he was and he did not recognise Cecilia.

She caught Richard's eye over the head of the children. There was a question in hers. He raised his eyebrows in response and tipped his head to say he would tell her later.

They gently took one of George's arm each while Rupali managed the children. George's breathing was laboured and loud. They walked him home slowly, carefully avoiding the dirt and stones on the ground. Where they couldn't dodge the detritus, they picked him up and carried him. Cecilia was relieved that it was not far. The railway quarters were near the station, as they had been in Mahoba.

Once they got him to the bungalow, they put him to bed.

Cecilia started to make some chai. The two little ones were with Rupali. The older children, back from work and school, were crowded into kitchen with her and Richard. They had been to see their Papa in his bed. Cecilia looked around at them. Heavy questions hung in the air, she knew they must be answered. She took a while to make the chai, pondering what to say. She decided not to lie to them.

After handing them steaming cups of the sweet, spiced tea,

she asked Richard, 'What happened, what is wrong with Papa?'

Richard, sitting at the table with his head in his hands, looked up at her, eyes brimming with sorrow.

'I don't know so much, Mama. Papa was never happy since he came to us. He was always melancholy. I tried everything I knew to cheer him up, Mama, nothing worked. Not even seeing those two talented hockey brothers I had told him about. I wanted him to coach them, like he did with us. But he was not interested. He was not interested in anything.'

'He was sick in his mind when he left here, Richard. The loss of the babies was too hard for him to bear. But now he is sick in body too.'

'Yes, Mama. He has been ill in his body for about two months,' Richard paused and looked around at his siblings, 'he asked me to bring him home. He said he was dying,' the children gasped collectively, 'and he wanted to die at home. With all of us around him.'

Her stomach lurched, she knew there was truth in George's prognosis of his own condition. The children were all crying, Cecilia not knowing which of them to comfort first. She felt bad as she pitched her voice above their wails.

'Children, shh. Papa needs peace and quiet. This noise is not helping him.'

They immediately quietened down. Now she could only hear their sniffles. 'Papa is very ill. But he may not be dying. Helen, Gertie, please fetch the doctor from the Railway Hospital. Let's see what he says.'

The doctor, an old and wizened Englishman, asked to see George alone, spending about an hour with him. Cecilia and the children waited outside the bedroom. Cecilia felt taut throughout her body as tension gripped her. She knew the doctor's news would not be good. She was determined to stay calm in front of the children.

They all jumped back as the doctor opened the bedroom door. His eyes met hers over the heads of the children and he said, 'Mrs New, may I speak to you alone in the kitchen?'

The doctor closed the kitchen door behind him. He had an unsteady gait and a manner that did not inspire confidence. She knew the outcome of George's illness. She needed the doctor to tell her how long George had left.

'Mrs New,' his voice was monotonous and slow, 'Mr New has pneumonia. He is very ill. He has no will to live, either.' He was clearly trying to break the news gently to her, under-estimating her ability to understand the situation.

'How long?'

'Not long, Mrs New. Not even days, I would estimate. I think hours.'

'We lost four tiny babies. I think his love of life went with them. It is sad as we have other children who need him.'

The doctor shrugged, 'Not many people have your strength, Mrs New.'

'I do not think I am strong. I am as sad as my husband. Sadder, even, because I carried all the babies and lost a daugh-ter before I even met him. But I cannot think of myself all day, doctor. I have no time to cry and mourn them. I have other children who rely on me. I have a job and responsibili-ties.' She realised she was sounding bitter.

The doctor raised his eyebrows in response, but said noth-ing. He took off his stethoscope and folded it into his medical bag.

'The best thing you can do now, Mrs New, is sit by his bedside and talk to him. Say your goodbyes, let the children say goodbye too. Make sure his path to the next life is smooth. Make sure he knows he is loved. Once he has passed, contact me at the hospital and I will help arrange the funeral service for you.'

She remembered her manners, 'Thank you Doctor.'

She did not see him out.

She gathered the children into the kitchen. They were watching her, worried about what she was going to say. She looked at them all and took a deep breath, buying herself time to think about how she would break the news.

'God will be taking Papa to heaven soon.'

They started crying again, but all of them quietly, the wails seemed to have been cried out of them.

'But Papa will be able to hear you when you talk to him. We need to sit with him, tell him we love him.' She paused, 'We should say goodbye to him. It will be too tiring for him for us all to sit with him at once. Perhaps you should see him in twos.' She knew that going with a sibling would be helpful for both themselves and George. 'Richard, please could you organise this. I need to go to the church and get the priest to give him the Last Sacrament.'

Richard co-ordinated his siblings into twos to visit their father. He made sure each pair only spent a few minutes with George, so as not to tire him too much. How proud she was of her firstborn, he had grown up into a lovely, caring young man.

The priest came and administered the Last Rites with little grace or fervour. He had seen too many people in this state and was immune to any sadness.

The children were in bed when she heard a gentle knock on the door. A nurse stood there. 'The doctor sent me. I am from the hospital. He said you might want some help.'

Cecilia opened the door and beckoned her in. She showed her where George lay breathing ever shallower, forced, breaths.

The nurse examined him gently and said, 'Just a couple of hours left, I am sorry to say.'

Cecilia said softly. 'I know it will be soon. Will you stay with me to the end?'

'Yes, I will. Then I will help you prepare the body.'

The nurse took a chair in the corner of the room and sat down. Cecilia sat gently on the bed and stroked George's bony hand. After a while, they heard his breath change, growing even shallower. His body twisted suddenly, making her jump from the bed. Just as suddenly, it relaxed and he sighed, as if his action had pushed the rest of the air out of him.

The nurse walked over to the bed and check his heart and pulse. 'It is over,' she said. She closed his eyes and placed a rupee on each to weight them shut.

Chapter Eleven

'It's time we opened that office in Quetta, Mrs New. We should return to the plans we had some time ago.'

Cecilia's thoughts strayed to George. If he hadn't been so stubborn, they would have moved there years ago. He would not have contracted the pneumonia that killed him.

Pandit frowned, 'Are you not in agreement with me, Mrs New?'

Shaking her head back into the present, 'Oh, I am Pandit, I do agree. I was just lost in other thoughts. I am sorry.'

'Then we need to plan.'

They spent the next few hours working out a way to open a new office in Quetta. Pandit still wanted to move there, and have her manage the Multan office, but he was not sure his health would withstand the move. However, he told her, he wanted to try. 'I am growing quite old now, Mrs New. But I do not want to give in to "Time's wingèd chariot", as Andrew Marvell would have it called.'

'Pandit, no more talk like that please. "Time's wingèd chariot", indeed. You have many more good years left in you.'

He laughed, 'I like your confidence, Mrs New. So, it's decided, then. I shall move to Quetta and build up our office there. You will stay here and manage the work. We will keep in contact through regular phone calls, telegrams and letters. Like we did before. It was successful then.'

'When shall we start, Pandit?'

'Let us start tomorrow. Also, we must make time for your legislative research and drafting. It is very important indeed. To you and to these Chambers.'

The next day, Pandit brought his servant to pack his books and files. He turned to Cecilia at the front door and said, 'Farewell, Mrs New, we will be in touch soon. I will wire you when I arrive and let you know the address of the new office. These are exciting times for both of us.'

'They are indeed, Pandit. Good luck.'

After he had left, she moved her own books and files into his office, sitting at his desk with a smile. She was looking forward to managing the office permanently, stepping up to her responsibility and making Pandit proud of her.

At home, life after George was settling down. There was still a sadness in all of them, she reflected. The older children were philosophical yet thinking more about their own lives than their father's death. Little Joseph and George seemed to have forgotten him already. She had loved him but that love had ebbed away over the years, replaced with sadness and grief that washed the high tide of desire away. Whenever she thought about her husbands, she remembered Maurice. Life with him was so happy. Even after more than twenty years, she loved and missed him more than she missed George or Christopher.

She was now living openly as a widow – a working widow who had an important job. She would not be cowed into marrying for the sake of appearances. She was in her forties, no longer a naïve young girl. Let the gossips gossip. Let the men in charge challenge her, she would challenge them back. She was no longer going to live by other people's expectations.

Family life was changing too. John had moved to Howrah to live with Richard and work with him on the railway. She was still living in the railway house in Multan, as Alfie was working in the sheds and training to be a driver. Cissy had just met a nice young man called Christopher and she was sure they were on a path to marriage. Gertie was courting too. She seemed very keen on her young man, Stephen.

Helen was getting increasingly religious and talking about becoming a nun. She told Cecilia she felt lost and alone in the world, that God was her only family now. Cecilia had tried to reassure her that they were her family and she was her mother. Not her birth mother, indeed, but the woman who loved her and brought her up as her own daughter. Helen was not convinced and Cecilia was crushed.

She spent many hours pondering Helen's words and concluded that if Helen really wanted to become a nun, then she would not stand in the girl's way. The family would visit her as often as possible.

Cecilia took Helen to the convent to begin her new life. It was a dark and imposing building, which brought back terrible memories of Richard's birth. She took a deep breath and pretended to be relaxed as they stood in the huge empty lobby. She shivered. They were greeted by a small, elderly nun who shuffled over to them with an air of importance that was at odds with her walk. Her tread echoed around the bleak entrance hall, a sound of foreboding to Cecilia's ears.

'Helen New?'

Helen nodded. Cecilia watched her beloved stepdaughter. She was so young and looked nervous as she put down her small suitcase.

'Well, come along then. Follow me.' The nun turned and started to shuffle back in the direction she had come.

Cecilia hugged Helen tightly. Then breaking the hug and holding her shoulders, she wiped her tears saying, 'We will come and see you on Saturday, so it will not be long.'

The nun turned back to them, 'There are no visiting hours. This is a closed order. You will not see each other again.'

Cecilia's heart jumped in shock. Helen's head was bowed, her dark hair flopping over her face. 'Did you know this, Helen, that it is a closed order?'

'Yes Mama. I need a new family now. I will miss you at first, but I will get used to it. And so will you.' She was firm in her tone.

'But what about your brothers and sisters? Gertie especially will miss you. I will miss you too.'

'This is the right way for me. I want to devote my life to God. I will pray for you all every day.'

'But you are only seventeen. How do you know that you want this for the rest of your life? A closed order? I had no idea. You didn't say. You might change your mind in a few years. You might want to get married and have children?'

'But Mama, I do not want to have all the sadness. My Mama died when she had me. You and Papa had so much sadness when you lost my brothers and sister. I do not want that for me. I want...'

The nun interrupted calling out to them, 'Come along, come along, we cannot waste more time.'

Helen picked up her suitcase, 'I am sorry, Mama, I have to go now. I love you. Thank you for all you have done for me. You were a good Mama.' She turned and walked towards the nun without looking back. Cecilia watched them disappear through a large wooden door. It slammed behind them, echoing its finality around the enormous lobby.

The pain of love and loss hit her again, she had to get out of this horrible place. She walked out of the convent into the relentless sunlight of the day. She blinked. And blinked again, as her tears spilled over. She was bereft, she had lost another child.

When she told the other children, she was surprised by their reactions. The older ones, including Gertie, were disappointed but not too upset. They were more interested in their own lives, looking forward, not back. They were courting and not bothered by any events at home.

Little Joseph and little George were upset but didn't really understand, so they carried as normal. They were sweet children with George's kind nature. But Joseph, even at seven years old, showed signs of the melancholy that plagued his father. Cecilia hoped he would grow out it. She determined to show him how much she loved him. She was sure that knowing he was loved would make all the difference to him and his moods.

In the meantime, her work continued apace. Being responsible for all the litigation in Multan, there was a lot to manage. She employed another clerk. Regular calls from Pandit in Quetta helped them keep in touch as they discussed each case and how to progress it.

Her main work was the citizenship for Anglo-Indians. She spent many hours working on the data she had collected and trying to construct a compelling argument, one that the British would see was of benefit to them. Eventually, she landed on the idea that the British would need a workforce in reconstructing Britain after the Great War. Many Anglo-Indians had died for the British in the war, so there was a moral imperative on the British to repay such sacrifice. Cecilia realised that the British would be unlikely to act on a moral imperative but included it in her paper, to add weight. She created an argument that making Anglo-Indians British citizens would give the British the opportunity to have them come to the UK, filling the gap in the workforce. In addition, she wrote, the shrinking trade of opium to China over the last few years, had led to more people being needed in the mother country to create new industries and sources of wealth. She calculated how many hours they would work and how much they would collectively generate for the British economy. The figures were impressive.

When she had completed her paper, she sent it to Pandit for his approval. She knew that the final version would have his name on it, not hers. This rankled with her. She kept telling herself, if the paper was taken on by the British, and if legislation was enacted, then the object of the exercise would be realised. That was what she wanted above all else, so it wouldn't matter whose name was on the document. But a little bit of her still felt it would be fairer if she were given at least some of the credit.

Cecilia unlocked the bungalow door after returning from work one evening and jumped back as an excited Cissy threw herself into her arms.

'Oh Mama, Mama,' she shrieked, her long dark hair loosened by her excitement and cascading over her slim shoulders, 'Mama, Christopher has asked me to marry him. I said yes!'

Cecilia held her daughter at arm's length, 'This is a surprise, bette. You are only eighteen. Are you sure?'

'Oh, yes, Mama. I really love him. I am so sure, I want nothing else.'

'What about your education?'

Cissy shrugged, 'No need Mama. He has a good job on the railway, so I will not work. It doesn't help a marriage.'

There was a heavy pause, laden with things unsaid. They looked at each other for a long time until Cecilia broke the silence. 'If you are happy and sure, then it is good. I love you. I want you to be happy.' She hugged her daughter.

Inside herself, she was disappointed that Cissy was not going to carry on with her studies. All the time she had put into supporting her daughter's education was wasted. Cissy did not value it.

When she let go of Cissy, Cecilia smoothed her own pale green sari and said with conviction, 'Now tell me, have you made any arrangements?'

Cissy skipped into the kitchen where Aktbar was stirring a dhal. He put two plates in front of them, then left the room.

'Well?' Cecilia asked scooping up the dhal with a chapatti, 'What are your plans?'

'The Church of the Holy Redeemer. In November.'

'That is very soon. What about the banns.'

'We will get a licence, Mama, it will be easier. Then I will be Mrs Goffney. I can't wait.'

The wedding went smoothly. But it was bittersweet for Cecilia. Her children were together and she watched them with pride. And the five children she had lost were with her too. She imagined all of them, at their right ages, being among the guests, chatting to their siblings, creating a happiness that was never to be. She missed Helen, who would never be at family events again.

No one else seemed to notice. It was her own private torment, there was no one to share it with, no one to confide in. She was alone. As she had been for many years, even during her marriages. Papa had passed three years ago and she still ached for his love and kindness.

For everyone else it was a happy day. Cissy looked radiant in a cream-coloured lace dress with a grey cloche hat. Christopher was handsome in his guard's uniform. They were in love. It radiated through them as once it had radiated between her and Maurice. She looked at them fondly and prayed for their happiness to last for ever.

She went back to work, travelling between Quetta and Multan, as she had been doing for some time now. But Cissy's words, '*I will not work. It doesn't help a marriage*', had hurt her. She wondered since if she had done the right thing by working at all. She was beginning to realise that her children might feel resentful. She had always thought they would appreciate that she was working for them and for their future. Their resentment was borne of their youth, she decided, it would wear off when they were a little older. Once they had gained more life experience.

'I have had a letter from the British administration,' said Pandit, 'about our paper on citizenship for Anglo-Indians.'

'What did they say?'

'Well, it is cautious. They say they are interested in the idea and wish to explore the matter further within the Indian Civil Service and the UK central government.'

'Well, at least they have replied and they have not rejected the idea. So there is hope.'

'Yes, indeed, Mrs New. Now, the question is, do we leave the matter with the British and wait to hear from them? Or do we somehow press our case further? If so, how?'

'I think we should ask for a meeting with them, Pandit. They could easily forget the matter. And now is the time to press our case, as they are still wondering how to rebuild the country. We are presenting them with a solution. If we leave the matter, it may be too late.'

'Very wise, Mrs New, very wise. Negotiation is always about timing, I agree. I shall reply and request a meeting, as soon as possible.'

'And, Pandit, might I suggest we garner letters of support from important people, like the Sorabjis, the Aga Khan, Eardley Norton, Annie Besant, the people we have met and discussed it with. Gandhi too? If we have other people on our side, and can prove it by showing the British letters, we will strengthen our argument.'

'You are right again, Mrs New. Please organise that.'

'I will, Pandit', she agreed, once again irked that she had the idea and would do the work but Pandit would get the credit. She knew it wasn't his fault, it was the way the system was, but it still galled her.

'Gertie, are you pregnant?'

Gertie stopped as she walked past her mother in the yard. 'I...'

Cecilia looked at her daughter's burgeoning belly and raised her eyebrows, 'I think you are showing.'

'Oh, Mama, I was about to tell you. I think I am.' She burst into tears.

'Come here, Gertie, you need a hug.'

'Oh Mama, are you cross with me?'

'Let me tell you something, bette. I had Richard before I married Mr Roche, his father.'

Gertie wiped her eyes, which were wide in astonishment, 'Is that so, Mama? Really?'

'Yes, we were very much in love. But I was sent away to a horrible convent to give birth to hide my pregnancy. I will not let that happen to you, bette. What are you planning to do?'

'Stephen and I want to get married before the baby arrives.'

'Are you sure? It is a very big decision. You are only fourteen.'

Like her sister before her, Gertie radiated an innocent happiness.

277

'Yes Mama,' Gertie replied, 'We love each other. I know we will be very happy.'

'What about your education? You are very clever. You should continue it, you know.'

And, in a near copycat conversation of the one she had had with Cissy the previous year, Gertie replied, 'I do not need more education, Mama. Stephen has a good job. I want to stay at home with the baby. That is the best way for a marriage to work.'

There was a silence. Her words hit Cecilia's heart as shards of disappointment.

'It is not good for a woman to work,' said Gertie, tilting her tiny chin upwards, 'it makes the children lonely.'

'So, were you children lonely?'

'Of course we were, Mama, we missed you so much.'

Cecilia put her head in her hands and said in a low voice, 'I didn't know. You had Papa and Rupali. I didn't think you noticed when I was away. I always missed you all. So much.'

'We did notice, Mama. Rupali is nice but she is not you. Papa was not very talkative. He did not really play with us. We wanted you, our Mama. You were always such fun.'

'I had to work as we needed the money and I wanted to make our lives better. There were so few places that would take me, that I had to travel a long way to and from work and college. It was not easy being a working woman.'

Cecilia felt the energy seep out of her as she protested her past. Gertie was telling her what Cissy had already said. She didn't like what she was hearing. It made a mockery of her whole life. She wondered how she had got it so wrong.

Gertie placed a hand on her shoulder, 'Mama, we all love you. We just wanted more of you, that's all.' Then she left the room. And left Cecilia with her thoughts.

278

On another happy family day, in May 1920, Gertie married Stephen O'Connor. Her body swollen with child, she beamed at her family and guests. Stephen was a fireman on the North West Railway and many of his colleagues attended the nuptial mass and reception. They were exuberant. Gertie wore a pale blue gingham smock trimmed in white braid. And she had borrowed Cissy's wedding hat and shoes to complete her pretty outfit. John was her witness and signed the registry with a flourish of fraternal pride.

For the same reasons as Cissy's wedding, it was a bitter-sweet day for Cecilia. This time, though, there was more sadness heaped upon her from Cissy's and Gertie's comments about her work. She was upset that her motive was not understood. They resented her career. The thought weighed her down. She had let down her dead babies by not looking after them properly and she had let down her living children by not being with them often enough. She was a failure. Her loneliness invaded her thoughts, every moment of every day, it seemed.

Joseph and George were growing up fast yet still needed her attention. She gave them all of her time when she was at home. But work was also pressing, the meeting with the British administration was important and was scheduled to take place in Quetta, and she had to attend. It was too important to miss. A letter from Pandit with the date of the meeting meant that she had to leave the next day.

She felt low on the journey to Quetta. She was travelling to a meeting where a man would take the all the credit if it went well. And she would take the blame if it didn't.

Pandit seemed relieved to see her, which cheered her up a little. She soon found out why.

'The British have brought forward the meeting to this afternoon, Mrs New,' he her told as he hurriedly packed some

279

files into his briefcase, 'We must leave now in order to get to their office in time. Come, come.'

So it was, with no preparation, she found herself meeting the British administration and putting her argument forward. They met two men, one older and one quite young. Both had airs of polished superiority. The room was book-lined and the tables and chairs shiny dark wood. There was a large fireplace. An unnecessary feature in India, she thought. Both men sat at the table. The older one, who had a grey trimmed moustache and neat beard, sat at the top. The younger one, pimply and nervy, sat on his right. Her document was in front of them.

As soon as they sat down, Pandit asked her to explain the argument she had outlined in her paper.

She had written it so long ago, she couldn't easily recall the details. But she was energised by the challenge and began to explain her argument without notes. She could tell the civil servants were listening with intent. Pandit was smiling at her, impressed and proud. When she had finished, the room fell silent. The large grandfather clock near the door ticked loudly, its sound echoing through the silent room and through her tense body as she waited for their response. After some time, the older man spoke, but to Pandit only. His voice was deep, so sonorous that it drowned out the clock and created its own echo around the room.

'Thank you. We find your argument intriguing. You are right, the mother country needs rebuilding after the Great War. That process has begun already. There are other matters, of course. The recent partition of Ireland has meant that there are economic considerations there too. And many of your so-called Anglo-Indians have Irish forebears. They might be needed in the Northern part of Ireland now.'

The thought of her children being repatriated to Ireland

sent her stomach into a flutter. But she did not show her worry as she said, 'Very well, what are the next steps?'

Both men turned to her shocked that she had spoken, then back to Pandit as though she had said nothing. Once again, the older one spoke, 'We need to discuss this internally. And with other countries in His Majesty's Dominions – there are many issues to consider. We will be in contact in due course.'

It was clear the meeting was at an end. The civil servants stood and, in turn, shook Pandit's hand. She moved forward to shake their hands too. They turned away to gather their papers ignoring her completely. She bit down her fury as she and Pandit were escorted out of the building by a lesser employee.

After they returned to Chambers, she spoke to Pandit, 'Did you see how they ignored me? Even though it was me who outlined the argument and gave them all the information they need.'

Pandit nodded, 'It is the way of things, Mrs New.'

'I want to change it – it is deeply frustrating. All my work goes unacknowledged. It makes me angry.'

'Well, it won't change in my lifetime, Mrs New. Perhaps yours. But I have limited time left, I fear.'

She looked at him in astonishment, 'Pandit, what do you mean?'

'Well I am over seventy now, Mrs New. My doctor tells me that I am incurably ill.'

'I don't understand.'

He smiled, 'It is not immediate, Mrs New. They tell me I have a few years yet.'

'I don't know what to say.'

'But I do, Mrs New. I will be reunited with my wife and daughter at last. Only then will I be truly happy. Now we have work to do, so I will say no more about it except that I intend to leave this practice to you. You have earned it, Mrs New.'

She was stunned. Never had she ever thought about his passing or his plans. Her heart plunged with the thought of him dying and soared with the thought of a secure future. She said, 'Pandit, that is very kind indeed. But let's not talk of it now. It is too upsetting.'

He nodded, 'Very well, but we must talk about this another time,' and returned to his office.

Still reeling from Pandit's news, both his illness and his plan to leave the practice to her, she decided to go to Mass in Quetta before returning home. Since Victoria's death, she had avoided the church, the memories were still too raw. But she needed to pray for Pandit.

Chapter Twelve

As she walked into the familiar church, Cecilia caught her breath. There was a man standing in a middle pew and, for a second, she thought he was Maurice. Her heart started to hammer but instantly slowed. She shook her head remembering Maurice had died over twenty years earlier. This man was very young, probably the same age Maurice was when she had first met him.

Shivering with the shock, she braced herself, striding to the front of the church and taking her place in a pew in front of him. She turned slightly and swished her blue sari around her legs to sit down, making sure she caught a glimpse of him as she did so. This man was tall and handsome, with red hair, he was in uniform too. He was so like Maurice – it took her breath away. She smiled to herself. How nice it was to see someone who brought back such happy memories. Memories from a time so long ago when she was young and in love, sure that life would be a serene walk through happiness.

She thought of the times when Maurice scooped her in his strong arms and twirled her around the room as though they were romantic lovers in a novel. The times he told her she was beautiful, that he was lucky to have her as his wife. The times he kissed her, tenderly, hungrily. His gentle, attentive lovemaking, his lusty lovemaking. A much better lover than her other husbands.

And she remembered how much he had loved their children. He was such a proud father, unashamed of telling anyone who would listen.

Her throat was dry and tight, her body trembling. She kept turning subtly to see this young man, with her heart thumping and her ears full of the sound. Even though she was now in her forties, she could feel a physical attraction to him. It was making her feel excited and young again.

She realised she had turned towards him too often when he started smiling back at her. Hastily, she turned to pay attention to the service. She reminded herself that she was here to pray for Pandit's recovery. She tried her best to concentrate on the service, on the task at hand. But she couldn't.

She left the church in an embarrassed hurry at the end of Mass, looking away as she passed him in the aisle, nearly running into a donkey that was resting in the shadow of the church door.

She heard fast steps in the dry dust behind her. Looking around, she saw he was catching up with her. He was wearing a kilt, she noticed. It must have been heavy but it didn't stop him from moving quickly in the midday heat.

As he reached her shoulder, he said, 'You are beautiful.' Cecilia could feel again her blood pulsing in her ears as her heart pounded hard in her chest. But she carried on walking at the same pace.

He was walking bedside her now. 'You are beautiful,' he repeated.

Continuing to walk and without looking at him, she replied, 'I am old enough to be your mother.'

'So,' he retorted, 'doesn't stop you being beautiful.'

After a pause he said, 'My name is Thomas Weightman. I am a Private in the Black Watch.' He held out his hand.

Cecilia felt a little stab of disappointment – he wasn't Maurice after all – even though she knew it was a ridiculous thought. Without breaking step, she shook his hand, 'Cecilia New. Law Advocate.'

He smiled – a wide open smile that made him look even more handsome. 'So, you are beautiful and intelligent.'

Cecilia felt her heart ache for Maurice – this young man was even using his words.

'May we go for a walk one day?' he asked. Then added, 'Soon.'

She thought about young women of his age. Their firm bodies unmottled by age, unstretched by childbearing. Why would he be interested in her? It was improbable.

Then she thought of Maurice. She wondered if he had sent her this young man to make her happy again. Life had been so hard, perhaps she should have a little diversion. She decided to give him a little encouragement.

'That is a nice idea, but I do not live in Quetta, I am traveling home to Multan this afternoon.'

A disappointed shadow fell across his face, 'But will you come back again?'

'Yes, I work both here and in Multan.'

'Will you be back soon?'

'I don't know. I expect so. I am here quite often.'

'Please, if I give you my name and address will you write to me and let me know when you will be here again.'

She rummaged in her bag for a pen and paper and gave them to him. He leaned on a nearby tree stump, scribbled on the paper, then handed it back to her. She glanced at it. His address was near her office. She put the paper into her bag and smiled at him, 'I will write. But I have to leave now and pack my bags.'

'Please don't forget me,' he pleaded, 'You are the most beautiful woman I have ever seen. I want to get to know you better. Please write.'

She nodded, not wanting to appear too eager. 'Goodbye.'

She turned away and noticed that her body felt lighter and seemed to want to skip. She forced it to a slow and measured step in case he was looking.

She smiled to herself the whole of the journey back to Multan. She was excited that this handsome young man was paying court to her. She felt more boosted than she had for years. Yes, he was younger than some of her children. Certainly younger than Richard and John and possibly younger than Bridget would be now, if she had lived. She decided to flirt with him, for sheer fun.

More good news came in when she was back in the office. A small article in the newspaper noted that Cornelia Sorabji had become a member of Lincoln's Inn in London. The first Indian woman to do so. Her old acquaintance had been successful in her campaign.

An even smaller article noted the passing of Pandita Ramabai, a social activist promoting the rights of women. The first woman to be given the title "Pandita". Cecilia had heard of her work. She knew that Pandita and Cornelia worked together on occasion. She felt a sadness but also a gladness that Pandita's work had left a legacy of improvement for women.

Another pamphlet told her Regina Guha had also died recently before she could complete her struggle for a woman's right to practise law in India. There was a chance that her legacy would be upheld – the courts were still debating it. Their Chambers were still involved in the drafting and passage through the courts but she had not kept in contact with Regina herself. She regretted that now. Cecilia was determined to become a fully qualified barrister practising in India, under

Indian law. In that way, she could honour Regina and all her hard work.

In August, Christopher Michael O'Connor, was born. Cecilia was delighted to have a grandchild. The prospect of playing with him, looking after him yet not having everyday responsibility for him, was enticing. She stayed with Gertie and her husband for some weeks. Once Gertie was back to form, Cecilia decided to go back to Quetta.

She told herself that she needed to talk over a number of cases with Pandit and to check on his health. But the real reason was that she wanted to see Thomas. She wrote to him, as she had promised, asking him to meet her outside her office the day after she arrived. Her heart was beating fast as she posted the letter, hoping he would not have forgotten his offer to take her for a walk. Or even his somewhat unbelievable protestations that she was the most beautiful woman he had ever seen.

To her surprise and pleasure, the day after she arrived in Quetta, Thomas was waiting on the veranda of her office as she left work. Her heart jumped as he reminded her of Maurice all over again, tall and handsome with an easy manner.

He stubbed his cigarette into the sandy ground and smiled, 'Well, it's been a long time. You are even more beautiful than I remember.'

'Thank you, Maur…' she stopped herself in time.

He didn't seem to notice, 'Are you still able to walk out with me? I am sure I am in a queue of men for your attention. I hope that you will favour me.'

What a load of rubbish he is talking, she thought. But she said, 'I have many suitors, Mr Weightman, but today I am choosing you for a walk in the park.'

He tipped his head, 'I am flattered, Mrs New. Truly I am.'

They fell into step, the leafy boulevard built by the British soon giving way to the crowded noisy streets created by the Indians. The small park was about ten minutes' walk away and they chatted amicably as they strolled. She was aware passers-by would think they were mother and son, but she didn't care.

He told her about himself. He was an only child, his father lived in the UK. His mother had died very suddenly when he was about six-years-old, so he barely remembered her. He was stationed in Quetta and really enjoyed life in India. He went on, 'But I enjoy it a lot more now I have met you.'

She just about stopped herself from bursting into laughter. He must assume that I am really daft, she thought, if he thinks I believe what he is saying. But it was fun and she was enjoying the game.

'Don't be silly. I am in my mid-forties. How old are you?'

'I am twenty-one,' he replied with an air of defiance, 'any-way, age is just a number.'

'I have children older than you.'

'So?'

'I am too old for your flirting.'

'No, you are not. I am not flirting either, I am telling you what I see. I see a beautiful woman.'

She smiled. 'You are very persistent.'

'I want to get to know you better, that's all.'

'Well, I am enjoying your company. You make me laugh with your comments.'

'I don't want you to laugh, I want you to believe me.'

She felt a slight stab of panic that she might have offended him and turned him off her. She did not want to do that – she was having too much fun.

'Sorry – I didn't mean to offend you. Come, sit on this bench in the shade and let's talk a little more.'

He was mollified. They sat together, chatting long into the evening. As the light fell, the noises of the animals grew louder and the noises of the children grew softer. They did not notice, they were so engrossed. They talked about general things, nothing of any importance, but everything was important.

During the conversation, she decided she wanted to continue to see this young man, but she did not know of his intentions towards her. Surely, he didn't want a physical relationship? He could have that with girls of his age. He probably just wanted to flirt with her to practise.

When she felt it was time to go, she stood up and dusted off her sari. 'I have to get back now. I need to be at work in the morning, then I am returning to Multan in the afternoon.'

'A busy lady indeed. Let me walk you home.'

'I am staying with friends nearby, there is no need.'

'Nevertheless, I will walk you back and then I can enjoy your company for a little longer.'

He lit a cigarette as they strolled out of the park into the balmy Indian night. 'When will I see you again?'

'I will be back again soon. Pandit's health is not good, so I need to be here quite often.'

'Well, I am sorry that he is not keeping good health. But I am glad, if it brings you back to Quetta.'

Though he was voicing her secret thoughts, she said nothing.

'I am not sure when exactly. I need to be in Multan for a while, then I am going to Howrah.'

'Howrah? That is a long way away. The opposite direction from here. Why are you going there?'

'My son is getting married.' She watched him for his reaction but the gathering darkness made it difficult to see any expression.

'Your son?' I know you said you had children older than me, but I didn't really believe you.'

'Richard is twenty-six. A few years older than you, indeed. He has been working on the railway at Howrah for many years. He met his intended there.'

'I hope one day I will meet him. And his wife. Please write to me while you are away. I will miss you. You are excellent company.'

He took her hand and bent down to kiss it gently. 'I very much hope to see you again.'

She watched him go, his jaunty step propelling him. He didn't look back.

She went into her lodgings with a smile. She knew she was in charge in this relationship. He was fun, definitely an enjoyable diversion from real life.

At work the next day, Pandit told her that he had received a letter from the British about their paper. 'They said there are moves for independence throughout the Empire. The issue would need to be resolved consistently. It will not be quick or easy to make any legislation. Every colony would need to have a say in the matter and negotiations could take years.'

'Well, we should keep up the pressure and ask them periodically about progress.'

'Mrs New, this is why I am happy to leave the practice to you – you are a woman of sound judgement and inspiring vision.'

'I do not want to lose you, Pandit.'

He smiled, 'As my illness gets worse, Mrs New, so I will hand over more work to you. That seems to me the best way, a gradual process.'

Her eyes filled as she said, 'You are the wise one, Pandit, I am honoured to know you and to work for you.'

Richard's wedding was a lovely occasion. All the family managed to make it to Howrah and she was enveloped in her love for them all. She still ached for her lost children. And today especially for Maurice on this, the wedding day of their firstborn. All the memories of Richard's birth came flooding back, she was feeling overwhelmed by the emotions.

Richard's bride, Mary, wore a delicate white dress with pink shoes and a small veil. She seemed a lovely girl, pretty and radiant in her bridal love. Richard looked at her as if he adored her, it was a look that his father had often given Cecilia. She knew that her firstborn, child of love, would be a loving husband. And father, when the time came.

Back in Multan, she received a letter from Thomas, telling her he was being deployed to Britain for some months, to help build the railway there. She was disappointed. Somewhat disproportionately, she thought. They had only had two walks, nothing else. He had brightened her life with his lively manner and flirtatious ways. She realised she was going to miss him, more than she should. He ended the letter by saying he would try to get back to India as soon as possible as he was keen to see her again. She folded it and put it in her desk for safe keeping. She would write a friendly letter to him soon, she decided. But not yet.

Some months later, a telegram arrived in the Multan office. She tore it open and read:

Pandit very ill. Come as soon as possible.

Cecilia hastily packed some clothes and took the next train to Quetta. She hurried to the office as soon as she alighted. Pandit lived above it with a housekeeper to see to his domestic needs. Up until now, she had never entered his home.

His housekeeper, Mandeep, nodded in recognition and gestured her in. Cecilia glanced around. There were photos of

Pandit's late wife and daughter on the walls everywhere. She knew their deaths were the saddest event in his life. Here was the evidence.

Pandit was, to her surprise, sitting in an armchair in the lounge, with a small table next to him. Photos of his wife and daughter were on the table too, along with a glass of water.

He looked frail and his whole body had shrunk since she had last seen him. A blanket over his lap looked as if it were covering nothing, as if there were no legs underneath. His arms were fleshless bones. She was shocked at the sight of him, wondering why he was not in bed.

He saw the look on her face and knew exactly what she was thinking. He fought to get each word out. His raspy voice creating hesitations between each word, she had to lean close to his lips to hear his words. 'I... will... not... lie... down... to... die... Mrs... New. That... is... not... the... way... I... want... to... meet... my... wife... and... daughter.'

She knelt beside his chair and laid her hand over his, 'What can I do to help you, Pandit?'

His breath was shallow and the effort he put into talking was painful to see.

'Carry... on... our... work... Mrs... New. The... practice... is... yours... now.'

'Oh, Pandit, I don't want you to die. I love you. But thank you. Thank you.'

'Thank... you... Mrs... New. You... have... been... a... daughter... to... me. Thank... you.' A solitary tear ran down his sallow cheek.

His head fell suddenly onto his shoulder as his eyes closed. He was sleeping, taking shallow, hoarse breaths. She kissed his papery hand, its mottled thin skin stretched over large veins. He stirred gently in sleep as if he knew she was with him. She stayed with him until his breathing deepened and he seemed more at peace. Mandeep tucked the blanket around him. Cecilia spoke to her in Urdu asking when the doctor had visited last. Mandeep said he had been that morning. The doctor had said Pandit would die in the next few days.

Cecilia saw Mandeep's eyes fill with tears. She felt united with Mandeep, freed in this moment from the caste system, by their love for this kind and gentle man. She broke convention, hugging the sad housekeeper tight, letting her cry on her shoulder for what seemed like hours. Her own tears rolled too.

They were with him, each holding a hand as he passed away three days later. He smiled as he breathed his last. A smile that told them he was reunited with his wife and daughter. He was at peace. They hugged each other again, sad that he had gone but relieved that his suffering was over.

There was a lot to do after Pandit's death. The administration involved in taking over the Chambers was time-consuming. Cecilia also wanted to inform many other people of his passing. People he had helped or supported, people who had debated with him and were inspired by his ideas. She wanted him to have the recognition and respect he deserved. She wrote to everyone who had come into their office to discuss the issues of the day: Jinnah, Gandhi, the Sorabjis, Annie Besant and Eardley Norton. They all wrote back with warm words but Norton's letter also noted:

> I remember Pandit was keen for women to have equal rights, especially to practise law. Regina Guha was impressed by him. It is sad that she died before the Act was passed earlier this year. Rest assured, her work means that you can work freely as a lawyer now.

She read the letter with increasing excitement. The passing of the legislation had escaped her. She usually picked up that type of news from pamphlets. She had not had the time to read any of them lately. She was free to lead the Chambers openly, to blaze a trail for women now and in the future. She could feel the burden of secrecy lift from her shoulders as excitement coursed through her body. Life would be so much easier now.

She replied to all the letters, telling all these important people that she was now leading the practice and continuing Pandit's work. Her letters were clear she would be supporting a peaceful transition to self-rule and seeking clarification on the rights of mixed-race people. In each letter she included a summary of her document and asking them to support the rights of Anglo-Indians in all their discussions. The work was continuing the way Pandit had wanted.

She wrote to Thomas in England telling him the news:

> I will run both branches of Chambers and travel more often between Multan and Quetta. Pandit has also left me his houses in both towns so it will make life even more easy and more financially comfortable.

She didn't know if Thomas received her letters, he had never written back in the past.

He turned up, unexpectedly, at the Multan branch a few weeks later. He opened her office door with a flourish and a big smile, 'Hello, I am back.'

She jumped, 'I didn't know. You didn't write or anything.'

He lightly touched her arm, 'I didn't get a chance to write. The Regiment just sent me back with no notice. But I was happy about it as I knew I would see you.'

Still a charmer, she thought to herself. But her heart was beating fast. She had forgotten how much she was attracted to him, how he looked so much like Maurice. She quickly reminded herself that she was in her late forties and he was only in his early twenties.

He looked around the office, 'So, all this is yours, now that your Pandit has died.'

She nodded, 'It is such a relief to be in charge and to be able to act openly. But I would rather he were alive.'

'Why?'

'Because he was a wise man and always kind to me.'

Thomas shrugged, 'He was old. And now you have his offices, you are rich. And still beautiful.'

She smiled a small smile, 'Well, life is a little easier now, that is for sure.'

'I would like us to step out together. I want to spend time with you.'

'You are very young. Too young for me.'

'Age is nothing. Irrelevant, as I said before. Anyway, I am nearly twenty-three.'

She laughed. 'You are far too young. I am nearly forty-eight.'

He laughed too, 'I am old enough to see your beauty and your kindness.'

'My children will not be happy.'

'Why not?'

'They won't like you being so young. Besides, people in the town will talk. I will be the subject of gossip.'

'So?'

'I have been gossiped about often in the past. It wasn't pleasant.'

'I understand. We could just start stepping out in private. Where no one knows us.'

She sighed, 'I don't know, I don't know. That is sneaking about. I did enough of that when I was training.'

'We can always stay at home. In your houses, here and Multan.'

'That is sneaky too. You are so young, you think it will be easy. I am old enough to know things are never easy.'

'Look,' he said firmly, 'I do understand. I want to be with you. But you must decide what you want.' He leaned in kissing her lightly on the lips, sending quivers through her body. He whispered, 'You know where I am.'

He left.

On the journey to Multan later that day, she thought about what she would do. She knew he was lying. She didn't know what his motive was, but she decided she didn't really care. If he wanted her money, he wouldn't get it. After Christopher had stolen her cash, all those years ago, she had opened an account with the Punjabi National Bank. She was the first woman to open an account in her own name. If money were his motive, he would not be successful.

He was young and attractive, fine company with an easy manner and a quick wit. He looked so like Maurice. She was lonely, still bearing the responsibility of raising young children, as she had done every day for the past twenty-eight years. And bearing the weight of grief and her children's resentment. In addition, her workload was heavier than ever.

She needed some fun, she decided. How many years was it since she had danced? Since she had enjoyed the company of a man? Since she felt her burden lightened? It was time for a change. He was surely using her while he was in India, there were so few women that soldiers could meet here. She assumed he would go back to Britain and find himself a wife eventually. She was fine with that. She would toy with him, have a discreet liaison. They would part ways amicably. Both parties satisfied. She would play along and pretend that she believed all his protestations, letting the game unfold. It was a thrilling prospect.

She wrote to him and asked him to meet her the next time she was in Quetta. She told him she would like to spend more time with him. His reply came back quickly, she realised he must have written it straight away:

> I miss you so much. I cannot wait to see you again and spend more time with you. There is no other woman I would rather be with. I will meet you from the train at Quetta station.

True to his word, he was waiting at the station when her train pulled in. He spotted her quickly through the noisy crowds of people, some dragging multiple suitcases or herding animals, some doing both. Above the noisy, dusty chaos, she heard him call her name, 'Cecilia, Cecilia, over here.'

And there he was. The crowds and noise fell away. She could only see him, standing there alone. It was as if Maurice had come back to her. She found herself running towards him. Reaching him she hurled herself into his arms. He staggered, taken aback by the momentum. She suddenly noticed every-one around them was looking at them and smiling, touched by their reunion.

A Sikh woman in a shimmering orange shalwar kameez said, 'It must be lovely to see your son again.'

They jumped apart, Cecilia adjusting her burgundy sari in embarrassment. Recovering quickly, she smiled and replied, 'Yes, it is lovely thank you.'

The crowd smiled benignly at them. Thomas reached for her bag. They walked away quickly – slightly apart from each other.

In the house, Thomas put down her bag. 'Well, that was a greeting.'

She laughed, 'I forgot myself, I was so pleased to see you.'

He laughed too, 'Well, I hope that means you like me.'

'Yes, I do,' she replied watching him carefully for his reaction as she said, 'you are good company and you make me feel young again.'

He moved towards her and took her in his arms, 'I have been looking for a woman like you all my life'.

'This old?'

'I have never been interested in girls my age. They are silly with empty heads.'

'I think we should just spend some time together and see what happens. We cannot be outside together easily. Did you see the way people looked at us at the station? That woman thought we were mother and son.'

He laughed loud and long, 'May I take you to bed and prove that we are not?'

'You may. Why would we spend time outside anyway?'

'Indeed. We have all we need here. Just you and me.'

She was surprised to learn that she was his first lover. He was more nervous than she had anticipated but was eager to learn and to please her. She enjoyed teaching him and they spent a satisfying day enjoying each other's bodies. After, as they lay in each other's arms, dozing happily, she marvelled that, at last, she had found a lover eager to experiment and was uninhibited in his efforts.

She heard him sigh and sat up to look at him.

'Are you alright?'

'You make me feel amazing,' he said, 'I had no idea it could be so good.'

'Well, there is a lot more we can do, you know. A lot more fun in store.'

He sat up suddenly. 'You can't get pregnant, can you?'

'No, no. I have been barren for years. Thank goodness. I have been pregnant enough.'

'I only want you – not children.'

'Well, I still have two young children I am bringing up. They won't make any difference to us.'

'Why not?'

'Because we can keep our relationship in Quetta. No need to go to Multan. They won't need to meet you.'

He looked crushed, 'But I love you. I want to meet them.'

'Let's just enjoy this for now. Think about that later.'

He didn't protest as she kissed him, using her expert fingers to excite him once again.

He left to get back to the barracks early the next morning. She went downstairs to work. She found her thoughts reverting to the day before, her mind crowded with intimate memories. She had never been so physically satisfied, not even with Maurice. Then she had been so young and inexperienced. Their relationship had been short, there was no time to grow to understand each other's needs or proclivities. Sex with Christopher was something she feared. George was a kinder lover than Christopher, but he was dull with it, leaving her unsatisfied. Thomas was so inexperienced, she could teach him to love her in ways she had always dreamed of and never dared to vocalise before. He was eager and not shocked by any of her requests. In return she did things for him that she had never done for her husbands. And enjoyed them too. She smiled and smiled. His future wife would be thankful for the experience she was giving him now.

He turned up that evening, staggering under the weight of a large box, a cigarette tilting at the corner of his mouth.

'What's in there?' she asked as he set it down on the table with a bump.

'It is called a gramophone. Have you heard of them?'

'I think so – it plays music, doesn't it?'

He took it out of the box gingerly, 'Yes, it does. I hope I didn't break it when I put it down.'

She watched as he fixed it together, 'Where did you get it from?'

'It belongs to the Regiment. They've let me borrow it.'

'How does it work?'

He lifted out a large black disc and twirled it in his hands, 'It is on this. The gramophone plays it with a needle. The music is in these grooves, see?'

She didn't see how it could work. She watched as he carefully put the record in the middle of the machine, wound up the handle and placed the needle arm on the edge of the disc while it spun around. Music rose up and filled the air.

'It's an American called Duke Ellington. A new style of music called jazz,' he grinned at her, 'it is music for dancing.' With that, he grabbed her by the waist and swung her around. 'Dance with me, my Cecilia.'

They danced around the kitchen, the music weaving its sound into the room, leading them in their moves. Cecilia felt near to tears, she had forgotten what it was like to dance. To dance for the sake of dancing. Losing herself in dance was so invigorating, yet she had not done it in years.

Once they had danced to the record three or four times, they sat down exhausted and happy.

'Thank you,' she puffed.

'You told me that you loved dancing. We cannot go to dances. So, I brought the dancing to you.'

She kissed him. 'I really appreciate it.'

Suddenly, he was on one knee, looking up at her with pleading eyes. 'I love you Cecilia. Will you marry me?'

She laughed loudly, she couldn't help it. 'That is a good joke, Thomas. Very funny.'

His face fell, 'I wasn't joking. I love you. You are everything I want in a woman. You are beautiful kind and clever. I want to be with you forever.'

'It is a silly idea, Thomas. I am so much older than you. I want us to enjoy each other and you to go back to Britain and find yourself a wife.' She smiled, 'A grateful wife.'

He stood up, 'Look, I don't want other girls, I want you. I don't want to sneak about. I love you and am proud to be with you. I want you to be a proper part of my life. I want to be a proper part of your life. I want us to be married and proud.'

She could see his point of view. She loved to be with him too. They enjoyed each other's company and it *was* wrong to stay inside just because of gossip.

'Let me think about it,' she said, kissing him again and whispering in his ear, 'In the meantime, let's go to bed.'

After Thomas had left to go back to the barracks, she thought about his proposal.

In some ways it was ridiculous, she was so much older than him. But then, in other ways, they made each other happy. And wasn't that the point of a marriage? It was about time she had some happiness. She thought how society accepted men who married women a lot younger than themselves. Even her dear Papa had taken a much younger woman as his second wife, no-one thought it was odd. It was so unfair that women had to live by different standards. The notion of unfairness grew in her mind, as it once again reared itself in her life.

The dawn of the next day heralded her decision. She had challenged conventions all her life, why stop now? She had Richard, her first born, before she married. She had become a lawyer and lived as a widow. She would defy convention again.

Yes, she would marry Thomas. They would be in public together as man and wife, showing their happiness to all. Gossip and social conventions would not come first, she decided. She had always carried the weight of gossip, why should she stop now?

As soon as Thomas walked through the door that evening, she said, 'Yes, I will marry you, I accept your proposal.'

He twirled her around the kitchen in excitement, 'I am so happy, I love you, I love you.'

She laughed, and kissed him thoroughly. 'Let's go to bed and celebrate.'

And they did.

Afterwards, Thomas lit a cigarette and smoked his way through planning the wedding. 'We will need to have the banns read. We need to go to the church to organise that.'

'Well, tomorrow's Saturday and we could go then.'

'I can get leave at the end of the year. We can marry then.' He checked his diary. 'If the banns are read starting from Sunday, we can get married on New Year's Eve. I think the Regiment will let me do that. I need to check first, though.'

'That way we can start 1925 as husband and wife,' she said, stroking his arm. 'I can't do much to organise it as I have to go back to Multan tomorrow and be there for a few weeks.' She moved her fingers down his body. He kissed her hungrily; they celebrated again.

Chapter Thirteen

When she was back in the Multan office, there was a call from John.

'I am getting married!' he shouted, full of joy. 'In December!'

She stopped herself from saying, so am I, and replied, 'Well that is happy news, bette. What is your wife-to-be's name?'

'Ethel. Ethel James. She is so beautiful, Mama. She is fourteen and lives in Santragachi with her family. We are getting married in Howrah.'

'Have you set the date yet?'

'Of course, of course. I am so excited. It is 6 December. You will be there, Mama, won't you? With Joseph and George? I am inviting everyone.'

'Of course, I will be there,' as she hurriedly wrote down the details. 'I will bring them too.' She was relieved the date didn't clash with the day of her wedding to Thomas.

'I can't wait for you to meet Ethel, Mama.' John carried on, 'I am sure you will love her as much as I do.'

'I can't wait either, bette. We will be with you then.'

She put the phone down. That would be four of her children grown up and married. With Helen in the convent, there was only Michael and Alfie left of the older ones to settle down. She was sure it would not take long.

Thomas was writing to her with updates. He confirmed he had booked the Catholic Church in Multan for 31 December. She smiled at the prospect of marrying him and shocking everyone.

Rupali helped her pack for the wedding trip. She watched as the ayah set about sorting out their clothes. In the seventeen years or so that she had been with the family, Rupali had grown stockier and plainer but still had her kind, placid personality. She never complained and always worked with great diligence. The children all loved her. Rupali was so loyal to them, it moved Cecilia's heart. She remembered how she had chosen her in a hurry, for her sweet nature and frumpy looks and, in all honesty, her immediate availability. She had proved to be a huge asset. She had seen Cecilia through all the baby deaths and looked after all the additions to the family with gentleness and love.

Cecilia felt moved to ask her, 'Do you not want to get married and have children of your own? Why do you stay with us?'

Rupali looked startled at being asked a personal question, 'Oh Memsa'ab. I could never marry, look at me. No man would have me.' She gestured to her large body.

Cecilia squirmed as she thought about a reply. It was true Rupali's unprepossessing presence would not make her a suitable match for most men. But she didn't want to say anything to hurt this lovely woman. She needed to say something positive and truthful.

'You are loving and kind, Rupali. You will be a lovely wife and mother, with those qualities.'

'I am too old now, Memsa'ab,' she replied, more to herself. Then her face brightened. She smiled, showing a beauty that few people would ever see, 'But I love you – and your family. The children are precious to me.'

Cecilia touched Rupali's arm gently, 'We love you too. All the children love you. When we go to the wedding, I want you to enjoy it as a guest. Not as a servant. Please.'

'Thank you, Memsa'ab. Thank you so much. I will.'

As they were about to leave, followed by the boys carrying their bags, there was a knock. Cecilia opened the door. She gasped as she saw Thomas leaning on the doorframe, smoking a cigarette. He was grinning.

'What are you doing here?' she asked, surprised, 'You should be in Quetta.'

'I had a few days off. I was missing you. I thought I'd come and see you.'

Her heart started beating fast, desire coursing through her body, he had such an effect on her.

Cecilia turned to Rupali. 'Please could you take the boys into the yard and wait for us there.' She ignored their curious looks and nodded to Thomas, 'You had better come in.'

He followed her into the kitchen.

She turned to him and whispered, 'You can't be here.'

'Why not?'

'You just can't. No one knows about you and we are just going to leave for my son's wedding in Howrah.'

'Then I will come with you. I am your fiancé, after all.'

'No! That would be impossible.'

'Why?'

'I haven't told them about us.'

'I don't understand.'

'They will think you want me for my money,' she paused, 'not that I have much money.'

He hesitated, just a little, but long enough for her to notice. 'I know you have money – I am not a fool. You have two houses and a law practice. I know you will leave them to your children. Even if we marry, you should still leave it all to them.'

'That is my plan. Everything will go to my children equally. My will is clear. I will not change it even after we get married.'

He kissed her and changed the subject, 'I have missed you so much. And I want you. Now.' His finger reached under her choli.

She pushed him back gently, 'We can't, the children are in the yard. They might hear us.'

'We can be quick and quiet. We can lean against the table.'

She had missed him so much. She was yearning for his body, so she gave in to their mutual desire. It was urgent and satisfying. With the added edge of the children and Rupali nearby, it felt daring and risky too. So, all in all, she thought afterwards, it was highly enjoyable.

She smoothed her hair back into place and said, 'You can come with us. I cannot tell my family that you are my fiancé yet. I need more time to think about how I break it to them. We must say we are friends.'

He shrugged, 'If that is the only way we can be together, then I shall come. I may have to return to Quetta before you leave Howrah anyway. I will have things to do for our wedding.'

'If you leave earlier than me, we will allay suspicion.'

The wedding was both simple and joyful. She saw the happiness that infused John and his pretty young bride and focused on it to control the sadness that always threatened to engulf her on family occasions. She was also excited to be in the proximity of her young fiancé, hugging the delicious secret of their forthcoming nuptials to herself.

At the wedding breakfast, she introduced Thomas to her older children, telling them he was a friend. They all seemed curious, but were too preoccupied with their own socialising to say much. Thomas was smiling and chatting to them all, handing around his issue of cigarettes, which were gratefully received.

A little later, she overheard a conversation between Richard and John, 'So, who is he?' asked Richard, 'Why would Mama have such a young friend? Surely, they have nothing in common? He must be thirty years younger than she is.'

'You aren't suggesting he is her beau, are you? That's ridiculous.'

Richard laughed, 'No, no, she is old enough to be his mother, or even grandmother. I expect he wants her money, to charm it out of her.'

'Mama is not stupid. She would know if he was just wanting her for her money.'

'Yes, but she is lonely. And there's no fool like an old fool.'

'You are right there, for sure.'

They both laughed and went away, puffing on Thomas's cigarettes. Their words pierced her heart. Her beloved sons, calling her an old fool. She had no idea they thought so little of her. After all the years she put into bringing them up and the sacrifices she had made for them.

'Mama.' She turned to see Michael walking towards her. She smiled at him.

'Mama,' he said again, 'I have some news for you.'

'Oh?'

'Yes, I am going to Dublin next week.'

'Dublin? Why? How long for?'

'I want to meet our family there, Mama. And look for a wife.'

Another child of hers leaving, making his own way in life. A good thing, she knew, but a hard reality for her to face. 'Will you come back?'

'If I find a wife and she wants to come here, I will.'

'What about Alfie? You are living with him now. He will be alone.'

'Alfie is bad tempered and selfish. I will be glad to get away from him. The railway will find someone else to share his bungalow, I am sure.'

'I want you to be happy,' she sighed, 'I want all my children to be happy. I will miss you so much.' She hugged him hard.

Michael seemed pleased she had not made a fuss and sauntered away.

She watched them all, reflecting that many things in her life had not turned out the way she expected. She had worked so hard for her children, to give them security and improve their life chances. But they didn't appreciate it. Her girls resented that she worked so hard, her older boys thought she was a fool. Michael was leaving for Ireland without another thought. And Alfie was so unpleasant and selfish, he was a disappointment, even though she loved him.

She watched her younger sons running around and playing together. She wondered what they would be like when they grew up. They were such affable boys, with friendly personalities. Her experience told her that they may not always be that way.

It made her want to be with Thomas all the more. She needed to live life for herself now. Marrying Thomas would be the first step. She was not worried about the age difference. She was not a lonely old fool either. Her money was safe in the bank. Thomas would not have access to it. She had made sure of that. They were a good match. She would scandalise everyone, that was an excellent reason for marrying him.

Thomas moved towards her, away from talking to Cissy's husband. Keeping his distance, he said, 'You have an interesting family. I enjoyed meeting them. But I have to return to Quetta now.'

308

She nodded, restraining herself from touching him. She said, loud enough for those nearby to hear, 'Goodbye. Have a safe journey back to Quetta. I will see you there again at some stage, I expect.' She knew her tone was false. She hoped it sounded genuine to others. Thomas turned on his heel, working his way around his future family, saying goodbye and making it clear he was going to Quetta alone and not back to Multan with Cecilia.

After he left, Cissy walked up to her, 'Mama. Tell me the truth. Who is this Thomas and why did you bring him to the wedding? He is not a family member, after all.' Her daughter's brown eyes were soft with sympathy. Cecilia felt moved enough to bring Cissy into her confidence. But not yet.

'I will tell you tomorrow. I have something to ask of you as well. But now is not the time. I am leaving for Multan with Rupali and the boys after breakfast. I will talk to you before I go.'

Cissy raised her eyebrows, creasing her beautiful face, 'Very well, Mama. I will wait until the morning. It is all very curious.'

Cecilia laughed. 'The wait will be worth it, I promise.'

The next day, as Rupali helped the boys to pack, Cecilia asked Cissy to walk to the fruit stall with her, 'To get some fruit for the train journey home,' she explained to the others.

Together, mother and daughter strolled in peaceful unison through Howrah's grimy, noisy streets. The sounds of trains pulling in and out of the large station nearby added to the cries of the animals, the calls of the street sellers and the shouts of the children. Cecilia leaned in closer to Cissy, 'What I am about to tell you is a big secret. You must not tell anyone until I say. You must promise me.'

'Of course, Mama, I promise.' Cissy's eyes were alight with excitement.

'My news is that I am going marry Thomas on 31 December.'

Cissy stopped. 'No, no. He is so much younger than you.'

'He is 25 years younger than me. But I do not care. He loves me. If I were a man and he was a woman, no one would say anything.'

'That's true, Mama, I suppose,' Cissy conceded, 'but how do you know his intentions are true. He may be after your money.'

'Of course, I have thought of that. I am not a fool. My money is safe in the Punjabi National Bank. Many years ago, your father stole from me. I have not kept money in the house since then. I learnt my lesson.'

'Papa stole your money? Do you mean papa George? Or Christopher?'

'Your real Papa, Christopher. He was a mean man. He drank too much. He hit me and stole from me. I had so little money, I couldn't pay for a doctor when you all were unwell. It was not a happy time.'

'Oh Mama, I didn't know. You have never said.'

'It was many years ago, when you were a baby. He was your Papa. I did not want you to think ill of him.'

'Oh, it must have been hard for you.'

'Many times, Cissy. Many times.'

'I am starting to understand a little more now that I am married myself.'

'Are you happy, Cissy?'

'Oh, yes Mama. But I am just learning that life is complicated. If you are happy with Thomas, you must marry him, I think. I was just a little shocked, I suppose.'

Cecilia smiled at her, 'Thank you, bette. It means a lot to me.'

They walked on, in renewed harmony.

'I said I wanted to ask something of you,' Cecilia spoke after a pause.

'You did. What is it, Mama?'

'I would like your husband to be my witness at the wedding. And you to be my attendant.'

'Yes we will.' Cissy smiled, 'Of course we will support you, Mama. You have always supported us.'

'But you mustn't tell anyone, remember? After the wedding, I will tell them all myself. Then they can't object. It will be done.'

Cissy laughed, 'Your secret is safe with me. You are incorrigible, Mama.'

'Well, it is easier to apologise after doing something than to ask for permission. I think that is advice to heed for most of life.'

'I will not forget that, Mama. Now, it is time to get the fruit and get home before everyone wonders where we are.'

'Very well. I will see you both at the Church of the Holy Rosary in Quetta on 31 December at 3 o'clock. It is where George was christened.' She didn't say it was also where Victoria's funeral was held. She did not want them to be reminded of that terrible time.

Chapter Fourteen

The wedding took place during a normal Mass, so there were a number of congregation members attending. The wedding party itself was small. Only Thomas's witness Percy Wales, along with Cissy and Christopher, were there. Of course, Cissy and Christopher brought their delightful little two-year-old daughter, Brigit Cecilia. Cecilia smiled at having little Brigit with them. It was poignant, as her own Bridget had never attended a family event. It helped blot out the memory of her cradling Victoria's dead body in the front pew of this very church, all those years ago.

Thomas and Percy wore their dress uniforms. They both looked handsome and smart in their kilts. Their jackets had epaulettes with brass buttons shined to perfection. Cecilia wore a dropped waist floral dress in sapphire blue. The colour had always suited her and it was not one she had worn in her previous outings as a bride. Cissy and Christopher were smart in their best Sunday clothes and little Brigit was dressed in a white party dress with a red ribbon at the waist.

Cecilia and Thomas pledged their vows, focusing on each other intently. They ignored the curious glances from the congregation, who were clearly aghast at their age difference. Cecilia kept thinking back to the day she had married Maurice. Thomas was so like him, it was as if she could start life over again. With Maurice by her side, as he should have been.

As the Mass was ending and Father Meyer was giving the blessing, they heard a shout from the back of the church. Everyone turned.

Alfie was standing in the aisle, a look of fury on his face. He was dishevelled, his clothes awry, stubble on his chin.

Cecilia looked at Cissy, a look that said, 'What is he doing here?'

Cissy shrugged.

'Mama,' Alfie shouted, 'Do not marry him! I forbid you. He is a scoundrel.'

He started to make his way down the aisle but his progress was slow. He was staggering and clearly drunk.

The congregation gasped with a frisson of excitement and expectation. This wedding, already a talking point, had become even more interesting. The priest stood still in shock. Only Thomas and Percy were quick to react. They ran towards Alfie, kilts flying backwards in their wake. They each grabbed one of his arms to frogmarch him out of the church. But Alfie, emboldened by drink, youth and indignance, fought back. He kicked, pushed and wriggled so much that Percy was compelled to deliver a sharp uppercut to his chin. Alfie collapsed to the floor. The congregation gasped in unison, enthralled at the scene unfolding before them.

Cecilia suddenly decided to take charge. She ran to Alfie, who was sitting up now, shaking his head as if there were a bee buzzing inside it. She bent down and hissed to him, 'Get up, you have to leave. Now.'

Using a pew to lean on, Alfie pulled himself up. Taking no notice of Cecilia, he stood in front of Thomas and raised his fist, 'You,' he shouted again, 'get your hands off my mother.'

'Too late for that,' Thomas smiled. The congregation gasped again, thrilled, as they realised the implication of his comment.

313

In a move misjudged by his drunkenness, Alfie roared and lunged at Thomas, arms flailing. Thomas stepped aside. Alfie fell at his feet in a crumpled heap, too stunned to be embarrassed. Thomas and Percy picked him up and dragged him out, Cecilia and Cissy following them.

In the fresh air, Alfie started to sober up. Still aggressive, his voice threatening, he looked at Thomas and said, 'You are a scoundrel. I am pleased I stopped your wedding. You must not marry my mother.'

'You were too late. We are already married,' said Thomas through an angry smile. 'I am your father now.'

Alfie lunged again uselessly. This time Percy caught him and leant him against the church wall. 'Look boy,' he said, holding Alfie by the throat. 'Go away. This is none of your business.'

Cecilia, with a rush of protective love for her wayward son, shouted at Percy, 'Let him go.'

Alfie slid down the wall and sat against it, defeated. He hung his head between his legs and stared at the dusty ground. The little group was silent as they watched the congregation file out of the church, looking at them with curiosity and not a little regret. It was obvious the show had now ended. When everyone had left, Father Meyer walked over, his vestments clinging to him in the heat of the day.

'I am very disappointed in you all.' His voice was stern, 'That is not the way you should behave in church.' He looked at the downcast Alfie: 'Young man, your mother is entitled to do as she wishes. I agree this is an unusual wedding, but getting drunk and starting a fight in church is unacceptable.'

Alfie muttered something unintelligible, as Cecilia felt the need to smooth things over with the priest. 'I am so sorry, Father Meyer. This is something I will deal with. I apologise for interrupting Mass.'

To their surprise, Father Meyer laughed, 'Well the normal congregation were given a show today. I expect they may bring their friends to the next Mass to see if there is another episode. So, I might find the numbers will increase as a result.' He left, walking back to the church, still laughing. Cecilia breathed a sigh of relief. Thomas, Percy, Christopher and Cissy laughed too. Alfie smiled. Then Cecilia remembered something she had wanted to ask the minute she saw Alfie.

'How did you know about the wedding, Alfie?'

The sudden shot of tension between Cissy and Alfie was felt by all of them as the atmosphere changed again. 'Well?' Cecilia asked again.

Alfie replied, 'Cissy told me.'

Cissy handed Brigit to her husband, walked over to Alfie and kicked his thigh, 'Why did you say that?'

'Because it's true.'

Cissy kicked him again, harder this time, 'But I told you to keep it a secret.'

Cecilia was furious. Turning to Cissy, 'You promised to keep it a secret. You promised.'

'I was so excited, Mama. Alfie noticed. He nagged me until I told him. It was his fault, not mine.' Cissy's voice had heightened into a self-pitying whine, 'He nagged me.'

Alfie jumped up, seemingly sober and recovered, 'You told me without me asking, you liar. Anyway, it was good you did. I am sorry I didn't stop the wedding but at least I tried.' He looked at Cissy and her husband, 'Which is more than you did. This man will ruin our mother's life. I know he will.' Alfie stumbled out of the church gates. They watched as he staggered down the crowded street.

Cecilia turned to Cissy, 'You have let me down. If it weren't for little Brigit here, I am not sure whether I would see you ever again.'

315

Cissy was crying, 'He kept asking and asking until I gave in. Alfie made me do it.'

'Cissy, you must take responsibility for your own actions. Alfie is a nuisance, I grant you. But no one can make you do anything.'

Her voice still wheedled. 'But you said it is easier to apologise than ask permission. I was only doing what you told me. So, it's your fault too.'

Cecilia exasperated, angry that her wedding day had been ruined, said tightly, 'Thomas and I are going to our home now. The rest of you can do what you like.'

She grabbed her new husband's hand and led him through the church grounds. He stopped to light a cigarette, leaning on one of the brick pillars that were bookends of the metal entrance gate.

He raised his eyebrows, 'Well, we will always remember our wedding day.'

'I am sorry. I wanted to tell my children in my own time.'

Thomas touched her hand, 'Look, I didn't marry your family, thank goodness. I married you. And I want us to go home.' He smiled at her, a smile with lustful intent, 'I will show you how much I love you and why I married you, Mrs Weightman.'

'Good, but I hope you will show me more than once, Mr Weightman.'

Chapter Fifteen

Their marriage was successful, contrary to all predictions. Cecilia hugged the joy of their relationship to herself every day. They enjoyed each other's company, spending many happy hours in and out of bed. They both carried on with their work, Thomas sometimes coming to Multan with her when she was working there. She often brought Rupali and the boys with her when she worked in Quetta. He was a loving stepfather to Joseph and Christopher. His youth and vigour meant he had time and energy playing sports of all kinds with them.

They relished the scandal that accompanied them wherever they went. Telling everyone they were husband and wife then watching them react was a constant source of amusement. She and Thomas used to mimic people's reactions when they were alone at home together. It became a running joke, something they shared that no one else knew about. Their little secret.

They were in Quetta when she decided to tell Thomas that she had received a letter from Alfie.

'He's getting married in April,' she told him.

'I am surprised he has found someone who would marry him.'

'You still haven't forgiven him for what he did at our wedding, haven't you?'

'No, I haven't. More than that, he upset you. He has never appreciated you. He doesn't contact you. You are such a good mother. He chooses not to see it. I doubt he ever will.'

Sadness engulfed her heart at the truth in his words. Even so, she still felt the need to defend her son, 'He's a young man, Thomas. Being with his mother is not a priority at his age.'

'He is five years younger than me. I saw your beauty and kindness the moment I set eyes on you. It is a shame he is not mature enough. He should appreciate his mother. If my mother were still alive, I would always be in contact with her.'

'Perhaps he will change now he is getting married. He has been moved to West Ridge in Rawalpindi, so he is setting up by himself.'

'Perhaps his bride will calm him down. What did he say about her?'

'Very little. His letter was mainly about himself. Typical Alfie. But he did say her name is Sophia Fernandez. She is nineteen and from Goa.'

'Well I hope she is strong enough to put up with him. What date are they getting married?'

'It's the thirtieth.'

'I think I can take leave around then, so we can travel to-gether.'

She took a deep breath and told him, 'His letter says he doesn't want you there. Only me.'

Thomas jumped up in anger, 'That's ridiculous! I am your husband. His stepfather. I have every right to be there.'

'It is his choice.'

'It sounds as if you are supporting him. You should be loyal to me. I am your husband. He started the trouble on our wedding day. Not me.'

'But he's my son and he is getting married. I don't want to miss his wedding day.'

Thomas walked out of the house without replying. She knew, from experience, that it would not be worth following him. He would, she predicted, calm down in his own time and then propose an idea that would be a good solution.

Sure enough, he was back a few hours later with a smile and a hug for her, 'I am sorry I walked away like that. I was just cross, that's all.'

'I understand. It is silly of Alfie to hold a grudge. It's been over three years now.'

Cutting off her reply, Thomas butted in, 'I want to be with you when your son marries. It is important. I will come with you anyway. We just won't tell Alfie in advance.'

Cecilia was alarmed.

Thomas continued, 'I promise you that there will not be a scene. If things get difficult, I will leave straight away.'

'Anyway,' he grinned, 'it is better to apologise than ask permission, as you always say.'

She laughed, 'Well, if that is the only way we can do this, then let's do it. And you must keep your promise.'

'Of course, of course.'

'So, we will just join them at the service. You stay at the back while I go to the front pew, as the mother of the groom.'

'Happy to do that. I will be discreet.'

Sophia was beautiful, Cecilia thought, as she watched her walk up the aisle with her father, Joachim. In her bridal dress, she was waiflike. Her long dark hair framed her face and large brown eyes. Her little head was topped with a fashionable cloche hat. She was short with such a tiny build that she looked like a little girl playing at dressing up. She was not yet twenty, still a child really. Much like Cecilia herself had been when she had married Maurice. Back when she was naïve enough to think that loving Maurice would ensure her life would be happy for ever; back when she thought she had all the answers to life. The young think they know everything, she observed, it is only when you get older that you realise you know nothing.

Cecilia watched her son as he took his bride's hand. He looked proud and happy. Grinning and brimming with love, he kissed her. Sophia blushed and dropped her head modestly. Cecilia wondered how long it would last. Sophia seemed a docile girl and Alfie had such a difficult temperament. How would she cope with him? How long would they be happy, she wondered.

She really knew so little of Alfie her son. He had been drunk such a lot and so rarely at home that she had spent little time with him, especially over the last few years. He was almost a stranger. Although he seemed to take after his father, Christopher was at least kind and loving on occasion; Alfie didn't seem to have that capacity. She hated to admit it but Alfie wasn't a nice person. He was selfish to the point of cruelty. It was a devastating realisation for her.

She wondered why he had turned out that way. She had brought him up the same as her other children. She had loved him just as much, though he made it a challenge most days. Perhaps losing his father so early made him difficult. George was a good stepfather, although his patience with Alfie's wilful behaviour had worn thin on many occasions. Alfie tested him deliberately every day. Perhaps her absences while she was at work, or pregnant or looking after the other children had a bad impact on him. But none of the other children were like Alfie, so that couldn't be the reason. She probably would never know. It was depressing to think that she had brought up such a person, after she had put in so much effort to improve his behaviour.

She watched the bride and groom walk down the aisle. Alfie staggered slightly. Sophia gripped his arm to right him. It was clear that Alfie was drunk. She raised her eyebrows. At least Christopher waited until afterwards, she thought wryly. Alfie was so young, he had turned twenty-two just a few days earlier. To be drunk on an occasion such as this was not a good sign for his married life.

Thomas joined her at the wedding breakfast. Alfie was too busy talking to his siblings to notice, Thomas leaned into whisper, 'Too much to drink in the church, eh? And more drinking now? That poor girl. How will she deal with him?'

Cecilia shook her head sadly, saying nothing.

'It seems that your son is the scoundrel. Not me.'

'You are a right. You are a good man. I am sorry to say Alfie is not.'

As if he had heard his name over the sound of the party chatter, Alfie looked towards them. His eyes settled on Thomas. He looked both astonished and furious. He pushed his way through the crowd, faltering with each step. Cecilia tightened her hand on Thomas's arm, saying, 'You said you would not cause any trouble, remember?'

There was no time for him to reply. Alfie had reached them and was standing in front of Thomas, very close to his face. 'What are you doing here? You are not welcome,' he hissed.

Cecilia could smell the drink on his breath from her distance. She knew it was time to diffuse the atmosphere, 'I asked Thomas to come,' she lied, 'because I wanted to share your happiness with him.'

Alfie's eyes glared, his nostrils flaring. She thought he was about to hit Thomas. Suddenly Sophia appeared at the arm of her husband,

'Alfie, what is happening?' she asked, looking at each of them in turn, her pretty face creased in a questioning frown.

'Darling, this is my Mama,' Alfie's voice had changed completely to soft and tender. How quickly he could turn, Cecilia thought. He has not changed since he was a child.

Cecilia stepped between Thomas and Alfie and hugged her new daughter-in-law, 'Welcome to the family.' She raised her eyebrows and gestured to Alfie and Thomas, giving an ironic curtsey.

There was a startled silence for a few moments. Then they all burst out laughing. It seemed the bubble of tension had burst.

But it hadn't. When Alfie stopped laughing, he changed again. He said in a curt tone to Sophia, 'This is my mother's husband. He is not welcome.'

'But he is your family, Alfie, he should stay,' said Sophia, bewildered.

'No. I will never accept him.' He addressed Thomas, 'You must leave now.'

They all watched with mounting fear as Thomas slowly pulled a packet of cigarettes out of his pocket, taking one out. He tapped it on the packet, put it to his lips and lit it. He blew the smoke upwards, to Cecilia's relief. She had thought he would blow it in Alfie's face. Thomas offered a cigarette to Alfie. She saw Alfie wonder whether or not to take it, eventually deciding to take him up on the offer. Thomas lit Alfie's cigarette.

After taking a couple of puffs Alfie seemed to calm down. But with his third drag, he blew smoke straight into Thomas's face, 'Thanks for the cigarette. But now it is time for you to go.'

Cecilia shot Thomas a warning glance, which he heeded. 'Very well,' he said, 'if you insist. Cecilia, we are leaving now.'

'No,' shouted Alfie, 'My Mama must stay. Leave her here

where she belongs. Mama, you must choose between him and us.'

Cecilia stared at Alfie for a moment and then asked, 'Why don't you like Thomas?'

'He is a scoundrel and too young for you.'

'But he is my choice, Alfie. We love each other.'

'Don't be ridiculous, Mama. He is using you. He wants your money.'

She heard Thomas's intake of angry breath as he stood at her side.

'And you, Alfie, do you want my money?'

'I'm entitled to it,' replied Alfie very quickly. Then realising his mistake, 'No, no. I was joking. I don't want your money, Mama. I don't want this villain to take your money, that is all.'

'Thank you, Alfie, now I know. You are not worried about me because I have married a younger man. You are worried for yourself. That I may not have any money left for you to inherit.' She leaned towards him, 'May I remind you it is my money. I have worked for it. What I do with it is up to me.'

Alfie's voice hardened into a threat, 'I have only your best interest at heart, Mama. As I said, you must choose between us and this boy,' he spat the word at Thomas.

Alfie, Sophia and Thomas all looked at her. The rest of the gathering had silenced and were watching, waiting for her reply. She knew this was the moment she must make a choice. A choice that would have huge repercussions. If she chose Thomas, she might never see her children again. But she would have Thomas and a happy marriage for the first time since Maurice, more than thirty years earlier.

If she chose her children, she would never see Thomas again. Yet she saw little of her older children. John, Cissy and Gertrude were all married with families of their own. Michael was in Ireland and may never come back. Alfie was too selfish to spend time with her. But they all may forgive her eventually. In the meantime, she would have some happiness with Thomas. It was a risk she was prepared to take. It was about time she made decisions for herself now.

She stepped towards her husband, her heart pounding as they all watched her, 'I am leaving with Thomas now. I love you, Alfie, and all your brothers and sisters. I have my own life to lead. My future is with Thomas. Please come and visit us any time.'

She kissed a shocked Alfie and pecked Sophia on the cheek. She took Thomas's arm and walked out.

Once they were a safe distance away, Cecilia started to cry. She rarely cried these days, all her life's tears had been spent mourning the children and husbands she had lost when she was younger. Now, she thought she might have lost her living children. She couldn't bear the thought. Thomas led her to a small side street where he could hug her without being seen by people.

She leant against his shoulder and sobbed. He stroked her back, saying nothing. When she had calmed, she wiped her eyes and nose and said, 'I might never see my children and grandchildren again.'

'They will get over it and come back to you, I am sure of it.'

She hiccupped, still sniffling, 'I hope so. I don't know what I would do without them.'

Thomas put his fingers on her chin and tipped her face up. He leaned down and kissed her on the lips, tender and loving, 'I don't know what I would do without you, you know. Thank you for choosing me.'

Time proved Thomas right. Her sons and daughters contacted her over the next few weeks. Relationships were re-established with all except Alfie. She wrote to him regularly but never received a reply. She sent him and Sophia birthday and Christmas presents and waited hopefully to hear back from them. But nothing appeared.

Until one day a letter arrived:

> 6 March 1929
> Number 67
> Railway Quarters
> Rohri
> Sind
>
> Dearest Mama
> I have some news for you. You have a new grand-daughter!
> Sophia had our first baby yesterday. She is beautiful. We have called her Myrtle Josephine. It would be lovely if you could come and see her. As it is a long way to travel, you will be welcome to stay a few days.
> Your loving son
> Alfie.

She was excited to hear from Alfie at last. She was delighted she had a little granddaughter too. She resolved to visit them, she had a relationship to rebuild. She also wanted to see little Myrtle. She wrote a reply telling him she would be with him as soon as possible.

When Thomas returned from work, she was already packing her bags.

'Alfie and Sophia have had a baby girl. He wrote me a letter, look,' she raised it aloft, 'he has invited me to stay awhile.'

Thomas snatched the letter from her. He read it, screwed it up and threw it on the floor.

'He has got a cheek! No apology, no mention of his wedding. No mention that he has had nothing to do with you for the past year or even more.'

'I know,' she shrugged.

'So why do you want to go?'

'Because he is my son.'

'I don't understand.'

'No, you wouldn't. You don't have children. You will never understand.'

'No, I won't. They have always come first. Come before me.'

Cecilia sighed, 'Don't be ridiculous. I chose you, didn't I? I want to see Alfie and make up with him. I also want to see my granddaughter. You can come with me if you like.'

'I am working. I cannot come with you.'

'Very well. I will not to be too long. I love you.'

As she leaned in to kiss him, he flinched.

'Oh, please don't be cross with me. I do love you. I will miss you and I will hurry back.'

He shrugged, 'I don't want him to hurt you again. That's all. You are blind to his ways and how bad he is. I am just trying to protect you.'

'And I love you for it. But life is short. We have to make amends wherever we can. I know that more than anyone.'

'Yes, you do.' Thomas seemed to relent a little. He hugged her and gave her a little kiss on the cheek.

'Safe journey,' he said, 'I hope you will not be gone long.'

When she arrived at Alfie's railway bungalow, a short walk from Rohri station, he greeted her with a hug. He led her to the kitchen, which was large and airy. He ladled her some chai that his servant had made earlier. As he gave it to her, he said, 'I am pleased to see you.'

326

She decided not to talk about the past, 'I am too, Alfie. Let's not fight again. Now,' she patted down her pink dress, 'Where are Sophia and the baby? I can't wait to see them.'

Alfie hesitated, she saw that he was nervous. It was rare for Alfie to show any anxiety as he was doing now.

Cecilia frowned, 'Is there a problem, Alfie?'

'No, Mama. Not a problem.'

'Oh good. Where are they, then?'

'Sophia is resting, Mama.'

'And the baby. Where is little Myrtle?'

'There is a problem, Mama.' Alfie sat on a chair, his head in his hands.

'I thought you said there was no problem?'

Tears streaked his face as he looked up at her. She had a memory flash of her little Alfie looking up at her when he had done something wrong, all big eyes and ears. This grown-up Alfie looked no different. Her heart went out to him, as it always did.

'It is the baby, Mama. She was deprived of oxygen when she was born. She is retarded.'

Cecilia gasped in shock, 'Oh no. That is terrible.'

Alfie wept unreservedly, she had never seen him cry like this, not even when he was young. 'Sophia is not well Mama. She is tired from the birth. She is sad about the baby. She is very low and won't get out of bed to look after her.'

'I will stay a few days to help, Alfie. I will talk to Sophia. I remember I could not get out of bed when your brothers and sisters died. I understand what she is thinking.'

'Oh, thank you Mama. I knew you would.' He threw his arms around her and hugged her tight.

Suddenly, the penny dropped for Cecilia. Alfie hadn't missed her. He didn't care about her. He was using her because he needed help and had no one else. He would not have contacted her otherwise. Thomas was right. He would always hurt her.

Unable to resist tackling Alfie on the subject, she held him at arm's length.

'Alfie, you wrote because you wanted me to deal with this for you, didn't you?'

Alfie looked at her in surprise. He shook her off him, 'Of course, Mama. Why else would I contact you?'

'You are very selfish, Alfie. You only think of yourself.'

'Mama, I needed you, so I wrote. I cannot see the problem. I am thinking of Sophia and the baby. Not myself.' His eyes were wide with hurt.

She gave Alfie a cold look and said, 'You will never change, Alfie, I know that now. But Sophia and Myrtle need help, I am doing this for them, not you.'

Alfie smiled. He'd got his way, she thought, that was all he cared about.

She went to see Sophia in bed. The shutters were closed. She was lying in the dark. Awake and staring at the ceiling. Sweat and tears had glued her hair to her face.

Myrtle was asleep in a little basket on the floor beside her. Cecilia looked at the tiny baby and saw beauty in her wide features and peaceful smile.

Cecilia sat down on the bed. She placed her hand on top of Sophia's. Sophia didn't stir. Cecilia said nothing for a long time. She barely knew this young girl but this was a tableau of intimacy they would both remember all their lives. Myrtle stirred and started to cry. Cecilia gently picked up her new granddaughter and soothed her.

'Thank you for giving me such a beautiful granddaughter, Sophia. I am very proud of her. And you.'

At last Sophia reacted, 'She is retarded. She will never be

normal.' Tears flowed down her cheeks, onto her neck, soaking the collar of her nightdress.

'She is your baby. She deserves your love.'

'I can't love her. Alfie has said he doesn't love me anymore because of her.'

Cecilia felt a bolt of rage at Alfie. But decided not to make things worse, 'I expect he was just upset and getting used to the news. I am sure he loves you both.'

Sophia sobbed, unconvinced. Her pretty little face had aged with the worry and upset.

In a firm, kind tone, Cecilia said, 'Hold the baby, Sophia, and look at her innocent face.' She handed Myrtle to her mother, 'She needs you.'

Sophia said nothing. But she did look at Myrtle and softened just a little.

'I lost two daughters, Sophia. One was eleven-months-old and one was just three weeks.'

Sophia looked up at her in surprise, 'Oh, I didn't know. Alfie never said.'

'Well he wouldn't, would he? It didn't involve him. I also lost three baby boys as well. Five babies all told. I miss them every day, even now. Every single day the pain still grips me.' Cecilia's eyes were filling with tears at the memory, 'So I know how precious life is. Any life. Myrtle needs you. She is your baby. It does not matter that she is retarded. What matters is that she is loved.'

She could see that Sophia was coming round. All the poor girl had needed was some kind words. Words that she hadn't got from Alfie.

'I don't know how to look after such a baby, Mama. I don't know what to.'

'I have an idea. You need a good ayah. My ayah has been with me for over twenty years. She is excellent. She is calm and kind. I am sure she will be a good ayah for you. We really don't need her anymore now that George is fourteen. I haven't had the heart to tell her. I am sure she will be pleased to have a little one to look after again.'

Sophia smiled, a smile that brought life back to her pretty face, 'Oh thank you Mama. That is such a good idea. Alfie always speaks highly of Rupali. He really loved her.'

Envy pricked Cecilia's heart. She knew her children loved Rupali and she was glad they did. It still hurt her to hear it said out loud. What she wanted to hear that they loved their Mama. She stood up, kissed Myrtle's forehead and stroked Sophia's hand. 'I will ask Rupali to come. And I will stay with you until she gets here. I will look after you both.'

Alfie was waiting for her in the kitchen. Her voice was stern when she spoke to him. 'Go into the bedroom and tell Sophia you love her and the baby. And mean it, Alfie.'

He jumped up, 'Yes, Mama.'

'It was terrible of you to say you didn't love her because of Myrtle's condition. Terrible.'

'I didn't mean it Mama. I was just upset.'

'She thinks you meant it. Go in there and make it right between you. Now.'

Alfie started to walk out of the kitchen. As he reached the door, she said, 'I am going to send a wire to Rupali to ask her to be your ayah.'

Alfie turned with a look of happiness on his face, 'Oh, I like that idea Mama. I love Rupali so much.' She fought hard to ignore the pain of his words.

Alfie frowned, 'She won't be able to read a telegram, though.'

'No, but Joseph and George will read it to her. I will send the telegram now and stay with you until she gets here.'

He gave a small nod and said quietly, 'Thank you Mama.'

A month later, Rupali had settled well into Alfie's family, she loved little Myrtle, giving Sophia gentle guidance on how to look after her. Once Cecilia had seen everything was calm, she left. She went back to see Joseph and George in Multan and to work there for a short time. The boys both had jobs on the railway now and were happy to see her.

Work was light in Multan, which meant she could return to Quetta and Thomas. She was missing him terribly. The train was, as ever, hot, crowded and dusty. People were everywhere, squashed into the aisles and corridors. They were even on the roof or clinging on to the outside, fingers gripping tightly to the metal slats of the shutters. Every moment of the journey made her more eager to be home in the quiet safety of Thomas's arms.

She alighted with relief. The air outside, oppressive though it was, felt fresh compared to the stifling train. She took deep breaths as if it were the cleanest air she had ever breathed. She began the walk home, stopping to buy some large mangoes from the fruit stall on the way. They were ripe and soft, she knew they would be a delicious welcome home treat.

She wasn't sure if Thomas would be at home yet, but decided to enter the house quietly in case he was, so that she could surprise him. She opened the door softly and listened in the hallway. She heard nothing at first. Then, muffled noises seemed to be coming from the bedroom. Curious, she walked quietly towards the sound. As she neared the bedroom the noise became louder and more recognisable. Lovemaking. Her heart started beating faster, a sense of foreboding descending on her with every step.

She opened the door as gently as possible and peered into the room.

She had a good view of them, they couldn't see her. She stared, not wanting to believe what she was seeing. The shock froze her brain and stopped any thoughts. Horror rooted her to the spot. When they finished, they collapsed together on the bed with their arms around each other, sated. Cecilia shook her head vigorously to bring some thinking back. Taking a deep breath, she opened the door fully and stepped into the room. Neither of them heard her.

In a calm voice, calmer than she was feeling, she said, 'I hope you enjoyed that.'

They both jumped, holding the sheet over their bodies.

'Cecilia,' said Thomas, shocked. 'What are you doing here?'

'It is my home.'

He looked at the girl, 'You had better leave,' he told her in Urdu, '*Alvida.*'

The girl stood up, naked. Cecilia noticed, with envy, her young firm breasts and lithe body. She couldn't have been more than nineteen. She scrambled into her choli and sari. She hurried past Cecilia as she left without looking at her.

Cecilia and Thomas stared at each other. By some mutual unspoken agreement, they said nothing until they heard the front door close.

As it shut, Cecilia said, 'Well?'

She walked out of the bedroom into the kitchen. She put the celebratory mangoes on the table, knowing they would never now taste sweet. Thomas walked into the kitchen, his crumpled clothes askew.

'It meant nothing,' he said.

Her voice was heavy with sarcasm as she tried not to lose her temper, 'It looked like it.'

'Honestly, Cecilia. You have been gone so long. I didn't know when you would be back. I was desperate.'

'So it's my fault, is it?'

'Yes, if you had been home it would never have happened.'

332

'So, what do you do when I am in Multan. Sometimes I spend weeks there.'

She saw him squirm as he tried to think of an answer. Eventually with a small voice, he said, 'I know when you are coming back when you are in Multan. But this time I did not know. I couldn't wait any longer.'

She knew there was a reasonableness in his words. She was fifty-three now. Her hair had greyed, her body thickened, she no longer looked young. He was only twenty-eight. He needed more frequent sexual satisfaction than she did. But she wasn't yet ready to forgive him.

'Who was she?'

'I don't know. I don't even know her name.'

'Bravo for you. Just pick up a girl and satisfy yourself with her. What a hero you are.'

'Please Cecilia. Forgive me. I would never hurt you. Never.'

'But you have hurt me.'

'Only because you found out.'

'You really do think it was my fault, then?'

Thomas nodded without conviction. She knew it was pointless arguing. He would always blame her. His words made her think he had been doing this for a while, getting away with it because he knew when she would be back from Multan. The core of steel inside her tightened.

She spoke to him as if he were a child, 'We will not say any more about this. I will not go away for as long, so you do not become that desperate again. I will not tell you when I am coming back. This way you will have to behave, as you will never know.'

Thomas looked at his feet, chastised. He said nothing as she swept from the room, leaving him alone.

She never felt the same way about Thomas after that. She still loved him, enjoyed his company, even let him back into her bed. She just couldn't lose the doubts that were running through the back of her mind. Was that the first time, had he always been unfaithful? Did he really not know the girl? Was he still seeing her? Or other women? Was he just using her to get her money? Would he leave her? Would all the tittle tattle about them be right? Would he make a fool of her, as everyone was sure he would? Her mind never rested. She was determined not to see this marriage end. She would not be proved a fool.

For his part, Thomas seemed to be back to the man she met, that man she fell in love with, the man she thought had been sent to her by Maurice. He was loving, attentive, fun to be with and still an enthusiastic lover. There were times when she almost believed it had never happened. That she had never stood in her bedroom doorway and watched him having intercourse with a beautiful young woman. But she couldn't erase the memory, however hard she tried.

A telegram arrived from Alfie. Sophia had had a second child. A little girl they called Dagma Elizabeth. Both mother and baby were healthy – Cecilia had not known that Sophia was even pregnant. She was relieved to read of the baby's safe arrival, a normal little girl would be just what Sophia needed. But she decided to not to visit them. That would entail leaving Thomas for too long. She would wait until Thomas had some leave and they would go together. She was sad to miss seeing Dagma while she was a new baby but she had to do what was needed for her own life and to keep her marriage intact.

A letter arrived from Michael:
    My dearest Mama

I have some news. I have a wife. She is beautiful, Mama, I know you will like her very much. Her name is Mary, but we call her Polly, and she is a cousin. We got married in Sandyford in August and she is expecting our baby in May next year. We will be back in India around Christmas time. I have secured a job as a shed man on the railway in Lahore. We will live there. We will visit you first though. I am so excited Mama and looking forward to seeing you again.

Your loving son

Mickie

She was glad he was coming home, relieved that he would be settling in the land of his birth and she was looking forward to meeting his wife. She enjoyed the company of Mary, Ethel and Sophia, her daughters-in-law. Having another one would be a pleasure, she was sure.

She was amused to note that Michael had signed himself "Mickie", which is what his brothers and sister called him now. And they called Richard "Dickie" these days too. Perhaps it was time for her to follow suit.

When Mickie and Polly arrived in India, they first stayed with her and Thomas in Quetta. Polly was a quiet girl, barely making any sort of sound. She looked exhausted, whether from the journey or the pregnancy Cecilia wasn't sure. Her skin was pale and there were dark rings around her eyes. Her belly was swollen already, she looked more than four months gone. Throughout their stay, she remained in their allotted bedroom, resting. Cecilia looked in on her regularly, rarely managing to get a word of conversation out of her. Mickie, she noted, seemed to ignore his wife, showing very little concern for her. He spent the time playing cards and drinking with Thomas and his friends.

Cecilia knew she should not interfere but couldn't help but ask, 'How is Polly? What do you think is wrong with her?'

She heard a sharp edge to his voice as he replied, 'She is fine, Mama, a little tired. She needs to rest, that's all.'

Rising to his anger she asked, 'Do you think you should check on her more often?'

'I said, she needs rest,' his tone hardened again, 'I leave her to have it.'

She decided not to push the argument further.

One day, Polly responded by smiling when Cecilia laid a cup of soothing sweet chai on the bedside table. It was a wan smile, but at least it was a reaction, something that she had not done since arriving. In a soft tone, so that no one outside the room could hear, Cecilia asked, 'How are you feeling?'

Her voice faltered, 'Terrible, Mama. The journey was awful, I was seasick and pregnancy sick the whole time.'

'It sounds awful, Polly. But here you can keep resting, I will look after you.'

'That will not be possible, Mama. Mickie wants to leave today. He says he must see Alfie and then Cissy before we set up home in Lahore.'

'He cannot mean that. You are not well enough to make so many long journeys.'

Polly sipped her chai shrugging, 'Mickie makes the decisions, not me. I have told him I am too tired. But he thinks it will do me good.'

Cecilia thought back to her lost babies and the terrible impact their deaths had had on her life. She looked at the young pregnant Polly and decided to try and stop Mickie from leaving. In so many ways, Mickey was as stubborn as Alfie. But she would never forgive herself if something happened to the baby without her saying anything. She marched her anger to the kitchen, stopping at the door and taking a deep breath to calm herself.

Mickie and Thomas were at the kitchen table, smoking and playing cards. They were sitting in easy camaraderie, each with a glass of whisky at his elbow. Cecilia busied herself at the stove, doing nothing in particular. 'When do you plan to leave, Mickie?' she asked in what she hoped was a casual tone.

'Later today, I think,' answered Mickie, taking a gulp of his whisky.

With a huge effort, she controlled her voice, 'I do not think Polly is well enough to travel.'

'Nonsense, Mama.' He laid a card on the table, 'Trump,' he said to Thomas, 'my trick,' and he gathered the cards laying them neatly in a pile next to his glass.

'Please put your cards down, Michael. This is important.'

Mickie threw his cards on the table in temper, 'What is it, Mama?'

'I said I do not think Polly is well enough to travel.'

Mickie sighed, 'Oh Mama,' he said exasperated, 'You worry too much. Polly is just a little tired, that's all. Meeting Alfie and Cissy will perk her up, I am sure.'

But she was not going to give up that easily, 'Michael, I lost five babies. It is a terrible thing. It will be a blight on your lives forever. You want your baby to be safe, don't you?'

Mickie jumped up in anger pushing the table towards Thomas. The drinks spilled. Thomas made a play of picking up the dripping cards and wiping them on his trousers.

Mickie stomped over to Cecilia, an air of menace in his step, 'This is my decision, Mama,' he hissed in her face, 'it is nothing to do with you. Polly is my wife. I decide what she needs, not you. Leave us alone. Stop going on about your babies. I am sick of hearing about them.' He left the room, slamming the door.

She heard him shouting at Polly, 'Get up and pack. We are leaving. Now.'

Glaring at Thomas who was pretending not to hear, she ran out and followed Mickie.

'Look,' she pleaded, 'don't leave like this. Let me take Polly to Lahore and settle her in there. You can come after you have seen Alfie and Cissy.'

Mickie paused, as though he were considering the idea. His shoulders straightened. He said, 'No, Mama. She is my wife. She does what I say.' Turning to Polly, who had been folding clothes in silence, he snapped, 'Hurry up! We are leaving now.'

Cecilia put her hand on the trembling girl's arm. 'Sit down, I will pack for you,' she glared at Mickie with a look that said don't you dare stop me. He didn't. Cecilia packed their meagre possessions into two small holdalls and handed them to Mickie. He grabbed Polly's hand and pulled her up with little or no care for her condition.

'Goodbye, Mama. I will let you know when the baby arrives,' his eyes still blazed with anger. He added, 'Don't expect an invitation to stay.'

He dragged his wife behind him as he left. She turned her head to Cecilia and gave a small smile, acknowledging her mother-in-law had tried to help her.

The noise of Mickie slamming the front door echoed through the bungalow as she walked back to Thomas in the kitchen. Expecting some comfort from him, she was shocked when he said. 'Why did you interfere?'

'I was trying to keep the baby safe.'

'But it is nothing to do with you.'

'The baby is my grandchild. It has everything to do with me.'

'But it is Mickie's decision what they do, not yours.'

338

'I just wanted to stop him making a mistake, something they would regret for ever.'

'You don't know everything, you know. Let them be.'

He looked at her with contempt for the first time. It chilled her to the depth of her being. The age gap was showing. His immaturity against her life experience.

Mickie wrote her a short letter some weeks later telling her that Polly was fine and the reason for her tiredness was that she was expecting twins. Cecilia was thrilled when she received it, although she felt that it was unlikely that her daughter-in-law was "fine". She was a frail girl and carrying twins would be difficult. Giving birth to them would be worse. But she decided to take Mickie at face value. She wrote back telling him how pleased she was for them, how excited she was to be a grandmother to twins. Mending their relationship was more important than ever now, she thought.

A telegram arrived in May. Its message as shocking as it was stark:

Polly and babies dead. Please come now. Mickie

She did not know how long she sat there. It could have been a few minutes. It might have been hours. Slowly, she started to function through the unbearable shock. She must get to her son. He needed her. He had asked her to come. Her beloved son was suffering and she had to be with him. She had to get to Lahore as soon as possible.

She packed a few clothes, and scribbling a message to Thomas telling him where she was going, leaving it on the table next to Mickie's telegram.

The journey was long, hot and crowded, no different to the hundreds of others she had taken over the years. Except this time, the train was taking her to a triple tragedy and a grieving son. She prayed for the souls of frail Polly and her two dead babies. Her relationship with God had waxed and waned over the years, over her many tragedies. Now, though, she felt a spiritual charge as never before. She spent the journey with her eyes closed in prayer, blocking out the noise, smells and every other distraction.

After the train had pulled into Lahore, she moved her mind out of praying, looking around, bringing herself into the present. She saw the curious design of the station – it was built like a red brick castle, with turrets, thick walls and slots for gunfire.

It was a short walk to Mickie's railway bungalow, once more through the clean leafy boulevards that were the imprint of the British. She sat on the bench on the veranda and waited for him to come home from work. It was a shady spot, making the heat just about bearable.

Mickie arrived three hours later. As he opened the gate, he saw her. His face lit up and he ran to her.

'Oh Mama, you came, oh Mama.' He flung his arms around her, hugging her hard.

'Of course. You asked me.'

Mickie started to cry as he led her into the house. He sat at the kitchen table, gesturing for her to do the same. 'It was awful Mama, awful,' he said without preamble, 'There was blood everywhere. The babies were both boys. I so wanted boys. Now I have nothing. What am I going to do?

She looked at him. Her children seemed to have an unremitting capacity to disappoint her, she thought. Mickie hadn't mentioned poor Polly. He was only talking about himself.

'What happened?'

'I don't know, Mama. The nurse said she was too weak to give birth to twins. I am not sure myself, she seemed strong to me.'

'She was weak and frail when you visited us last December. All that travelling had tired her out.'

She saw Mickie's body stiffen in anger, yet she carried on talking, 'She travelled a lot after you left us. I expect that didn't help.'

His eyes flashed, 'Are you saying this is my fault? I have lost my wife and two sons. How can that be my fault?'

'It's not your fault. But you should have seen how unwell she was. And looked after her better.'

'Get out,' he hissed, 'I am your son, I thought you would help me. But you just take her side. Like you did in December.'

'I was trying to help. I think you should have been more thoughtful towards her.'

'I have had enough. Go home, I don't need you.'

They stared at each other, neither of them wanting to relent.

With a sigh and not another word, she walked out of the bungalow, towards the castle-like station to make her way home. She had only been in Lahore for a few hours, it was a wasted journey.

Sadness engulfed her on the journey back. She was sad for the loss of Polly and the babies, sad that her sons were turning into such unpleasant men. Sad for the hours of sacrifice and hard work she had put in to bringing them up to be good people. All of which was to no avail. She arrived in Quetta full of unspent tears. Tears that she had held back until she could get home and shed them in private.

But home was no respite.

She walked into the kitchen to find Thomas having sex with a young woman across the table. All three were stunned for a moment. Then Thomas continued his activity, gasping between thrusts,

'Get out and let us finish.'

341

She did.

She went for a walk in the park, where she sat on a tree stump and cried. People passing by looked at her with curiosity. Goats, sheep, cattle and dogs too. She didn't much care.

Her tears did not stop falling. If it weren't for her work, which she found stimulating and satisfying, her life would be very bleak indeed. She had eight living children who, if they gave her a thought, resented everything about her. Her marriage was in tatters. Everything was such a mess. She stayed for hours in the park until she had made up her mind. Once again she resolved not to break up with Thomas in the face of his philandering. She had too much to lose.

She returned home late in the evening. Thomas was out. She was relieved not to have to face him.

He came back the next morning 'I am sorry,' he said, 'I should not have done it or said that to you.'

'Why did you do it, then?'

'I don't know. You were my first lover. I wanted to try others. I think that is why I did it this time. And last time.' He paused. 'They were the only two times, I promise.'

Her look said she didn't believe him. But she wasn't going to turn it into an argument.

'It is not fair to me, Thomas, please do not do it again.'

'I won't Cecilia,' he promised, 'I do love you.'

But she realised he was lost to her.

She knew the telegram would hold terrible news. It seemed her life was becoming one long stream of bad news. Her hands trembling and her heart pumping, she opened it with trepidation.

Sophia dead. Baby Sophie healthy. I need you. Alfie.

She sat down as if all the air had been punched out of her. Her head in her hands, another death another tragedy. When would it all stop? She told Thomas, though they spoke very little these days.

He didn't seem perturbed, 'You are going to go to him?'

'He needs my help. He has a disabled little girl, a tiny child and a new baby. And no wife.'

'As ever, he only contacts you when he needs you.'

'I know. But he is my son. There is no choice. Besides, I need to work in the Multan office for a while. He is in Rohri. I will combine the two trips.'

'So, you will be away for a while.' It was a statement. There was a vestige of hope in his voice. Hope that he had clearly tried to strangle, but failed.

'I don't know how long I will be. It could be weeks or even months. It depends what Alfie needs and how work in Multan goes. I am now a Barrister with much more responsibility. At the moment Alfie and my work must come first.' They looked at each other, each knowing what that meant. For them and their marriage. Neither said anything. The wall between them, the one that had been building for years, had now reached its full height. There was no way it would ever come down.

On the way to Rohri, she had time to reflect on her marriage. They had once been so happy, thriving on each other's company and defying convention. And now it had all gone. They were awkward with each other, wary as though they were untrusting strangers. Was it their age difference? Partly, she supposed, the fault lines of the age gap had been exposed over the last few years. Was it her frequent absences for work, dividing her time between Multan and Quetta? Partly again. Qualifying as a Barrister had involved a huge amount of work and running the two offices had been very demanding too. Was it her children? Partly, again, she realised. Thomas had no idea of the love a parent has for a child. He had often been frustrated with her over it. But what could she have done? They were her children. All eight of them needed her at some time over the years. She would never let them down. They both knew that.

Bungalow 67 in the Railway Quarters at Rohri was spacious with a large mature garden. A family house. Alfie was at work when she arrived but Rupali was home, looking after the three children. She cried with relief and happiness when she saw Cecilia. Cecilia hugged her, once again defying convention. She was pleased to see her former ayah who she had grown to love and still missed.

'Tell me, Rupali, what happened?'

'Oh Memsa'ab. It was terrible. The baby was very big, she weighed fourteen pounds. Too big for the young Memsa'ab. That is what the doctor told us.' Rupali started to cry.

A little girl bounced into the room. She was pretty, her hair in pigtails. She was wearing a blue gingham dress, 'Who are you,' she demanded, legs stomped apart, hands on her hips.

Cecilia smiled at her boldness. 'Are you Dagma?'

'Yes.'

'Then I am your Nana. We have not met before. But I have a little present for you.'

Dagma held out her hand, 'What is it? I want it.'

Cecilia made a play of not being able to find anything in her pockets. She shrugged an exaggerated shrug, 'Oh dear, I can't find it, I must have lost it.'

Dagma squealed with delight, 'It's in your pocket, I can see it Nana. You haven't lost it.'

With that, she jumped up and reached into Cecilia's pocket, pulling out a waxed paper bag and peering into it. 'Laddoos,' she shouted, 'you bought me laddoos.'

Cecilia stroked Dagma's cheek, 'You are as bright as a button, Dagma. And very cheeky too. Yes, I have brought you laddoos to share with Myrtle. What do you say?'

'Thank you, Nana, thank you. I will give Myrtle hers.' She turned to leave but at the door she paused as if she had been struck by another thought, 'Where is my Mama? Why are you here?'

The baby started to cry, Rupali comforted her. Cecilia picked Dagma up. She wondered what Alfie had told her about Sophia's death. Probably nothing, she concluded.

'Your Mummy was not well. Her body stopped working for her.'

'Why?'

She knew she couldn't lie to this clever little girl. She needed to explain it in a way she could understand. 'We don't know why, bette, sometimes this happens. It means that you will not see your Mama anymore. I have come to be with you and Papa for a little while until we can sort things out for you all.'

Dagma's bottom lip stuck out, 'But I want my Mama. I want to see her.'

Hugging her tight, Cecilia soothed, 'Of course you do.'

Just as suddenly, Dagma wriggled out of Cecilia's arms, switching the subject in the way only three-year-olds can do, 'I am going to give Myrtle some laddoos.' She happily ran out of the room.

When Alfie returned, he said, before he even greeted her, 'What am I to do?'

She had already thought it through, knowing that Alfie was interested in her solving problems for him. Just as she had done when Myrtle was born.

'I think you should ask Cissy to take Myrtle and Dagma to live with them. Rupali is good at managing Myrtle so she can stay too. We should contact the nuns in the children's home to see if they can look after little Sophie.'

Alfie looked relieved; his mother had come up with a good solution.

He said, 'I will go back to the station and ring Cissy's husband. I think he will agree.'

'I will go to the convent and speak to the nuns,' suggested Cecilia.

Cecilia decided to take Dagma with her to the convent. She was enchanted by her little granddaughter. Dagma was an intelligent happy little girl. Cecilia wanted to spend more time with her. Besides, she wanted to tell Dagma what was going to happen. She didn't trust Alfie to do it. Of the three little girls, any changes would affect Dagma the most.

On the way to the convent, she held Dagma's warm soft hand as her granddaughter skipped along the muddy path. She told her that the baby would need to stay with the nuns for a while.

'Because my Mama isn't here anymore, you mean Nana?'

'That is right, bette. The nuns will be able to care for Sophie properly. Babies take up a lot of time and your Papa has to go to work, so he can't do it.'

Dagma frowned, 'But what will happen to me and Myrtle? Will we stay with Rupali?'

'You and Myrtle will go and stay with your Auntie Cissy,' she explained, 'Rupali will go with you.'

'I don't want to. I want to stay with my Papa and you.'

'I need to go to my home soon. Your Papa will visit you at Aunty Cissy's house.'

Dagma charmed the nuns at the children's home. They told Cecilia they were happy to take in the tiny Sophie. They felt Dagma's lively personality was a good sign. Her baby sister would be just as lovely, they felt.

She told Alfie the news, 'I will take Sophie to them tomorrow. Rupali can take the girls to Rawalpindi. Christopher has agreed to take them in. I cannot have time off work. My job is too busy.'

'Let me go with them. I want to make sure they settle with Cissy and Christopher.'

'Good idea, Mama. Now I am off to bed. Your room is over there,' he gestured vaguely, leaving her in the hallway. There was no word of thanks or recognition that he was her host. She went to the kitchen and fixed herself some food. She had to concentrate on her grandchildren's needs now, Alfie was not a concern anymore. He wouldn't notice anything she did.

Chapter Sixteen

It was ten months before she decided to go back to Quetta. Life had been so busy and going back there was no longer an enticing prospect. The work in Quetta had lessened. She kept in regular contact with her clerks. She was able to manage everything from the Multan office. She had spent a lot of time at Cissy's. An extra motive was to make sure Dagma was thriving. She was so taken with this little girl, wondering if Bridget or Victoria would have been like her. She still ached for her little lost girls. Time with Dagma soothed her. Cecilia really loved her cheeky, intelligent company.

Eventually, she could put off going back to Quetta no longer. Work there was accumulating. She needed to talk to Thomas about their marriage. She had been writing to him. He had written back sporadically. She realised she was missing him. She was ready to forgive. She was determined to see what could be salvaged from the wreck of their marriage.

She was walking home to pack after her last day at work in Multan, when over the noise of the animals and the shrieks of the children, she caught the word 'Quetta' being shouted. She stopped and looked towards the sound. A young newspaper seller was waving a pamphlet in the air with wide dramatic arms:

> Earthquake in Quetta! Thousands dead! Earthquake in Quetta! Thousands dead!

She ran to him in alarm. Finding some rupees in her bag, she threw them down, grabbing a pamphlet. Not wanting to read it in the very public street she ran all the way home without stopping for breath, propelled by her anxiety for Thomas.

At home she tried reading it, a special edition about the earthquake. Her eyes could only skim the headlines, her panic stopped her from taking in any of the details:

> It had happened on 31 May, three days ago.
> A huge earthquake had killed tens of thousands of people, no final numbers yet.
> Most of Quetta has been destroyed.
> Evacuation of survivors beginning by train.
> Some survivors from poorer areas taken to two camps on racecourse.
> Governor General to open relief fund.
> Civil Lines badly damaged.
> Cantonment has lowest casualty rate.
> Military cordoning off the city for health reasons.

All she could think about was Thomas. Had he survived? If he had been at his barracks in the Cantonment, he might be alright. But if he had been at home, in Civil Lines, he might not have fared so well. Why hadn't he contacted her? Was it because he was dead? Or injured? Or in one of the rescue camps? She had to go to Quetta and find out. He could be lying injured and needing her. She had to find him. Trains were still working, it seemed, as the pamphlet said people were being evacuated by rail. The station was based in the Cantonment, which is why it must have survived. She decided to catch the next train to Quetta and do her best to cross any military cordon there without being seen.

Armed soldiers were roaming the station. They were asking people whether they were going to Quetta. Then turning them away if they were. When she was asked, Cecilia told them she was just going two stops to see her family. She didn't tell them she was a barrister as she knew they would not take kindly to her being a woman with a good job. She made herself out to be a friendly grandmother, one who, at the age of 59, was harmlessly truthful.

They were obviously fooled. She sighed with relief as she sat down. It took her a while to realise that the carriages were virtually empty, unlike every other journey she had ever taken. As the train pulled into each station, she could see armed soldiers preventing people from boarding. She slunk down each time so that she could not be seen. It took hours, her body stiffening and aching from crouching at each stop.

As the train pulled into Quetta station, she pressed herself onto the side of the carriage so she could see what was happening. The platform was full of people, all British. Soldiers were moving people into groups to ensure they boarded the train in an orderly fashion. Their efforts were going to be in vain she thought as she watched the crowd surge towards the doors.

To get off, she had to shove her way through the mass of people trying to board. It was scary but she was determined not to be knocked over or trampled in the rush. She spotted a soldier watching her. She knew he would question her. She would have to persuade him that she had good reason to be there.

Sure enough, as soon as she had emerged from the crowd, he was there with another soldier. They were very young and looked more nervous than she was feeling. One looked slightly older than the other.

'What are you doing here?' asked the older soldier.

'I have come to look for my husband.'

'There is a cordon around the city, you will not be able to look for him. There is a high risk of disease.'

'But I need to find my husband. Please take me to your... your... Sergeant.'

The younger one laughed, 'He is a Major. He is in the station office. We can take you there, but he will only tell you the same thing.'

'Nevertheless, I would like to talk to him,' she said politely but with a firm tinge to her voice. These soldiers were younger than her children, she would not be told what to do by them.

The older soldier walked in front of her, the younger behind as if they thought she would make a run for freedom. She smiled at the prospect of her, a 59-year-old woman, outrunning two young men in their twenties. It was ridiculous.

In the station office, the Major was sitting at his desk reading some papers. He looked up, frowning at her.

'This lady has come to search for her husband.' The older soldier told him.

The Major stood, gesturing her to the chair opposite him. He turned to the young soldiers, 'Go back to the platform. The crowds still need organising.'

After they left, he turned towards her saying, 'Now, what is all this about? You must know you cannot get into the city.'

'I have come to find my husband,' her voice brooked no argument.

He looked taken aback. She knew he was seeing an elderly Indian lady in front of him. One he expected to dismiss with a soothing word or two. He was not expecting her to be so assertive. He sat back down at his desk, shuffling papers with little conviction. He reminded her of the British civil servants that she and Pandit had met all those years ago. She knew that he didn't quite know what to do or say, he was unused to talking to women who were not his own servants. Or his wife.

To help him she said, 'His name is Thomas Weightman, he is stationed here, in the Cantonment.'

'The name is not familiar to me,' he said, 'what rank is he?'

'He is a Private.'

The Major's eyes widened in shock he could not conceal.

She stared into his eyes, 'I know what you are thinking. How can an old lady like me be married to someone as lowly as a private?'

He shook his head to deny it, but too fast and for too long. She smiled, his reaction was one she had seen over and over again. She still enjoyed it, even under these circumstances. She leaned in a little to make her point, 'He is twenty-five years younger than me. We have been married for eleven years.'

The Major gulped, growing pale at the thought. She waited for him to speak. Which he did, after he recovered his composure.

'If he was based at the Cantonment, he will likely be fine, there were no major casualties here.'

'But he may have been in our apartment and office at Civil Lines. I am a barrister,' she saw the Major look even more perplexed and squirm, 'My Chambers are there and we lived above.'

He cleared his throat, 'Well there were some casualties there, but not many either as most people escaped into the streets. As you know, the streets in Civil Lines are very wide.'

'Indeed,' she agreed, 'so now I need to find him.'

'Has he not contacted you?' His tone becoming superior again.

'Well, I assumed the telephone lines are down, or very busy.'

He had to concede a little ground she noted. 'They are busy. They are not down.'

She had had enough of the positioning and posturing they were both doing. 'Look,' she ordered, 'I need to get to my house in Civil Lines. I need to see if he is there. He may be lying injured.'

'He would surely be dead by now,' said the Major enjoying seeing her flinch, 'As it is, we have cordoned off Civil Lines, due to the threat of disease. You cannot enter.'

'Major. I have come all the way from Multan to find my husband. He is a British soldier. Surely you would want to know where he is and rescue him if he is lying in the rubble injured?'

Once again the Major looked uncomfortable. She knew he was out of his depth, dealing with her. To help him again, she said, 'Might I suggest that you let your soldiers escort me to my home and wait there for me. They can check that I am behaving myself.'

His face cleared as he realised this was a good option. She saw she had given him a way to get rid of her and save face. He left the room without a word and came back a few minutes later with the same two young soldiers.

'They will escort you. Do as they say.'

Not willing to let him off so easily, she issued a command as she left, 'While I am away, please check your Cantonment record. As I said, his name is Thomas Weightman. He is in the Black Watch.'

Suddenly the Major relaxed, laughing out loud, 'The Black Watch? They are not even based here.' His laughter echoed around the room, bouncing off the walls and ringing in her ears.

She left the office, reeling from the news. She walked in silence alongside the soldiers. She could not see any damage in the Cantonment. There was an eerie silence, none of the noise and bustle that she knew so well. It was replaced by the acrid smell of rotting corpses – animal and humans – assaulting her nose, seizing her throat and watering her eyes. The smell was not from the Cantonment itself, but was wafting in from the direction of Civil Lines. Were her eyes watering from the smell or because of what the Major had said? That there was no Black Watch stationed here? She didn't believe him. But with each step she took towards Civil Lines, her doubts were growing.

In Civil Lines, the buildings were damaged, unlike the Cantonment. It was her first sight of the devastation that had been wreaked on the city. Walls, roofs, doors were lying in haphazard piles. Tables, chairs, beds and all manner of furniture were strewn around the streets. Most of the ruins were unrecognisable, just piles and piles of rubble. There were choking clouds of thick dust everywhere. The scene was desolate, like something from a Biblical apocalypse.

The putrefying human bodies and rotting animal carcasses that she could smell in the Cantonment were here. The odour was overwhelming, the sights were bringing bile into her throat. She barely stopped herself from vomiting. The soldiers were similarly affected. She saw the colour drain from both their faces as she watched their efforts to stop themselves gagging.

As they drew near to her quarters, she saw two little boys, naked and covered in dust, playing on the rubble of her house and office. She had seen these two scamps before, many times. They used to run around the streets of Civil Lines, living off their charms, thieving when they had to. She had liked them. Few people did, but she saw their energy and intelligence. Life had given them a bad lot which was not their fault. She had always given them food and water when they knocked at her door. Now she saw debris had collected in their hair, their faces and eyelashes were clogged with dirt. Their dark little bodies had paled with the coats of dust that covered their skin.

They jumped when they saw her, 'Ah, Memsa'ab,' they shouted climbing down from the rubble of her house, 'How are you?'

'Don't go near them,' the older soldier warned, 'They will have diseases.' He waved them away with threatening gestures.

'I know them,' she said, 'I can speak to them in Urdu. They should not be here, it is dangerous. Where can they go?'

The younger soldier spoke, 'We can take them to the race-course, where their people are being looked after.'

'Very well. Let me speak to them.'

She saw the glare given to her by the older soldier. 'I promise I will not touch them.'

She smiled at the boys, 'Have you seen my husband?' She asked them in Urdu.

'Mr Thomas? Yes, we saw him a few days ago.'

'After the earthquake happened?'

Yes, Memsa'ab. He was here after the earthquake. He shouted at us to go away.'

'Did you see where he went?'

'To the station. All the white people went there.'

Her heart lurched again. Thomas had survived. Where was he? Why had he not contacted her?' The doubts that she had been fighting found a more permanent home in her head. With a huge effort, she pushed the negative thoughts aside, concentrating on the immediate task.

Out of the corner of her eye, she noticed that Pandit's filing cabinet was lying on its side. It had broken open. Papers spilling out of the dented drawers. She could see a letter with the British office stamp from Karachi, one that she had not seen before. It was poking out of an envelope, as if Pandit had never replaced it properly. It must have been important, or else he would not have kept it in his personal cabinet.

She bent down to pick it up. One of the soldiers shouted at her to stop. 'Don't touch it,' he panicked, 'it will be dirty.'

She ignored him, shoving it into her bag. 'It is clean, I assure you. But we need to go now, I have seen all I need to see. These boys tell me my husband survived. He is not here. That is all I need to know.'

She turned to the little scamps, 'You must go to the racecourse, where you will get food and drink. These soldiers will take you. I will come too. I want to see if my husband is there.'

She was glad, as indeed they all were, that the racecourse was behind the Cantonment, so that they had to retrace their steps; there was no need to walk into the poorest parts of the city, where the devastation and stench would be even worse.

As they neared the racecourse, the smell of death gave way to the smell of life: excrement, vomit and sweat. Nearly as pungent as Civil Lines, they all tried not to breathe it in. The soldiers took the boys to be examined by a doctor and Cecilia waiting in the tent at the gate to meet the General who was in charge.

He bustled in, full of his own importance and judgements. He was an older man, thin and harried. On seeing her, he stopped and said, 'If you are new, you need to go to the medical tent. Then you come back here to be registered. Bring your medical certificate with you.'

'But I am not intending to stay here,' she answered him crisply, realising that he, like the Major, also saw her as elderly Indian woman, another problem for him to solve.

He blinked, his eyes uncomprehending, 'What are you doing here then?'

'I am looking for my husband, Thomas Weightman. He is in the Black Watch.'

'There is no one from the Black Watch here. This camp is for Indians and we have registered every one of them. Most

356

of the British left on trains days ago. They mainly went to Karachi. But, as the Black Watch is not stationed here, you are
mistaken.'

Cecilia, annoyed by his attitude and pierced from hearing
again that the Black Watch had never been in Quetta, left
without another word. She made her way back to the station,
upset and confused. Thomas had never been stationed in
Quetta, although he went to the army barracks and wore the
uniform of the Black Watch. He had survived the earthquake
but had left Quetta without contacting her. Something was
wrong. Very wrong.

As she arrived back at the station, she caught sight of the
Major striding towards her along the platform with a horrible
smile on his face. 'Mrs Weightman. I don't think you found
your husband, did you?' His eyes were glinting with a nasty
triumph.

'I found out that he survived, that's all I need to know.'

'Yes, he did. He caught a train the day it happened. We
have his name as a passenger. No mention of him being in the
Black Watch though. Our list says he his is a lawyer.'

She did her best not to show him her surprise, realising she
was not entirely successful when he gloated, 'I know, I was
surprised too. I wonder why he said that? And why he has not
contacted you.'

He waited in smug satisfaction for her to reply. She said
nothing. Then he added, 'He was going to Karachi, he told my
clerk. He said he needed to get to the bank there.' This last
line was delivered with insincere concern, 'Why was he doing
that, would you say?'

'I really have no idea. But I imagine that, with Quetta no
longer existing, he needed to get his money from his PNB account.' She smiled at him through her supressed fear, 'He has

his own account, you know. I have my own too. Completely separate.'

He looked at her with barely disguised disbelief, 'If you say so.'

She forced a smile, 'I will be taking the next train to Karachi, Major. I have no doubt I will meet with my husband there.' She walked away before he could say any more.

She pushed herself into a seat by the shutters. She looked out over the parched countryside, thinking. Feelings of dread came to the surface as the realisation dawned that Thomas might have deserted her. But he could not have stolen her money, at least.

She suddenly remembered the letter to Pandit she had picked up from the rubble. Perhaps it would distract her from all the negative thoughts about Thomas.

She pulled the envelope out of her bag, a little puff of dust came with it. It had the crest of the British Consul based in Karachi. She pulled the letter out, shaking it to remove the rest of the dust. The woman next to her coughed pointedly. Cecilia checked the date and saw that it was years old. She realised it was the letter Pandit had mentioned and spoken about, but she had never seen. Cecilia shook it again aggressively, deliberately staring at the woman. Seeing the anger in Cecilia's eyes, she looked away, defeated.

Cecilia read:

> Your document provides us with a good basis for pursuing the idea of granting rights to Anglo-Indians. However, His Majesty's Government is minded to offer similar rights across its Empire and Dominions. Each country and dominion will have separate negotiations. We will begin these as soon as possible. Many people are needed in the United Kingdom in order to rebuild the country in the wake of the recent war.

I have been asked by the Viceroy of India to thank you for this exemplary work which will provide an excellent foundation for the future discussions.

Yours

Hugh Weightman

Clerk to the Viceroy

She stared at the signature, in shock. Weightman? Hugh Weightman?

She felt a prickling at the back of her mind, an inkling that she knew the name, Hugh Weightman. It was familiar to her but she could not think why. She knew she had met him before, but when and where was eluding her. It was decades ago, she knew that much. Staring out of the window as the arid countryside flew by, the memory came to her. Hugh Weightman was the clerk who broke the news to her about Maurice's death. She had started early labour with Bridget in his office. She had snapped at him when he offered to have his staff carry her home. He was the clerk who paid the military wives their husband's wages each week. He also gave them letters and ensured their replies were sent back. He was a kind man she remembered, thoughtful and caring. No wonder he had been promoted to work for the Viceroy.

Then another prickling in the back of her mind, another long-lost memory came creeping back. The day that a little toddler interrupted Mr Weightman as he dealt with the wages. A little boy, cheeky and lively. Mr Weightman had called him Tommy, apologised for his behaviour, explaining he was his brother. Tommy? His brother? Was her Thomas the brother of Hugh Weightman? The names and ages fitted. Yet Thomas said he had no family in India. Mind you, she reasoned, he said he was a private in the Black Watch, stationed in Quetta.

She looked at the address on the letter. She would go there as soon as she arrived in Karachi. Mr Hugh Weightman may no longer work there, but it was worth a try. If he wasn't there, someone might know where he had been posted. She could track him down and perhaps find Thomas through him. She leaned back in her seat, sighing with relief. She had a plan.

Karachi was huge city, a major port with many buildings belonging to the Raj. The East India Company had built them many years ago. Some were falling down, others had withstood the ravages of time. It was easy to find the Consul, it was in the most palatial part of the British quarters. A building of grandeur with turrets and towers. She was surprised to see that inside it was cramped and dark, with nothing of the internal splendour of other offices of the Raj she had seen.

She spoke to the young man at the front desk.

'I would like to see Mr Hugh Weightman, please.' She held her breath, expecting him to say that Hugh Weightman was no longer working there.

'Do you have an appointment?'

Taken aback, she replied, 'Well, no. But I do need to see him urgently.'

The young man, British and pompous, looked at her with an air of exasperation. She could tell that he, along with all the other British men she had dealt with recently, was seeing an annoying elderly Indian woman.

'He is very busy. You will need an appointment.'

'As I said, I need to see him urgently.' Her tone was firm.

He ignored it. 'Mr Weightman is the most senior member of staff here. His diary is always booked. I will make an appointment for you.'

He opened a large, leather-bound diary lying on his desk. Flicking through the pages, he found an empty one. 'You may have an appointment in two weeks' time, at eleven o'clock in the morning.'

He picked up a fountain pen, hovering it over the page, ready to write in her details, 'Name?'

'I need to see him today. My name is Mrs Weightman.'

On hearing the name, he dropped the pen spilling ink on the paper. It splayed like a blob of surprise. She watched the expression on his face. From shock to confusion, to the realisation that he had to do as she asked.

'I will see if he is available. May I ask what the appointment will be about.'

'You can ask, but I won't tell you. It is a private matter.'

He scurried away, his pomp draining from him with each step. His attitude had changed completely on his return. He smiled, 'You are lucky, Mrs Weightman, Mr Weightman has a free half-hour now. I will take you to his office.'

He proffered his arm for her to take as a gesture to her age and an apology for his previous implacability. She refused, 'I am fine, thank you.'

He led her through a maze of long dark grubby corridors. She didn't know how he knew his way around. All the corridors looked the same and seemed endless. He stopped by a large wooden door and tapped on it. They heard the man on the other side say, 'Come in.' Cecilia nodded at the young man to tell him she did not need him anymore. He slunk away.

Taking a deep breath, she opened the door. He was standing by a large ornate fireplace with an empty grate. In a flash she saw he really was the same Hugh Weightman, the one she had known all those years ago. He was older, of course. A few lines, thinning hair and a wider waist. But it was definitely him. She even saw a similarity to Thomas.

He looked at her in surprise. She was sure he didn't recognise her. But his manner was, as always, respectful. He wasn't viewing her as a nuisance as did so many of his type.

'I understand you wanted to see me urgently, Mrs, er, Weightman.'

'Yes, I have two matters to discuss with you. May I sit down?' She plonked herself in an old dusty armchair without waiting for a reply.

He sat opposite her on a flea-bitten chaise longue.

His voice was kind as he said, 'I expect these two issues are important. What is the first one?'

She nodded, 'Before we do, I want to say that I think our paths have crossed before. Many years ago. I was a military wife in Thatti and you were the ICS member who gave out our husbands' wages.'

She could see that he was beginning to remember as he said, 'My first posting. That was a long time ago.'

'I was Mrs Roche then, Mrs Maurice Roche. Though my own name is Cecilia.'

'Mrs Roche?' His face cleared, 'I do remember you. I thought you looked familiar when you came in.'

She wondered if he were making that bit up. She realised he was being truthful when he said, 'I remember how awful it was, telling you about the death of your poor husband. It stuck in my mind for years.'

'Not as awful as hearing it,' she replied tartly, immediately regretting her sharpness.

He coughed, embarrassed, shifting in his seat, 'Of course, of course. I am sorry. Very thoughtless of me. I know you went into labour with the news that day. I want to reassure you I checked with the other wives about your confinement. I heard you had a little girl.'

'My little Bridget,' she told him, her voice far away into the past, 'but she died when she was eleven-months-old.'

'I am so very sorry, I didn't know.'

'No reason that you should,' she said, slipping back into the present, 'but that is not why I am here.'

He raised his eyebrows, 'Please go on.'

'I am now married to a Thomas Weightman. I think he is your brother.'

Hugh Weightman smiled, 'Well I have a much younger brother called Thomas. The black sheep of the family, I am afraid. He is very young,' a polite clearing of this throat, 'a lot younger than you, Mrs Weightman. Thomas was born in 1901.'

It was her turn to smile, 'My husband is a lot younger than me, Mr Weightman. Twenty-five years to be exact. He was born in 1901 too.'

He spluttered and coughed, lost for words.

Cecilia said, 'I have a very clear memory of Thomas, when he was very young, bursting into your office. And your mother scolding him.'

'He was always doing that sort of thing. Always uncontrollable. He left home when he was quite young, about eighteen. We never saw much of him after that.'

'When I met him, he said he was a private in the Black Watch.'

'I doubt it very much. He was rarely truthful. He was too wild to accept army discipline. He always talked about joining the Army though. He stole a Black Watch uniform before he ran away. We believe he earned money through gambling and thieving. It broke my mother's heart. God rest her soul.'

'He said he had no family in India.'

'Patently untrue, as you can see.'

She pulled a photo of her and Thomas taken quite recently, one she always kept in her bag. She handed it to Mr Weightman who looked at it for a brief moment before saying, 'Yes, that's him,' handing it back to her.

There was pause, 'I must tell you something, Mrs Weightman.'

'Go on.'

'Thomas was here three days ago. I had not seen him in years. He told me he had just escaped from the Quetta earthquake.' He paused, 'And that his wife had died.'

Cecilia gasped, 'Sorry? Have I heard that correctly? He said I was dead?'

'Yes. He said you had died in the earthquake. He told me your name was Cecilia but didn't say that you were so much older than him,' all sense of politeness about the age difference had gone. 'He seemed distraught and asked me for money. He said he was leaving for Australia that day.'

'No, no, no.'

'There's more bad news, I am afraid, Mrs Weightman. He asked for money and I gave him some. He said he would repay me after he had been to the Punjabi National Bank to collect your account. I haven't seen him since.'

Cecilia felt as if her legs had given way, even though she was sitting down. Her stomach churned as she leaned back in her armchair trying to take in his words. Mr Weightman called for a glass of water. When it arrived, he placed it next to her on a side table and sat back down and waited.

She took a deep gulp, 'I must get to the bank and see what has happened.' She pushed herself up using the arms of the chair.

'I am sorry to have to remind you after this shock, Mrs Weightman. You mentioned you had two things to raise with me.'

'Oh, of course. I had forgotten. I have a letter to show you.'

She reached into her bag and brought out the letter he had written to Pandit.

He read it with a smile, 'I remember this and the excellent document.'

'Well, we put Pandit's name on it. I researched and wrote it. It is my passion, building a better future for my children and their peers.'

'Congratulations on such an influential piece of work, your intelligence and passion showed through. I should let you know that we are still doing as it said in my reply. We are still negotiating with all the other nations involved. It is a very slow process. Very slow.'

Unable to resist, she asked him, 'What status has it now? I want to know if my children will have the civil rights they deserve.'

'I understand your concern, Mrs Weightman. I believe the discussions are on-going. But it is no longer in my work portfolio, so I am not up to date.'

Her own wry view of life surfaced as she observed, 'Well, Mr Weightman. This is only the second time you and I have had a proper conversation. You have given me truly terrible shocks on both occasions. Perhaps our next conversation will contain a pleasant surprise. Like you telling me the appropriate regulations have been passed and my children's futures are secure.'

He smiled, 'I understand, Mrs Weightman. And indeed, I would like to convey good news to you. But I am due to be posted to Bahrain in the near future. I will make enquiries and revert,' he paused. Then making a decision, he continued, 'In fact, to help matters, I will personally push for the right resolution for you.'

She took out a piece of paper and scribbled her Multan address, handing it to him, saying, 'That would be much appreciated, Mr Weightman. Please write to me as I may not be able to come back to this office. I hope you are successful.'

'I will do my very best. And might I add, I am sorry about this situation. If Thomas had been a better man, we would have been a proper family. My wife would have enjoyed your lively company, I know.'

'Thank you, there has been a lot of trouble in my life. But I have survived. I, too, am sorry we haven't met under better circumstances. Give my regards to your wife and I hope your posting to Bahrain is successful. Now, please help me find my way out of this building. Or I might still be here next week.'

He laughed and called a staff member to escort her to the door.

She found the branch of PNB on the same street, at the corner, its colours bright and beckoning.

She asked the clerk to bring her a note of her balance, waiting for what seemed a long time. Her heart was pounding and her mind racing with different scenarios, even the hope she was wrong and Thomas would be waiting for her somewhere with open arms.

The clerk came back, with something of an embarrassed shuffle. He handed her a small, folded note. She opened it and read:

Your balance is 0

'This cannot be,' she said to him, 'I had many thousands of rupees in this account when I checked with you just last week. I rang and spoke to the Manager.'

'I think you may need to speak to the Manager again,' he said with a reverential bow, 'please follow me.'

He led her to the Manager's office, a crowded space which reminded her of Pandit's room in Multan.

The manager, a portly Punjabi with very little hair, gestured at her to sit down.

He sorted out a few papers while she watched him. He was taking his time, she thought, because he has bad news for me. She was right. 'Before this time, we didn't realise that you and Mr Thomas Weightman were a married couple.' He looked at her with steady eyes, 'There was such a big age gap, you see. Mr Weightman had an account here. But it held very little in the way of balances. Yours was always much healthier.'

He cleared his throat, 'Mrs Weightman, your husband came here three days ago. He said you had died in the Quetta earthquake.' He gulped, 'He emptied your account. He said he was going to Australia to start a new life. There were too many bad memories for him here. He was very upset.'

Cecilia said nothing. What could she say?

After a few moments, she stood up. 'Thank you for being so frank. I need to go to the port and see if he made good on his word about travelling to Australia.'

She could feel the manager's eyes boring into her back. Eyes that said, 'Why else would he have married you, but for your money, you silly old woman.' She knew everyone would think the same way, including her own children.

The port was her final hope. He may not have gone to Australia. It may have been another lie. She might discover him yet.

She found her way to the port, following the lines of people, donkeys and elephants all laden with goods and furniture, all moving in the same direction.

It was a heaving mass of chaos. People were shouting to one another, boarding boats by pushing and shoving. Cases and trunks were piled up on pathways, looking as if their owners had abandoned them. Sacks of cargo were being offloaded from boats and ships and flung onto the docks by reckless sailors. Port authorities were beating people with sticks to prevent them from looting the newly arrived goods. The trumpeting of distressed elephants, the braying of tired donkeys and the howling of wild dogs, combined to make her want to get away from the area as soon as she could.

Cecilia saw a sign to the ticket stall and pushed her way through to a small office. There was a straggly queue of listless people waiting outside. She was in too much of a hurry to join them. She pushed her way to the front with neither explanation nor apology. The line looked at her with curiosity but didn't protest. It seemed they were confused in these surroundings and thought she was just part of the pandemonium.

Once she got to the desk, she realised she unable to bear the mortification of admitting that Thomas was her husband. So, she told ticket clerk, 'I am looking for my son. I think he sailed to Australia three days ago, or possibly yesterday or the day before.'

'Do you want me to check the passenger lists?'

'Yes please, his name is Thomas Weightman.'

The clerk looked down the passenger lists while she waited. He was not fast, checking each name at least twice. Cecilia felt the excruciating agony of each second.

'Yes,' said the clerk with a note of triumph, 'I have found him. He boarded a ship three days ago. He paid on the day. Had a lot of money on him, it says here.'

'Is there any more information?'

'Yes, it says he was widowed in the Quetta earthquake. He wanted to start a new life in Australia.'

'I see,' she said, still in the role of his mother, 'I am just relieved he survived. I hadn't heard from him.'

The clerk smiled, 'I am sure he will write to you when he arrives. After all, every son loves his mother, doesn't he?'

Her acknowledgement was weak and she sloped out of the port office past the curious line of waiting people, the weight of indignity and shame bearing down on her with each step.

Chapter Seventeen

Her body had been failing for months, though her mind was as sharp as ever. She knew her time was near. She had moved in with Cissy because she was too weak to look after herself, but Cissy was busy with her own family, so Cecilia spent most of the time in bed, alone with her memories.

She thought about the last twelve years of her life. She had spent weeks, sometimes months, living with different children. Trying to rebuild her life after Thomas. She had felt endless humiliation and shame over those twelve years. Her anger had too often spilled over in the direction of her children and grandchildren. Her ability to find the positive had deserted her. She hadn't had a happy day since she found out about Thomas's treachery.

It wasn't just him that had made her so bitter. It was all the other tragedies that she had endured. All the sadness and loss. All the times she had swallowed her thoughts and feelings to keep others happy. It was as if there was no more room inside her. It had all started to overflow. None of her children understood what she had been through, or the sacrifices she had made for them. They were not interested in finding out either. Part of her bitterness was aimed at them, she knew. She had spent her whole career working to increase their life opportunities. Yet none of them had bothered to look at the new avenues their lives could have taken.

Her sons were railwaymen. Her daughters were house-wives. Their husbands were railwaymen too. They all resented the time she had spent at work when they were children. Time that she had spent to keep them financially sustainable, trying to make their futures easier.

Both Mickie and Alfie had remarried. Alfie's bride was Eva and they had little Myrna. Alfie had brought his older girls back together and they were living as a family in Kotri. Mickie had now had eight children with his new wife. It brought her peace to know that they were both settled again. She hoped they would have changed their ways. But she doubted it.

One good thing that had happened was a letter from Hugh Weightman. A precious letter. A letter she had kept among her papers. It told her that the negotiations across the Empire were coming to a conclusion. There was a *British Nationality Act* due to go through Parliament after India was partitioned. She felt her life's work was complete when she read it. She had been instrumental in securing rights for her children and grandchildren. They would be able to travel to other countries like Britain, Australia and Canada, starting new lives there if they so wished. They would have opportunities to study and be teachers, doctors, lawyers, not just railway workers. It was a triumph for her. Though a triumph that no one connected to her. She hoped the letter would be found after her death and her family, at least start to understand.

Partition was near, due in August, two months' time. She knew she would not live to see it. Outside she could hear the constant cacophony of the town. Rawalpindi was always loud and noisy. Now it was also a town wary of the imminent divide. It was steadying itself for an influx of Islamic people fleeing India – some had already arrived. The noise levels were increasing every day as they sought homes, food and clothes, making deals in the market, finding their place and space in their new surroundings.

Some of the noises were tense: loud and argumentative. Cecilia feared partitioning, for the changes it would bring, for the violence it had already brought to every community. There had been so much bloodshed already. She didn't want to die, but she feared that life for her in the new Pakistan would be even harder than it was in India of the British.

She remembered the young Ali Jinnah, who came to Pandit's Chambers many times. He was now the head of the All-India Muslim League. His lifelong dream of creating a new country for Muslims was coming true. From what she had read a few months earlier, he and Gandhi, Mountbatten and Nehru were all working together to create the Partition of India. She smiled to herself at the memories of Jinnah and Gandhi. Jinnah – how her loss of temper had led to him helping Pandit with his bundles. How Gandhi had been so diligent in keeping his promise to her beloved Maurice.

She prayed for the family she was leaving behind. She prayed her grandchildren at least would take the new opportunities their parents had ignored.

Cissy came into the room with a glass of water, 'Here Mama, for you.'

She struggled to reply, her throat was so sore and dry, her voice so weak.

'I don't have long now.'

'Hush Mama. Don't talk like that.'

Cecilia took a sip of water. It lubricated her throat so she could say what needed to be said, 'I am sorry for my bad temper. Tell the others please. I loved you all.' She lay back in the bed exhausted from the effort.

'Oh Mama, I remember that you were such fun when we were children. You always made us laugh and feel loved. I know life has been difficult for you since, er, Thomas left.' Tears spilled down her cheeks, 'Don't say sorry, Mama.'

'Don't cry, Cissy. I have outlived so many people that it is my turn now.'

Cissy nodded in silent acknowledgment. She sat on the bed, holding her mother's hand. Cecilia shut her eyes to rest awhile. She didn't sleep. She heard Cissy leave the room, closing the door in the manner of a nurse not wanting to wake her patient. A short while later, she heard a movement and turned her head towards it. Two men were silhouetted in the door frame. One moved forward.

It was Alfie. Her heart soared – her beloved Alfie had come to see her. Come to say goodbye. For all Alfie's frustrating behaviour, she still loved him deeply. She even had a sneaking admiration for his rebellious streak. She knew he inherited it from her – even if he hadn't used it in the best way.

Too weak to move, she watched him cross the room to her bed. He knelt down taking her hand. He was crying softly. 'Oh Mama,' he said, 'I've brought our new priest to see you. He is Father Joseph Cordeiro. He's going to give you the Last Rites.'

Cecilia struggled to talk. She wanted to tell him that, as a divorcee, she couldn't receive the Last Rites. Alfie guessed. He leaned towards her ear and whispered, 'It's alright Mama. I told him you are a widow. He is new, so doesn't know you. That's why I didn't bring Father Francis Kotwani. He would have known.' Alfie smiled with the air of a conspirator. Watching him, Cecilia thought, trust Alfie to lie to a priest. She had done it herself, too, all those years ago. When she told Father Theodore that she lived in Kohampur. So, perhaps she and Alfie were not that different after all.

Alfie moved aside and the young priest appeared by her bed. He laid his chalice, chrism and Missal on her table. She noticed he was a handsome man with broad shoulders and an aura of calm. He laid his hand on her arm. 'Cecilia, I know you can't talk. I will say all the prayers for you.' He had a strong English accent, just like the British civil servants she had met, although he had dark skin. She was certain that this young priest held a bright future. He sat in silence next to her bed for a minute or two. Then he began his ritual. His Latin praying was lyrical but he read from his Missal in more sonorous tones. He laid the host on her tongue and anointed her forehead with a cross.

'Cecilia. You do not have long left. I know you have had a hard life – Alfred told me. But you have led a good life – he told me that too. Your work here is done now. You will go to heaven and live with the Lord.'

He blessed her then crossed himself. As he left the room, he put his hand on Alfie's shoulder and smiled a sad smile. 'You did a good thing, bringing me here, Alfred. The Lord will not forget.'

Alfie wiped his tears as he moved to hold Cecilia's hand. 'I don't want you to die. Don't leave us. I know I have not been a good son, but I do love you. We need you here, Mama.'

She summoned enough strength to squeeze his hand lightly. Alfie cried harder. 'I don't know what to do, Mama. It is so frightening. Every night, Eva and the girls are scared. They hide in the house while the rioters are outside shouting and screaming. Little Myrna is so petrified. We can barely keep her from crying out.'

His voice dropped, 'And I am scared too,' he admitted. 'We will not be welcome anywhere after India is partitioned. I don't know what to do.'

Cecilia looked as intently at Alfie as she could. His face was ashen. He looked as if he hadn't slept for days. Now she wondered about the motivation for his visit. Did he really come to say goodbye to his mother who had put up with all his misdeeds over the years? Or did he want to use her to unburden himself, for his own ends? She thought, probably the latter. With so little time left, she didn't care. She needed to share something with him and felt a surge of strength from within. She spoke each word with a careful struggle.

'Go… where… education... is... better... for... the... girls. Make... sure... Dagma... goes... to... university. She... is... the... cleverest... of... them... all. You... will... be... able... to... go... anywhere, I... promise.'

She closed her eyes. Alfie jumped up, wiping away his tears. 'You are right Mama. I will make sure they get the best education.' He smiled, 'You taught me that. See I did listen after all.' He kissed her cold cheek. He went on, 'You are right. Dagma is so clever, we will make sure she gets the right education. She wants to become a doctor, you know. A doctor, our little Dagma. Can you believe that? Father Francis has connections to Bandra University. He will get her a place there. Just think of it, Mama. You will be so proud. A lawyer and a doctor in the family. And both women too.'

As he turned to leave, he paused, 'You were a good Mama. I know I didn't make it easy for you and I'm sorry. But you were kind to me, whatever I did. I didn't deserve you.' He returned to her bed. She felt his warm lips on her icy cheek. He said softly, 'Goodbye, Mama.'

Her eyes still closed, Cecilia gave him the slightest of smiles. The tiniest acknowledgement of his momentous apology. Alfie left quietly, head bowed, tears flowing.

She felt a sensation of peace flow through her weak body. A feeling of contentment that she'd never known before. In surety she knew that her children were all settled. Her grandchildren would have opportunities because of her life's work.

Especially Dagma. Her brilliant, beautiful Dagma would go to university and become a doctor. That was worth it all.

A few minutes later, with the loud, angry shouts, screams and drums of Partition rioters outside her house, Cecilia saw Maurice walk towards her. He was surrounded by her lost children. He reached out to her with a smile. She danced towards him, into his loving arms.

Author's endnote

The facts of Cecilia's life (births, marriages, deaths, locations) are recorded in the British Library's British India records. They are also on the Find my Past website. The historical backdrop and characters are real. The fiction lies in the narrative thread that weaves it all together. I had to create a credible story in the absence of any other information.

The characterisations are broadly fiction. There are some facets which I gleaned through meeting Cecilia's children when I was younger. I met Richard, Michael, Cissie, Gertie and Alfie, who was my grandfather. Some things I have been told by relatives who knew them well. For instance, Richard and Gertie were popular among their siblings as they were both calm and kind. I have reflected this in the narrative. The character of Christopher Keating was totally fictionalised. There is no-one alive who remembers him or anything about him, so I had to structure a narrative that worked around the facts.

The book would have been twice as long if I had followed the lives of all Cecilia's children until her own death in 1947. There were so many more births and tragedies. I decided to focus on Alfie and his family as they are my direct ancestors – Dagma being my mother. The anecdotes about Alfie are true. He didn't ever change. He moved his family to England in 1950 and they settled in Gillingham, Kent. He passed away in 1981.

Dagma didn't become a doctor, after all. She went to Bandra University in Mumbai as a teenager, staying with family friends. When Alfie moved the family to England she joined them, although she made it clear it was not her choice as she did not want to leave her studies. Once in the UK, she met and married my father, settled in Hertfordshire and had six children. After bringing us all up, Dagma took a degree and became a science teacher. I think she was cut from the same cloth as Cecilia. She died, aged 81, in 2012.

Having been moved by Cecilia's story, I created a website and podcast that uncovers stories of other women who have led amazing, but invisible, lives. On it, I included more about the background to the book and the process of researching and developing the story. You can find it at www.amazing-womeninvisiblelives.co.uk

Bernie Morgan
March 2021